PERCEPTION

W. B. SAUNDERS COMPANY
PHILADELPHIA AND LONDON   1962

AND MOTION

An Analysis of Space-Structured Behavior

KARL U. SMITH, UNIVERSITY OF WISCONSIN

WILLIAM M. SMITH, DARTMOUTH COLLEGE

With the assistance of MARGARET F. SMITH

The following illustrations in this book have appeared in prior publications of the authors
and are reprinted or adapted by permission from:

The Behavior of Man, Henry Holt & Co., Inc., 1958.   Figures 6-4 and 13-2.

American Journal of Physical Medicine.   Figures 2-7, 5-1, 6-1, 6-2, 6-3, 6-4, 6-5,
6-6, 6-7, 7-1, 7-2, 7-3, 7-5, 7-15, 7-16, 8-2, 8-4, 11-9, and 11-10.

Journal of Applied Psychology.   Figures 1-4, 3-3, and 3-4,B.

Journal of Comparative Neurology.   Figure 10-3.

Journal of Experimental Psychology.   Figure 7-4.

Perceptual and Motor Skills.   Figures 7-18, 8-1, and 8-2.

Science.   Figures 3-9, 3-10, 3-11, and 13-26.

COLLABORATING AUTHORS

SHERMAN ANSELL

ORLANDO BEHLING

JOHN GOULD

DONOVAN GREENE

PAUL GREENE

ROBERT JONES

CHARLES McDERMID

THOMAS MURPHY

RICHARD PINSKER

WARREN RHULE

LYNN WARGO

CHARLES ZWERG

CONTRIBUTING AUTHORS

DONALD KUGLITSCH

JUDITH JOHNSON

PREFACE

This book is the culmination of a set of ideas about the mechanisms of human perception and motion, how these mechanisms can be studied through the use of scientific television devices and electronic methods of motion analysis, and how the integration of perception and behavior can be understood in terms of the geometric and neural relations of the sensory feedback systems of motion. In order to determine the validity of assumptions about sensory feedback in motion and its relation to behavior organization, a large number of specific experiments have been conducted on the effects of displaced, delayed, and size-distorted visual feedback on different types of motions. We describe the results of these experiments, as well as giving a detailed account of the various electronic motion analyzers, closed-circuit television systems, and videotape recording set-ups that have made them possible.

In the search for truth about animal motion and its integrative mechanisms, we have rejected some widely accepted concepts about the reflex, the synapse, and the nature and significance of the learning process. We base our own interpretation of behavior organization on some ideas concerning the perceptual feedback relationships of motion and the neurogeometric mechanisms underlying them. We submit that the primary organizational factor of response is spatial, not temporal, and propose that the basic structural unit of the brain be conceived of as a differential detector, responding to differences in stimulation and sensory feedback.

The research presented in this book is concerned principally with the problems of spatially displaced sensory feedback. One chapter, Chapter 13, presents an introduction to an important new experimental area — that of delayed sensory feedback. We consider the problems of feedback delay and the implications of the experimental results in this field so significant that we have prepared a second, smaller book on this subject; it is entitled, "Delayed Sensory Feedback and Behavior."

Many individuals and groups have contributed to the research programs that made these two books possible. The main financial support came from the National Science Foundation, in the form of a number of grants to both major authors. This support was the basis for other aid received and enabled us to sustain our research on an independent basis. We wish to thank Dr. John T. Wilson and Dr. Henry Odbert for their helpful cooperation over the years when this research was in progress. Additional financial support has been provided by grants from the Public Health Service and the Research Committee, the University of Wisconsin, from research funds voted by the Wisconsin State Legislature. Preparation of the manuscript has been facilitated by financial support from the Ford Foundation to one of the authors.

The hard labor, laboratory routine, and data analyses that made this book possible were contributed largely by graduate student assistants, whose names appear as collaborating authors. Two undergraduates who made specific contributions to the research appear as contributing authors.

We appreciate the cooperation of the University of Wisconsin Television Laboratory in aiding the installation and maintenance of some of the video equipment and in providing special equipment for some studies. We wish to thank especially Edward Furstenberg, Robert Shult, and Charles Huber for their engineering assistance and technical aid.

The design and construction of electronic motion analysis equipment have been a critical part of this research. The construction of this equipment for our purposes was aided by Lawrence Anderson and Charles Boutelle.

Numerous studies in this book required the facilities of machine data processing, which were supplied by the Numerical Analysis Laboratory, University of Wisconsin, under the direction of Professor Preston C. Hammer.

One of the most critical experiments reported — that of delayed visual feedback — was made possible by the RCA Manufacturing Company Research Laboratories, Princeton, New Jersey, which generously permitted us to use their experimental videotape facilities for conducting a controlled study of concurrent delay of sensory feedback of motion. The technical assistance of W. D. Houghton and the participation of John W. McCrary in this research are greatly appreciated.

Additional tangible support of the RCA Manufacturing Company was the granting of a miniature television camera chain to one of the authors in the very early phases of this research, when financial help for buying such equipment had not yet been obtained. We also wish to thank the Dage Television Corporation, Michigan City, Indiana, for the loan of television instruments during these early stages of our research operations.

The studies on application of television and electronic behavior-recording techniques to research on infant control of the behavioral environment were conducted in the Pediatrics Department, University of Wisconsin Medical School, with the cooperation of Dr. Nathan J. Smith.

It is impossible to credit individually the great number of graduate and undergraduate students whose work as subjects was never easy and often trying. Many of these people were repaid only by points toward a course grade. We wish to acknowledge especially the participation of Professors Leonard Berkowitz, Gibson Byrd, Warrington Colescott, William Harley, Dean Meeker, and the late Louis Weinberg, who gave generously of their valuable time to act as subjects in the studies on artistic drawing.

Finally, we wish to express our gratitude to Professor Herbert Pick, who read one draft of the manuscript, for his many helpful suggestions.

THE AUTHORS

CONTENTS

ix

CHAPTER 1

CONCEPTS OF PERCEPTUAL-MOTOR ORGANIZATION

Behavior, especially the behavior of man, presents many aspects to the eye of the observer. Traditionally, psychologists have tried to deal with some of these aspects more or less independently. Thus, our textbooks have chapters on motivation, emotion, perception, motion, learning, thinking, and so on. One way to categorize behavior is in terms of several fundamental characteristics, or dimensions: (1) behavior is motivated, i.e., it is organized in terms of internal motivational and emotional states; (2) behavior is articulated with reference to

the stimulus patterns of the external environment; and (3) behavior organization changes in time. In this book we shall be concerned with the second of these characteristics — the structuring of behavior in terms of the perceived world.

In the normal individual, perception and motion are but two sides of the same coin: his reactions to the spatial and temporal patterns of the stimulus world. Motion and perception are considered to be space-structured and time-structured, as evidenced by their correspondence to the geometric properties of space and objects and the temporal patterns of stimuli. One of the distinguishing features of the human individual as compared with other animals is the high degree of precision with which he can articulate his movements to correspond to the properties of hard space (objects). However, with all the detailed knowledge of sensory, neural, and motor systems, there has never been a satisfactory account of how patterned motion is regulated. This question of the geometric organization of animal motion is still one of the central problems of science. Any advance we can make toward understanding it will throw light as well on other questions about human development and evolution, and the overall organization of behavior.

In the chapters that follow, we summarize some of the earlier work on motion and perception, and describe a number of our own experiments that are theoretically oriented and designed in terms of a space-structured or geometric conception of psychomotor behavior. Here we are studying perception and motion not as two separate forms of adaptation, but as one mechanism, adapting the movements of the body to the gravitational and three-dimensional characteristics of space. Both our theory and our experimental results contribute to our belief that the distinguishing characteristics of behavior in man and other higher animals are defined by the basic mechanisms of perceptual-motor integration.

Our theoretical formulation of the problem of psychomotor behavior has been both the inspiration for and the product of a number of new experimental techniques. Our electronic methods of motion analysis, which permit precise timing of the components of motion, have been developed over the past 12 years. More recently, we have adapted closed-circuit television and videotape recording to problems of perception and motion. One of our purposes here is to explore the uses of these techniques in behavior research.

THEORIES OF PSYCHOMOTOR ACTIVITY

Perception and motion have not always been thought of as equivalent or even comparable aspects of behavior. In ordinary thinking, as well as in most earlier philosophical and psychological treatments, perception has been as-

sumed to be a psychic function, quite different from easily observable motor behavior. The perceiving of stimuli and objects in space has been the subject of many investigations and theoretical analyses, but, in most cases, the study of perception has been considered to be independent of the study of overt motor organization.

However, in any overall description of behavior, it is necessary to relate in some meaningful way the events of perception and action. The behaving individual obviously adjusts his motions to his perceived environment. Conversely, all aspects of perception depend on certain movements, such as localizing and directional movements. The question can be put in several ways, depending on one's theoretical orientation. One can ask, "How do perceptions influence actions?" Or, "How does movement organization influence perception?" Or, "How does perceptual information change the organization of behavior?" Or, in our own terms, "What is the nature of perceptual-motor integration?"

Volitional Theory

Since the time of Greek science, perception has usually been classified as one of the attributes of mind, more in the realm of psychic experience than that of action. Classic theory of percipient events categorizes them as a mental integration of sensory processes, which can modulate the mental control of action. This ancient volitional view of the role of perception in motion has persisted to the present day, and still is used — expressed in somewhat more acceptable scientific jargon — to explain how the brain processes sensory information and makes it available in decision-making and the organization of overt behavior.

The experimental study of perceptual-motor interaction is coincident with the development of psychology as a science.

The original motor theory of perception can be said to have had its inception in the efforts of Berkeley[22] to explain three-dimensional space perception in terms of the kinesthetic cues from action of the eye muscles. With the emphasis on sensations and consciousness in the early days of psychology, theorists representing the structural and functional points of view turned consistently to sensations of movement to fill in the wide gaps in their qualitative sensory descriptions of mental life. From such thinking, we have inherited the motor theory of consciousness, the motor theory of attention and thinking, and the motor theories of perception.

Gestalt Theory

With the advent of modern experimental psychology, the problems of perceptual-motor integration were "resolved" by broad theoretical models of behavior based on learning theory, conflict motivation, and configurational principles of perception and behavior. According to the latter point of view, described generally as gestalt psychology,[153, 325] perception is exclusively "phenomenal" (i.e., observational) in nature, and behavior is a direct result of the organization of the perceptual field. In other words, the environmental field in which behavior occurs — the so-called behavioral field — is organized in perceptual terms. The laws of behavior and learning (called insight) are laws of perceptual organization. In substance, behavior organization is the action counterpart of the observed perceptual pattern.

Viewed historically, gestalt psychology formulates nothing decisely new about perceptual-motor integration except the concept of perceptual organization. Although this principle had an important impact on the more atomistic descriptions of behavior, it did not displace them in psychological thought. In its preoccupation with perception and perceptual organization, gestalt psychology failed to provide any real understanding of other aspects of behavior. The cleavage between perception and action remained, and could be bridged only by resorting to principles of psychic control.

Reinforcement Theory

The popular doctrine of modern experimental psychology represents a coalescence of various points of view about learning, conditioning, and memory, and their relation to motivation and perception. Thus, the traditional quantitative or arithmetic descriptions of behavior — though weakened by gestalt doctrine and other emphases on dynamic organizational principles—have become re-established. Reinforcement theory was stated clearly by Thorndike[304] a half-century ago, and is no more nor less valid today than it was then. The experimental facts of trial-and-error learning, respondent conditioning, operant learning, and so forth, have led to periodic reformulations of the salient features involved in learning, but the differences are primarily verbal.[136, 247, 279]

Running throughout most statements of learning theory is some recognition of the reinforcement principle — that the probability of recurrence of a response is a function of the number of times that the reaction has led to a reinforcement or perhaps the reduction of a drive state. Current reinforcement doctrine shows the pervasive influence of Pavlov's laws of conditioning.[205] The rat and the human individual are directed and motivated, not in terms of biological factors and organization, but in terms of the graphics and statistics of levers, push buttons,[247] and payoffs.[136] Reaching beyond the simplified experimental situations that gave it birth, reinforcement theory has been tailored to fit the facts in many areas of psychology. Thus, we find it as "information theory" when applied to problems of perception and communication,[127] as a "feedback theory" when applied to problems of perception and psychomotor activity in human engineering,[85] as an "anxiety-reduction theory" of clinical counseling,[193] and as a "payoff theory" of motivational psychology in social activity and industry.[188]

A Prospectus

In spite of continued enthusiasm for reinforcement psychology and all its implications for human problems, the underlying questions pondered by Mach, Helmholtz, James, and others still persist. What, in fact, is the basic biological organization of the human system? Is this organization one based on linear or quasi-linear chaining of conditioned or reinforced reflexes, and linear conduction chains within the brain? Just how are the organization and refinement of perception and motion to be explained? Can we discover in the patterns of human perceptual-motor behavior the critical features that distinguish man from other animals?

Many major problems of motion cannot be dealt with meaningfully in terms of traditional mentalistic, gestalt, or learning concepts. Such theories, for example, can describe in only the most general terms specific activities such as tracking behavior, localizing activities, spatial orientation, and the control of movement in object handling. In fact, our best general behavior doctrines cannot even explain why the eyes turn right to explore a stimulus appearing in the right visual field.

The area of research with which we shall be concerned in this book — the study of spatially and temporally displaced vision — is another case in point. Since Stratton's first experiments,[295-297] the facts of inverted, reversed, and otherwise displaced vision have been interpreted by traditional theories in a most superficial and inadequate manner. Faced with the enigma of explaining the interrelationships between the geometry of space and the geometry of motion, most psychologists have concerned themselves only with the question of whether the space-structured movements are learned or unlearned. Nothing has been said — in generally accepted terminology nothing can be said — of the mechanisms involved.

To take another example, all of our knowledge of the course of human development is violated by reinforcement interpretations of behavior. To apply the concepts of linear chaining of reflexes to the evolution of behavior patterns in the child cannot be justified. In the initial stages of behavior development in the fetus and neonate, learning is either altogether absent or proceeds in the most restricted way.[278, 326] The essential perceptual-motor organization in the young child is determined by differentiation of motions only incidentally directed by learning or insight.[96, 98]

A number of special phenomena of perceptual-motor development remain mysteries within traditional theories of perception and learning. "Imprinting" in lower vertebrates is one example.[169] The perceptual motivation of mammals in seeking light and certain patterns of environmental stimulation is another. Migration and homing represent still other examples. There is almost no systematic account of perceptually-guided motion within our general behavior theories.

In the conviction that a real understanding of the integration of perception and motion is the key to further advance in scientific psychology, how are we to proceed? We are certain that human psychomotor behavior is not sequentially organized in terms of unit responses chained by payoff and reinforcement. We are equally certain that human evolution is quite distinct from that of pigeon, rat, or monkey, and that what constitutes reinforcement for a rat may not act in the same way in human biological organization. We are convinced that learning doctrine cannot account for the organization of perception and motion, and that these two aspects of behavior cannot be separated from each other. Therefore, we propose to study perception and motion as one unified, integrated aspect of behavior organization. We shall be speaking not of how perception affects motion, or how motion affects perception. Rather we shall be concerned with how perceptual-motor behavior (in brief, motion) is patterned according to the spatial and temporal requirements of the environment. We shall be concerned as well with the biological mechanisms involved.

Further research on the mechanisms of the brain and their evolution may well turn on the problems of space-structuring of motion. For nearly a century, behavior science has tried to relate behavior with the brain by studying the sensory process and perception as a system of events divorced from motion. This phase has reached a dead end. Every major fact of human development, of psychomotor activity, of human motion, and of perception itself testifies to the barrenness of this theoretical approach, and of the derivative theories of learning and mental organization based upon it. We propose to start afresh, to try some new ideas, and to incorporate the science of motion into our overall understanding of behavior.

TOWARD A THEORY OF MOTION

The theoretical orientation of this book has developed over a number of years, in relation to a number of broad problems in psychology and physiology.

The central problem with which we are concerned — indeed, we believe it to be the central concern of behavior science — is the way in which animal motion is organized and regulated to conform to the geometric properties of the environment. To understand the nature of this perceptual-motor integration, we must understand the relationships of receptors, brain, and muscles to the structure and dimensions of space. We are developing, then, a geometric concept of motion organization, and are proposing a set of specific ideas about the nature of its neurophysiological regulation.

A broad theory of motion is not limited in its significance to the areas of perception and motion study, but has implications for other aspects of behavior as well. In the study of motivation, for example, we must account for the directing of behavior toward objects in the environment. The perceptual-motor system serves two closely-related functions in adaptive behavior; it regulates movements of the body with relation to environmental objects or situations, and it regulates movements of the receptor systems themselves in relation to the environment. Motivated behavior is directed behavior, but the orientation of the living system is maintained by its perceptual-motor activities. A more specific problem is to give an account of what we call activity motivation and perceptual motivation in higher animals — the drive to engage in perceptual-motor activities for their own sake. Further, we need to explain why animals must maintain themselves in certain limited geometric relationships with respect to gravity and other spatial characteristics of their stimulus field, or else suffer disturbance and disorganization of their patterns of behavior. There is no doubt that animals are motivated not only by their metabolic needs, but also by the demands of their motion systems.

A theory of motion also is related

directly to a meaningful account of animal evolution. In phylogenetic development, we see an ever more precise differentiation of movement patterns — an ever increasing ability to articulate motion in accordance with variations in stimulus patterns. The evolution of the brain in the animal series is correlated with this progressive refinement of perceptual-motor integration. Thus, the comparative study of behavior should be correlated with comparative neurophysiology to show how the characteristic motion patterns of different animal forms are organized and regulated by the specific sensori-neuromotor structures that have evolved in those forms. Most significant in this respect is the great leap forward in behavior organization of man, an advance correlated with his use of tools and his related ventures in the use of abstractions and symbolic behavior. The anatomical features of the human form that have evolved in relation to these advances in behavior organization are not so much refinements of the sensory surfaces as highly differentiated neuromotor systems, especially those of the cerebral cortex. The motion patterns that are distinctly human are the highly precise manipulations of the hands, alone and aided by tools; the marvelously flexible articulations of the speech mechanism; and the infinitely variable symbolic operations thereby made possible. When we understand how the human neuromotor system controls, regulates, and integrates these patterns of motion, we shall begin to know the nature of man.

Types of Movements

In organized patterns of motion, we recognize three movement components: postural, transport, and manipulative movements. These components can be defined operationally, by analyzing the movements of the body in specific integrated motion patterns. They also can

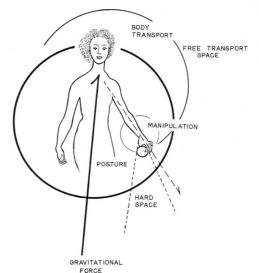

Figure 1-1. The three movement systems of space-structured motion and the stimulation patterns to which they are related. Posture is organized with respect to gravity, bilateral transport movements are organized with respect to free space, and manipulative movements with respect to hard space. Transport movements interact with both posture and manipulation.

be differentiated according to the geometric properties of the environment that support and regulate them. Finally, we believe that these movement systems can be related to different levels of the brain. A diagram representing the three movement systems is given in Figure 1-1.

The postural movements of the body are in general the "large" movements, which regulate body position in relation to the force of gravity and acceleration. Postural movements comprise the most primitive motion system in both phylogenetic and ontogenetic development. The older centers of the brain are organized principally for regulating the postural mechanism and integrating it with respiration and other vital functions.

Transport (travel) movements move members of the body, including receptors, e.g., the eyes, through fluid space, either air or liquid. Transport movements are intrinsically organized, mainly according to the bilateral symmetry of the body, with right and left members moving together or in opposition. These movements can be continuously controlled, highly precise movements, as observed in visual tracking or manual steering; or they can be free-thrown, discrete movements, as in walking, throwing, or moving the eyes from point to point in reading. These movements are integrated with postural movements, which support and direct them and control their magnitude. Transport movements and the finer manipulative movements are also interrelated, because manipulation depends upon the proper positioning of the member. For example, before an object can be grasped by the fingers, a travel movement of the arm must bring the hand to the object.

The third space-organized movement component is fine manipulation of the terminal members of the body or the receptor systems of the head. Here we include eye movements; manual manipulation; tongue, jaw, and lip movements; and movements of the feet in contact with the substrate. Manipulative movements are controlled according to the characteristics of hard space, i.e., the dimensions and position of objects. In Figure 1-1, the eyes are examining the contours of an object, and the fingers conform to its surfaces.

When we analyze the course of development in the individual, we see that the first movements to appear are the more generalized postural movements, followed by transport movements, and, finally, manipulative movements.[268] The development of the more specific perceptual activities follows this same course: from general to specific adjustments and from gross to fine discriminations. It is our belief that motion and perception are inseparably related. The development of perception in the child *is* the development of motion, and the

only valid understanding of perception at any level is in terms of the movements that define it. The so-called perceptual activities of detection and discrimination involve the adaptive movements of orientation and differential response whether these movements are large, easily seen, overt responses or minimal, implicit responses. The organization and stability of the perceptual field depend on movements of orientation, location, and differential manipulation that have become established in the motion patterns of the individual.

Neurogeometric Theory

The physiological problem posed by the characteristics of perceptual-motor behavior is to interpret the action of the response mechanism to account for space-structured motion. The concepts of linear reflexology and sequentially chained, conditioned movement patterns are not enough. The behaving system does not react to a multitude of discrete stimuli with independent, discrete stimulus-released responses. Rather, it reacts to a spatially organized environment in terms of detection of spatial and temporal differences in patterns of stimulation. Some of these patterns of stimulation are produced by external conditions and somatic movement; some, by internal activity. The important thing is that the individual reacts to differences, and continually produces additional differential stimulus patterns by his own activity.

The motion system never tends toward the homeostatic concept of equilibrium. If response movements resolved all of the stimulus differences and produced a state of stimulus equilibrium, the receptors and the brain would quickly become adapted and there would be no more stimulation.[222, 223] The theory to be defined here is that the neural mechanism of motion is both differential and dynamic, i.e., the system

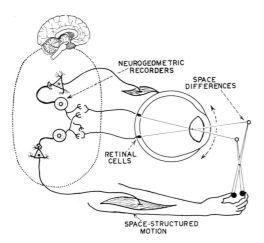

Figure 1-2. The principle of neurogeometric control of the motor system by detector neurons that respond to spatial differences in stimulation.

determines the pattern of motion by detecting differences in stimuli and generates further differences in order to maintain such control (Fig. 1-2).

Neurogeometric theory assumes that the central nervous system is composed of neurons and neuron systems that regulate the direction, pattern, and organization of motion in terms of detected spatial differences in stimulation.[259, 260] We postulate three types of such neurogeometric detecting or recording systems. Type I are intrareceptor detectors, which respond to differences in stimulation within a given receptor system. Type II are interreceptor detectors, which detect differences in stimulation between different receptors. Type III are efferent-afferent detectors, which detect differences between the efferent innervation of a movement and the afferent stimulus feedback of that movement.

Figure 1-3 illustrates the basic functional unit of these neurogeometric systems of the brain. We assume that a specific internuncial neuron acts not only as a conductor, as in traditional reflex theory, but functions also as a stimulus

differentiator, related to two specific afferent paths, e.g., from the eye. Such detector neurons are sensitive to stimulus differences in the afferent paths, and innervate the muscle system according to such differences. For example, when a difference in stimulation between two space points SP_1 and SP_2 exists, the internuncial neuron associated with these two receptor units is activated, leading to contraction of specific muscle cells. This contraction controls movement of the receptor system toward or away from the source of more intense stimulation, depending on the intrinsic integration of the particular sensorimotor system.

We call this primary differential conduction path a differential reflex unit. We believe that the whole central nervous system is organized in this way, rather than in terms of direct linear conduction. According to neurogeometric theory, every internuncial neuron acts as a space detector related to particular receptor points on the surface of the body or in the internal organs. These neurons are all "go-or-no-go" units. When a difference exists between receptor cells or between groups of receptor cells to which such a neuron is related, it conducts momentarily. When

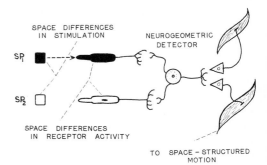

Figure 1-3. The differential reflex unit of neurogeometric theory. The internuncial neuron is conceived of as a genetically defined unit, which acts both as a differential detection system and a conduction system.

no difference exists — that is, when there is no stimulation of either receptor cell or when both cells are equally stimulated — the differential neuron is quiescent.

We assume that these neurogeometric reflex units are organized at three motor levels in the brain, corresponding to the three component movement systems described above. The differential space detectors of the postural system register variations in gravitational stimulation, due to acceleration of the body and positional variations of the body in relation to gravity. These detector neurons are related to the vestibular, kinesthetic, cutaneous, and visual receptors, and detect movement-produced variations in stimulation within each receptor system and between the different systems. The basic postural movements are integrated by the differential detectors at the level of the medulla, midbrain, and old cerebellum.

In the cerebellum, midbrain, basal ganglia, and cerebral cortex, there is a second neurogeometric system organized to regulate transport (travel) movements. The differential recorders of this system detect differences between stimulation of corresponding points on the two sides of the body or between adjacent or remote points on the same side of the body. Because transport movements are executed in free space, their organization and regulation are largely intrinsic, i.e., the pattern of transport movements depends for the most part on internal integrative mechanisms. Actually, we distinguish two transport systems, one processing information from the postural movements of the body, and the other integrating travel movements with manipulative movements. External stimuli can initiate travel movements (e.g., the appearance of an object in the visual field initiates a travel movement of the eyes), but only certain types of such movements are subject to continuous monitoring by

conditions external to the body. What we have called discrete movements, those free-thrown movements characteristic of walking, throwing, and the like, are regulated by Type II (interreceptor) and Type III (efferent-afferent) detectors and are integrated with postural movements. Their direction, rate, and duration are established at the start of the movement, although this pattern can be changed by external factors, such as an object blocking the path of the movement, or by shifts in posture. Continuously controlled travel movements, such as optical tracking, are controlled by Type I (intrareceptor) and Type III detectors, and integrated with both postural and manipulative movements.

The cortical projection systems, including the pyramidal system and the so-called sensory projection systems, are the neurogeometric mechanisms for the spatial control of manipulative movements. All three types of neurogeometric detectors function in this system to adjust fine manipulative movements to the dimensions of hard space, and to integrate them with transport movements in orienting and localizing.

Some direct evidence for neurogeometric theory, both behavioral and neurophysiological, will be presented in later chapters. For the moment, we shall point out what to us are some of the most significant implications of this theory and the areas where we have found these concepts the most fruitful.

We have long felt that any real breakthrough in understanding the functions of the brain has demanded a new orientation and a reinterpretation of the facts of reflex conduction. The traditional concept of the linear reflex has never surmounted the mystery of the synapse. Here at this break in the chain — the place where there is nothing there — traditional theory has had to postulate a decision-making agent which passes some impulses and blocks others. The nature of the agent has never been clear.

Certain chemical substances which affect the synapse clearly can raise or lower synaptic resistance rather generally, but cannot account for the rapid-fire differential responses so commonplace in animal behavior. To attribute decision-making powers to the synapse poses more problems than it solves. But to conceive of central nervous system neurons as responding only when a differential exists between two sources of input throws quite a different light on the problem. The synapse can be thought of as changing in conductivity over relatively long periods, due to general electrochemical conditions, but it is relieved of the responsibility of channeling — or blocking — each incoming stimulus.

We also have felt that the facts of learning need reinterpretation in behavior science. Too often learning concepts which are merely descriptive have been used to explain away the basic problems of behavior organization. It seems clear that the animal body is a space-organized system. The bilateral symmetry of the body itself, and of the nervous system, reflects a geometric ordering of vital activity that means as much to behavior science as it does to descriptive anatomy. Within this living system, the primary activities, including especially posture and locomotion, are genetically determined. The patterns can be interfered with in early development, but they cannot be modified to any marked degree beyond the species limits. In other words, the basic motion patterns of the individual cannot be learned, and before we can understand how behavior *can* be modified by experience, we must understand the organization of the patterns we start with. The responses that can be learned in any animal depend at the outset on the spatially organized motion systems of the species. Further, the conditions of reinforcement vary with the species. A reward for a dog may have no effect on man, whereas

man's behavior is often reinforced by subtle effects achieved by his perceptual-motor skills that could not even be discriminated by the dog. The more significant events in human learning elude analysis in an experimental tradition founded on animals.

It is our belief that the motion patterns that develop in the young animal or child — the space-structured postural, transport, and manipulative movements that appear in that order in both ontogeny and phylogeny — are as much a part of its genetic heritage as the gross anatomy of its body. The heritable mechanisms that regulate these motion patterns are the particular receptor and effector systems and the neurogeometric detectors of the brain. Each detector neuron relates specific receptor pathways to specific effector pathways. As an anatomical unit, it is subject to the vagaries of mutation, and the processes of natural selection and survival in evolution. The higher one goes in the animal scale, the more finely differentiated are these detector systems, permitting an ever more precise spatial control over movements. More highly developed behavior patterns are not a function of the refinement of receptor systems; the human eye and ear, for example, show no real improvements as detecting and discriminating devices over eyes and ears in certain lower animals. The progressive evolutionary changes in the behavior of higher animals are due to the refinement of their neuromotor systems.

Neurogeometric theory has some very direct implications for understanding the nature of motivation, particularly perceptual and activity motivation. A motion system organized according to our postulates is in a way a self-sustaining system, ever generating the conditions which induce further activity. We have said that the individual reacts to differences in stimuli. In resolving these differences, it continuously, by its own movements, produces new differences to which it must react. Here is a motivational system as compelling and more consistent than any of the traditional drive states. Moreover, when the geometric relationships between the individual and his environment are disturbed to any marked degree, and cannot be easily resolved, there are resulting disturbances in his whole emotional-motivational make-up. Some of these effects will be brought out in connection with our studies of displaced vision.

CURRENT RESEARCH

The concepts of space-structured motion, as we have developed them, represent both a general theoretical point of view, and a detailed experimental orientation to the problems of motion analysis and perceptual-motor integration. In writing this book, we have had two purposes: to review the historical development of the science of motion, particularly those investigations and ideas that have influenced our thinking, and to report in some detail a series of experiments designed specifically to test the concepts of neurogeometric theory.

The Problems

We have said that we believe the central scientific problem of behavior to be that of perceptual-motor integration, i.e., the regulation of patterns of movement to conform to the spatial order and dimensions of the environment. In our geometric theory, we have postulated that perceptual orientation, specific motions of the body, and their integration are regulated in terms of the relative spatial displacement of movement-produced stimulus patterns. Accordingly, we can test some of our specific hypotheses by systematically varying the conditions of displacement.

The general problem of displaced vision has been studied a number of times since Stratton first wore his inverting lenses.[295] Various experimenters have inverted, reversed, and angularly displaced the visual field, and studied the effects on behavior. In our own experiments, we have studied systematic conditions of inversion, reversal, combined inversion-reversal, various conditions of angular displacement, and size distortion of the visual field. We have also investigated conditions of temporal displacement of visual stimulation, i.e., delayed visual feedback. By analyzing the effects of displaced and distorted vision on various types of motion, we can define some of the conditions of perceptual-motor control, and make inferences concerning the differentiation of neural mechanisms involved.

The Methods

Our continuing investigations of the problems of perceptual-motor integration have been intimately involved with the development of some new research techniques. The most important of these are: (1) electronic methods of motion analysis and (2) the adaptation of closed-circuit television and videotape recording to behavior research.

ANALYZING MOTION. For behavior-recording and motion analysis, we have developed electronic techniques which record semi-automatically different travel and manipulative movements.[270] The prototype of this method of motion analysis was developed originally by Smith and Kappauf to record the lapping movements of the tongue in drinking in rat, cat, and dog.[257]

The diagram in Figure 1-4 describes the electronic recording methods by means of which we record differentially travel and manipulative movements in human motion. A very small electric current is passed through the body of the subject, and through objects or con-

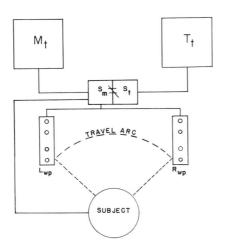

MOTION ANALYZER

Figure 1-4. Diagram of an electronic motion analyzer. A subthreshold current of about 100 microamperes is passed through the objects or controls to be manipulated and through the subject's body. Contact with the objects closes the manipulation relay (S_m), activating a manipulation time clock (M_t). Breaking contact causes the manipulation clock to stop and the travel relay (S_t) to close, starting the travel time clock (T_t).

trols which he manipulates. This current can then be used to key the relay unit (S_m) generating it and to operate recording devices and precision timers. Thus, when the subject makes contact with the first object at the top of the left work panel (L_{wp}), the relay S_m is closed and operates the manipulation time clock (M_t). When this contact is broken, a flip-flop circuit between relay units S_m and S_t operates a second clock, or travel timer (T_t). The travel clock continues to run until the subject makes contact with the first object at the top of the right work panel (R_{wp}), when the manipulation clock starts again. Thus, the times of the successive manipulation movements are summated, as are the travel times. When the subject touches the last object or control at the bottom of the right work panel, a stop circuit in the relay unit is activated, automatically stopping both clocks.

Variations of this basic circuit have been used to record the effects of spatially and temporally displaced vision on a variety of motor performances, including panel control motions, object manipulation, location reactions, tapping, drawing, handwriting, assembly motions, and tool-using operations. In developing our electronic motion-analysis units, we have used the most advanced electromechanical and vacuum tube relay circuits available in engineering literature. Thus, one product of this research has been the motion analyzers themselves, the utility and validity of which have been tested in thousands of experimental operations. We have reported a number of studies using these special methods in the motion-analysis literature.

DISPLACING THE VISUAL FIELD. In some of our first studies of displaced vision, we used optical devices to displace the visual field, as had earlier experimenters in this area.[217, 218] We used prisms in some systematic experiments, and also made observations on subjects who wore mirror arrangements to displace the visual field.

Most of our displaced vision studies have been made possible by the adaptation of closed-circuit television to the research laboratory.[273, 274] The use of the closed-circuit camera-monitor chain, the videotape recorder, and the stereoscopic television camera-monitor chain as scientific devices for the study of perception and motion has been both stimulating and rewarding. The television camera has proved to be a versatile experimental instrument, with great potential for many lines of research. In our vision studies it provides control over most of the spatial variables of significance in analyzing the phenomena of perceptual-motor integration.

Figure 1-5 shows how we have used closed-circuit television to displace the visual field. The television camera is directed at the subject's performance,

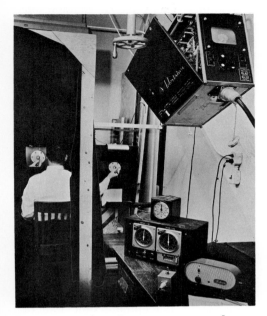

Figure 1-5. The television camera used as a scientific instrument to provide control over visual feedback. A screen prevents the subject from watching his own performance directly; he controls his motions by watching the televised image on the monitor screen.

and the televised image appears in a monitor. Screening devices prevent the subject from watching his own movements directly; he can control his performance visually only by watching the image in the monitor. Normal vision is simulated by locating the camera at an angle approximating the normal line of sight, and at a distance such that the image will be of normal size. Almost any condition of displaced vision can be effected by flicking a switch or shifting the position of the camera. The television image can be inverted or reversed by means of switches, or it can be inverted and reversed simultaneously. The visual field can be rotated to any desired angle by rotating the camera. By placing the camera at different positions in relation to the subject, we achieve the effect of "putting the eyes outside the head," the sort of effect one gets with

mirrors. Finally, we can use different lenses in the camera to increase or decrease the size of the visual image. In speed, flexibility, and scope of control, the television camera is an unmatched device for experimental manipulation of the spatial dimensions of visual feedback of motion.

From the time of our first use of television in the analysis of displaced vision and motion, we have considered the possibility of using a videotape recorder to investigate time displacement, as contrasted with space displacement, of the visual feedback of motion.[274] With the availability of such recorders, this objective in television methodology has now been achieved. As shown in Figure 1-6, the visual feedback of the televised image of performance can be delayed by inserting a tape recorder system in the closed-circuit television chain between the camera and the subject's monitor. The image is recorded on a length of tape traveling between the recording head and the playback head.

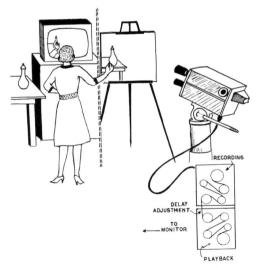

Figure 1-6. A dual closed-circuit videotape system, used to delay the visual feedback of motion. The televised image of performance is recorded on magnetic tape and played back to the subject's monitor after a delay interval.

The subject performs while the recording is being made and then sees a delayed image of his performance when the recorded signal is played back to the monitor. When two tape recorders are used, one for recording and the other for playback (an experimental set-up made available to us for a limited time by RCA Laboratories), the subject's performance can continue all the while he is watching a slightly delayed visual display. Television thus gives us experimental control over both spatial and temporal displacement of movement-produced visual feedback. One of our purposes is to analyze the interrelation of time and space factors in perceptual-motor integration.

Our interest in closed-circuit television goes beyond its uses in studying displaced vision, for we feel that this is an experimental technique with wide applicability in behavior research. In addition to the vision experiments, we have used television for exploratory observations in a number of areas, including infant behavior research and the behavior of fighting fish and pigeons with televised feedback. The use of television tape recorders to analyze information feedback and knowledge of results in learning has been extensively tested. Finally, different types of stereoscopic television systems are now being analyzed in relation to their applicability in behavior research.

SUMMARY

1. The problem of relating the events of behavior to the characteristics of the stimulus world has been recognized for a long time but never solved. The problem is described here in terms of a new conceptual orientation that behavior in animals is organized primarily in terms of geometric conformity to the spatial characteristics of the environment. Un-derstanding the geometric relationships between stimulation and motion is looked upon as one of the central problems of science today.

2. Traditional approaches to the problems of perceptual-motor integration — volitional, gestalt, and reinforcement theories, in particular — have been of limited significance in advancing knowledge concerning these basic questions. The widely accepted reinforcement concepts, which interpret motion in terms of linear and sequential chaining of unit reactions, fall short of a meaningful account of how behavior is organized. Alternative approaches to human behavior organization are indicated, in order to give some coherence to what we know about perception and motion, their evolution, and their neural basis.

3. A new theoretical approach to the problems of perceptual-motor integration, treating perception and motion as equivalent phenomena, proposes to account for the space-structuring of motion in terms of a geometrically organized regulatory mechanism. According to this theory, all motion is regulated by detection of spatial differences in patterns of stimulation. Such differential patterns are essential both for the process of stimulation of receptors and for integration of the specific space patterns of motion. Motion patterns are integrated at three levels — those of postural control, transport movements and manipulative movements.

4. Neurogeometric theory represents a revised interpretation of reflex doctrine in which differential action within the nervous system is based on differential input to the neuron from two sources of stimulation, rather than on decision-making powers of the synapse. Thus, the neuron itself is thought of as the primary detector of differences in patterns of stimulation, and somatic action is the adaptive response of the organism to these differences. This theory has direct implications for mo-

tion organization in development and learning, for theories of motivation, and for evolutionary doctrine. The more highly controlled and precisely articulated motion patterns in higher animals are due to the differentiation of these neurogeometric integrative mechanisms.

5. In our present research in perceptual-motor integration, we are concerned with spatial and temporal displacement of the visual feedback of motion. Several new experimental techniques have helped to determine the nature of these investigations. One is our electronic method of motion analysis, and another is the adaptation of closed-circuit television and videotape recording to behavior research. The future of television as a laboratory instrument seems assured, for it gives unmatched experimental control over almost all aspects of the visual feedback of motion.

CHAPTER 2

THE SCIENCE
OF MOTION

Understanding the organization of human motion patterns is an empirical problem as old as man himself, because the emergence of the human species hinged upon the development of tool-using behavior. Early man needed enough insight into the nature of his own motion not only to make and use tools, but to use tools to make tools. The machine tool tradition — the use of tools to make tools — originated in the most primitive human societies;[61, 131, 159, 316] for example, it is said to have been associated closely with the first use of fire by Peking man.[71] This prehistoric insight into human motion patterns was not confined to the idea of using tools to exert force. As Oakley has written, the tools of Stone Age man accomplished all

of the basic functions of modern machines, in percussion, cutting, scraping, piercing, shearing, and molding.[203] The prehistoric tool-maker necessarily must have conceived the relation between the tool and the human motion required for a specific use.

Within scientific tradition we can trace along several lines the development of knowledge about the organization and regulation of animal motion. In this chapter, we propose to survey three of these. First, we shall point out some of the highlights in the development of scientific concepts of how body motion is initiated, regulated, and integrated. Next, we shall review some of the developmental studies of motion, and, finally, we shall summarize various analyses of the organization of specific motion patterns.

It is interesting that all three of these areas of scientific investigation were foreshadowed in the late fifteenth and early sixteenth centuries by the work of a man now remembered primarily as an artist — Leonardo da Vinci. He was the first to make comparative physiological studies of motion in lower animals and in man, painstakingly recording his observations. He was also the only person prior to the twentieth century who systematically interrelated the anatomical mechanisms of motion in fish, birds, cats, horses, dogs, and man with physiological and graphic studies of their movements. Far in advance of behavior science, he defined the scientific problem of the changes in the body and its activities with age, and made careful observations of growth, development, and movement in young children. He also compared and contrasted characteristic motion patterns of men and women. He then went on to apply his scientific concepts of motion to the design of an untold number of novel devices and machines, including flying machines.

Although Leonardo believed in finite causes for animal and human motion, and may have been the first person to search for these causes systematically in relation to both anatomy and function, he still conceived of muscle action as controlled by fluids carried through body vessels — a heritage from the Aristotelian notion that movement is initiated by the release of animal spirits into the muscles by the brain. However, he had an intimate knowledge of all forms of muscular action, and may have had some idea of the reciprocal action of antagonistic muscles. He also made excellent drawings of the brain and receptor organs, which may have contributed to the development of more modern concepts of brain function more than a century later. Some of Leonardo's drawings, illustrating his knowledge of anatomy and motion systems, appear in Figure 2-1.

CONCEPTS OF NEURAL INTEGRATION

Late in the seventeenth century, Borelli described the nerve trunks as made up of nerve fibrils, and formulated the modern concept that muscular movement results from neural action.[29] However, the concept of the brain as the conductive mechanism of motion is ordinarily attributed to Descartes — a remarkable achievement for a mathematician and philosopher with very limited empirical biological experience.[10] Figure 2-2 contrasts Borelli's idea of the control of muscle action by nerves with Descartes' notion that movement results from external stimulation.

Advance in knowledge about the neural conduction mechanisms underlying motion coincides with development of the concept of reflex action.[246] The original observations proving that the brain or central nervous system is essential for motion were those of a British parish minister, Stephen Hales, whose experiments were systematically repeated by Whytt.[40] The experiments involved abolishing the central nervous system of the frog by tying off the head or pithing the spinal cord. Both of these operations were observed to destroy stimulus-released movement in the animal's limbs. Whytt also observed that only a small section of the spinal cord was necessary for stimulus-released movement, or reflex action. According to Carmichael,[40] Hales was the first writer to describe nerve conduction as electrical in nature, a fact that was not clearly established until the work of Sherrington[237] and Adrian.[1] Helmholtz[115] made some of the first systematic measures of the velocity of nerve conduction by measuring the latency of response of a frog nerve-muscle preparation when different points on the nerve were stimulated.

The traditional concept of the reflex is based on the notion of continuity of conduction between sensory systems and motor nerves innervating muscles. The discovery of the distinction between the sensory and motor nerve mechanisms was made by Charles Bell in the early

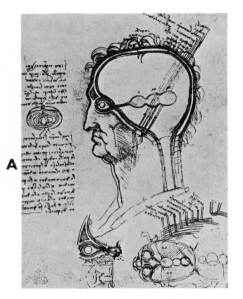

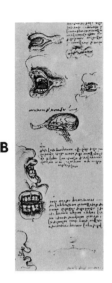

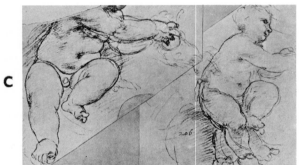

Figure 2-1. Leonardo da Vinci's studies of anatomy and motion. A. The eye and optic nerve system. B. Lip movements. C. Movements of infants. D. Movements of birds, dogs, human males and females. (From *Leonardo da Vinci*, Reynal & Company, 1956.)

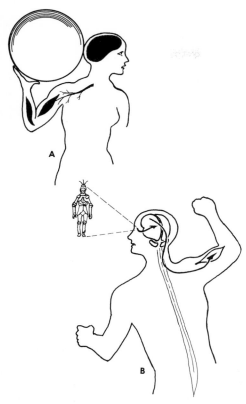

Figure 2-2. Borelli's concept of the neural control of muscle action (A), contrasted with Descartes' notion of reflex action, as movement produced by stimulation (B).

part of the nineteenth century.[39] Bell is credited also with discovery of the muscular or kinesthetic sense, but clear proof that kinesthetic sensory fibers are distinct from motor fibers was not made until the late nineteenth century. The original experiments differentiating motor nerves from the sensory nerves of the kinesthetic system were credited by Bain[11] to J. W. Arnold.

Early Neurophysiology

The concept of neural integration in motion grew out of the distinctions made between the mechanisms that control reflex action and those that regulate perceptually guided behavior and voluntary movement. These distinctions are credited to Marshall Hall and Flourens.[90] Hall showed that reflex activity in a frog persisted after decapitation.[237] In his discussion of motion, he distinguished among four types of movement — voluntary action, respiration, involuntary action of the muscles in direct response to stimulation, and reflex action. Detailed exploration of the brain itself as an integrative mechanism originated with the work of Flourens, who systematically isolated and studied the separate parts of the brain (forebrain, cerebellum, midbrain, medulla oblongata, spinal cord, and peripheral nerves) in relation to posture, motion, and perception. Flourens perfected techniques of neurosurgical extirpation and isolation of parts of the brain in animals and thus defined decisively the course of a major part of the science of neurophysiology up to the present.

The shift from general exploratory to more precise study of the brain was made possible by technological advances, including the development of electrical methods of stimulating the brain and of precise methods of recording movements — pneumatically, by means of the tambour (Fig. 2-3),[173] mechanically, by spring-driven and weight-activated recorders,[173, 191] and electrically.[183] With these improved techniques, the velocity of the nerve impulse was measured more accurately, the anatomy of the kinesthetic sensory nerves was established, the areas of the cortex which would produce movement when stimulated electrically were defined,[84, 94] and the electrical nature of nerve conduction was established with some degree of certainty.[237] Further, the first efforts were made to analyze the chemical and metabolic relationships in movement, and it was demonstrated that behavior can be modified by means of the metabolic action of the brain.[191]

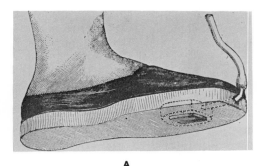

A

B

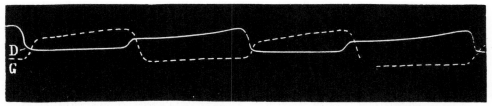

C

Figure 2-3. Some of the first instrumentation devised for the recording of human motions. A. Pneumatic pressure plate mounted in a shoe for recording human gait. B. Technique of carrying a smoked paper kymograph to record the movements of walking and running. C. A record of walking. (Marey.[173])

A remarkable pair of illustrations from the work of Mosso,[191] shown in Figure 2-4, are among the earliest graphic displays of direct study of the human brain. Mosso used a pneumatic lever to record the pulse of a subject who had an aperture in his skull as a result of a wound. The experiment disclosed that depriving the brain of blood by pressing on the carotid arteries led to marked changes in the cerebral pulse (as shown in the center line of the record), and to convulsions. The results were sufficiently impressive that Mosso decided not to repeat the experiment. Mosso was one of the outstanding original investigators of motion and the integrative system of the brain in relation to metabolic processes. Developing his own precision methods, he made systematic studies of motion, of muscular fatigue, and of the effects of sustained mental activity. He proposed one of the first sets of hypotheses about brain chemistry in relation to different levels of integrative functions, and outlined systematic experiments to test his proposals.

The definitive work on the integrative

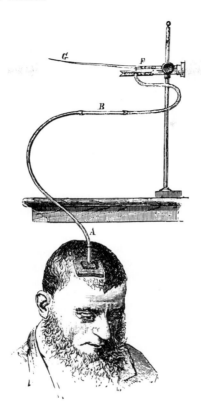

Figure 2-4. Mosso's studies of the brain and action. A. A pneumographic recording system attached to the head of a subject, located over a defect in the skull. B. Records of the pulse of the brain during overt action of the subject in response to pressure on the carotid arteries. (Mosso.[191])

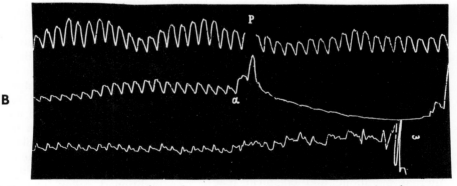

action of the nervous system is that of Sherrington, who adapted the myographic methods of Marey[173] to the study of reflex movements in decerebrate and spinal cats. Sherrington advanced to a very high level the reflex method of analysis of neural mechanisms of conduction and integration, and defined the principal hypotheses which still guide electrophysiological studies of neural mechanisms. By means of appropriately controlled stimuli, he quantified many of the properties of reflex control of movement, such as stimulus latency, refractory phase in neural conduction, inhibition, reciprocal innervation, inhibition of antagonistic muscles, reflex summation, recruitment, fatigue, and after-discharge. Above all, Sherrington defined clearly for the first time the properties of reflex action as determined by neural systems, and determined the general mechanisms of reciprocal control of antagonistic muscles.

Pavlov and the Growth of Learning Theory

Application of physiological knowledge of the nervous system to the understanding of general psychological events was blocked for a time by nineteenth century distinctions between reflex action, voluntary movement, and perception. Pavlov's studies on conditioned reflexes,[205] which were first reported in 1905, weakened this older point of view and opened the way for the general learning theories of behavior now so popular among psychologists. Pavlov's principal demonstration was that reactions to specific exteroceptive stimuli could be developed in dogs by associating these stimuli with unconditioned stimuli, i.e., stimuli naturally effective in producing the responses. In demonstrating how such conditioned reactions could be inhibited, generalized, extinguished, and associated with other reactions in so-called higher-order conditioning, he gave experimental reality to the many earlier doctrines that human learning and mental development are an outcome of temporal association of sensory experience and ideas. Perhaps his most striking demonstration was that internal metabolic and chemical reactions show the effects of conditioning even more clearly than overt behavior.

To Russian theorists, the term "conditioned reflex" represented the combined significance of the old doctrine of association of ideas and the notion of physiological determinism in behavior, and American psychologists found fully as much significance in Pavlov's work as did his compatriots. His experiments and theories achieved an end that all demonstrations of learning in psychology had failed to do, i.e., to prove experimentally that association of stimuli could modify vital mechanisms of both metabolism and motion. In this country, conditioning theory fostered the general belief that behavioral integration can be accounted for in terms of the temporal association and sequential chaining of reflexes. In the heredity-environment controversy, conditioning theory lent credence to the view of environmental determinism in development, with the emphasis on learning, as opposed to maturation. The chain reflex became a theoretical model of behavior development in the individual, and of organization of response at all levels.

Pavlov's lectures appeared on the American scene at a time when Thorndike[302, 303] was reporting his studies on animal learning and intelligence, and reformulating the old principles of association of ideas into laws of stimulus-response relationships in learning. Thorndike's ideas were potent in the then-developing field of progressive education, and provided, perhaps for the first time, a clear experimental base for an objective psychology. But his experiments with cats and puzzle boxes lacked the elusive but critical features of direct experimental control and manipulation of stimulus, response, and metabolic relationships that had been mastered by Pavlov. Further, Thorndike's concepts could not compete with the rich new set of pavlovian terms — conditioned reflex, unconditioned reflex, experimental extinction, higher order conditioning, and the like. The importance of learning as a basis of an objective and experimental psychology had been established by Thorndike, but the terminology adopted by the growing number of learning psychologists was derived from the conditioning experiment.

The application of conditioning theory to human motion and development was first formulated clearly by Watson,[317] and had considerable impact on psychological thinking. Some of his ideas were supported by experiments, although the results of these were not entirely unequivocal. His main thesis was that human development is a matter of chaining established reflexes together through conditioning. He believed that speech is developed by such stimulus-response chaining, and that thought is the implicit form of such chained reactions. Watson's[318] experiments on conditioning of emotional reactions in the infant, however, suggested a far more complicated state of affairs than he was perhaps ready to admit.

Since Watson's time, development of learning doctrine has followed an anticlimactic course wherein ever more elaborate theoretical models have been constructed. Human behavior in general, with varying emphases on verbal behavior, specific psychomotor behavior, perception, or emotion, has been forced into the mathematical or statistical molds prescribed by the particular theory of learning in favor. The most popular recent formulations of learning theory are those based upon the concept of reinforcement, as variously stated by Hull,[136] Skinner,[247] Spence,[279] Miller and Dollard,[188] and others. The term "reinforcement" refers generally to the process of strengthening or increasing the probability of occurrence of a response by following it with a reinforcing stimulus. Reinforcement is effected in various ways, by presenting or withdrawing reinforcers described as positive or negative. Secondary reinforcement represents the conditioning value of a previously ineffective stimulus that has been made effective by association with a reinforcer. Motion or behavior is molded or shaped (organized) through the action of reinforcement on particular responses. Learning theorists have gone on from these basic propositions to derive general laws of behavior relating motivation, emotion, and perception to the facts of reinforcement.

Weaknesses of Learning Doctrine as a General Theory of Behavior Organization

The impact that learning theory has had on psychology in general is out of all proportion to the events which it validly describes. The early promise of Pavlov's study of learning was to provide an answer to the question of neural integration in animal motion. This promise has by no means been fulfilled. In applying the generalized concepts of "learning mechanisms" to an account of complex behavior, including so-called abnormalities and conflict, learning theorists have for the most part passed over the basic question of neural integration. They have maintained that their theories can be significant at the behavioral level without reference to neurophysiological interpretations. This position can be disputed. The fact remains that behavior is a biological function, mediated by the response mechanism, and that theories of behavior organization must not violate the known facts of neurophysiological organization. On several counts, current learning theory cannot be reconciled with what we know of the behaving system.

One of the major weaknesses in learning theory is in its ambiguous interpretation of the role of the cortex in neural integration. It has long been known that speech in man and specific psychomotor activities in man and higher animals are integrated at the cortical level. Pavlov's work was generally accepted as demonstrating that the cortical integrative mechanism was equivalent with conditioning, or learning. It was felt — and is still assumed by many today — that the higher "mental" activities are integrated at the cortical level by means of learning.

The first doubt cast on this notion of the cortex as the seat of learning was in the 1930's, when it was found that dogs and monkeys with most[59] or with major areas[175, 330] of the cerebral cortex destroyed could still learn conditioned responses to sound and to light. In fact, most of the more complex phenomena of conditioning, such as generalization, inhibition, and higher order conditioning, could be demonstrated in such animals. More recently, it has been found that direct electrical stimulation of the hypothalamus can act as a reinforcer. Olds[204] showed that rats learn to press a lever in order to deliver a weak electrical stimulus to an area of their own hypothalamus, while Delgado, Roberts, and Miller[65] demonstrated that a somewhat stronger electrical shock to a different area of the hypothalamus sets up an avoidance reaction which can be conditioned to stimuli presented with the shock. No such reinforcement effects can be found at the cortical level. The notion that the cortex is the seat of learning has no direct experimental support, and one questions whether the neural integrative mechanisms of complex motions are, in fact, learning mechanisms.

Another major weakness of learning theory of behavior organization has been its explicit or implicit assumption that unit reactions are organized into larger complexes in terms of sequential chains. The more we learn about the motion mechanisms of the body, including those of speech, the less tenable the "chaining" concept appears to be. The development of motion patterns in young animals and children can be described best as a process of differentiation from general to more specific patterns, rather than the linking together of discrete responses. Even the developing patterns of speech are characterized

first by generalized movements of sound production, which only later are integrated with the more specific articulatory movements. The weakness of the "chaining" concept is apparent when one thinks of the process of learning a new skill, such as bowling. Here the new pattern of motion to be learned involves postural movements of the body, carefully timed movements of locomotion, sweeping transport movements of the arm, and, finally, precise manipulative movements of the hand and fingers. Several types of movement must be performed simultaneously, in an integrated fashion. How does one learn such a skill — by acquiring one response, then linking another to it, and another, and another? The idea seems absurd.

A third inadequacy of learning theory is that it provides no clue to the obvious differences in behavioral organization in different animals. When one studies learning capacity in rat and man, choosing patterns of response within the behavior repertory of both, no great differences can be found. The learning process — and its mechanisms — are assumed to be basically the same for all species. Then what is the significance of the very great differences in neural organization that appear in the animal scale? To what can we attribute the distinctive features of behavior in the different species — especially the characteristic behavior patterns of the human animal? To a generalized learning mechanism, possessed by all animals alike? We must look further than that for an answer to our questions. The problem of integration of perceptual-motor behavior has not been solved and will not be solved by running rats in a maze or giving them a lever to press.

Our own belief is that a meaningful theory of what learning is and its significance as a reorganizational process must be based on better understanding of the primary organizational mechanisms of behavior. The motion patterns that can be learned by an individual of a given species depend on the motion patterns with which he was endowed and the sensori-neuromotor mechanisms that define them. The problem is one of understanding behavior integration, but such an understanding cannot proceed independently of valid interpretations of the underlying neurophysiological mechanisms. Thus, we try to assess the significance of observations on motion organization in neurophysiological as well as behavioral terms.

DEVELOPMENTAL STUDIES OF MOTION

Some understanding of the mechanisms, the conditions of control, and the adaptive character of motion patterns can be gained by developmental studies, either phylogenetic or ontogenetic. Darwin[62] originated research on the evolution of adaptive motion mechanisms, and his comparative study of expressive movements in animals still stands as one of the few systematic studies in this area. All too frequently, general descriptive processes of animal behavior, such as instinct, motivation, learning, perception, and intelligence are assumed gratuitously to be the same order of events in all animals.[201]

Studies of ontogenetic development of motion patterns have been more numerous and more definitive. Many species of animals have been observed, both before and after birth, or hatching, in an effort to describe the normal course of behavioral development, to establish the maturational character of particular motion patterns, and to define the conditions essential to normal development.

Descriptive Studies of Motor Development

The first developmental studies by Harrison,[110] Matthews and Detwiler,[178]

and Coghill[50] pointed up the significance of analyzing the development of neural mechanisms for the general understanding of behavioral integration. Systematic descriptions of the course of development of motion in fetal animals have been given by Angulo y González,[3] Coronios,[54] Barcroft and Barron,[12] Windle,[329] and Smith and Daniel.[264]

Hooker[130] collected the first comprehensive data on the developing motion patterns of the human fetus. In particular, he defined the critical course of development between 8 and 14 weeks of fetal life. He described the first motion as a generalized mass movement involving torsion and twisting of the upper part of the torso. At first, any effective stimulus elicited the same generalized response. Two to three weeks later, specific limb movements could be elicited. Finally, at 14 weeks, or some five and one-half months before term, all of the finer movements of the body appeared, except perhaps breathing, vocalization, and some eye movements. All of these differentiated motions were elicited by specific stimuli applied on particular areas of the body. Thus, from the very first, the motions of the fetal body are space-structured in the sense that they involve an element of localized control, both in terms of the critical area of stimulation and the direction of the movement in relation to this source.

The critical period of development of motion in the fetus we have called the fetal motor sequence.[268] After birth, for the first few years of life, another course of motor development takes place. The postnatal motor sequence starts out with the generalized movements of the neonate, proceeds gradually through the halting, inaccurately controlled movements of the head; reaching; and crawling; and at about one year comes to involve well controlled motions of the terminal members of the limbs in different motion patterns. Eventually the postural, transport, and fine manipulative movements are highly integrated into the diverse activities of the young child. Further, these motion patterns are highly space-structured, in that they are adapted to the stimulus patterns of the child's environment. Perception and motion have not emerged separately; rather, the reaction patterns which have developed are both perceptual and motor in their organization (Fig. 2-5).

It seems clear from developmental studies that the appearance of organized motions in the infant is not dependent on practice, reinforcement, or conditioning. Conditioning in the fetus has been considered impossible by some investigators,[216, 277] difficult and unstable by others.[278] Even in the first few months of postnatal life, no stable consistent

conditioned learning has been observed.[176, 323, 326] Studies of motor development in infants and young children also indicate that the precisely organized perceptual-motor patterns with which the young child is equipped do not depend on specific learning or conditioning procedures.[96] The motion system of the child — as different from that of the pigeon, rat, or dog as his body and nervous system are different — is a part of his human heritage.

Maturation of Specific Motions

There have been many systematic studies of the development of specific motion patterns in children.[96, 97, 212, 213, 236] In general, these studies have de-

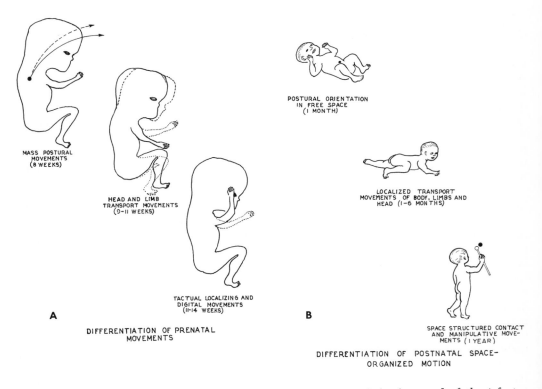

MASS POSTURAL MOVEMENTS (8 WEEKS)

HEAD AND LIMB TRANSPORT MOVEMENTS (9-11 WEEKS)

TACTUAL LOCALIZING AND DIGITAL MOVEMENTS (11-14 WEEKS)

A

DIFFERENTIATION OF PRENATAL MOVEMENTS

POSTURAL ORIENTATION IN FREE SPACE (1 MONTH)

LOCALIZED TRANSPORT MOVEMENTS OF BODY, LIMBS AND HEAD (1-6 MONTHS)

B

SPACE STRUCTURED CONTACT AND MANIPULATIVE MOVEMENTS (1 YEAR)

DIFFERENTIATION OF POSTNATAL SPACE-ORGANIZED MOTION

Figure 2-5. Spatially organized motion during development of the fetus and of the infant during the first year of life. In both fetal and postnatal motor sequences, development progresses from generalized postural motions of the trunk and limbs to transport movements of the head and limbs and finer motions of the extremities.

scribed the emergence of motion patterns on a flexible time scale, with generalized activities preceding the development of finer manipulative movements. McCarthy[179] has described language development similarly, as a sequence of transitional stages from gross activities of vocalization, through babbling movements involving repetitive movements of the chest and mouth, to fine movements of articulation of the lips, tongue, mouth, and throat.

There have been a number of demonstrations of rather specific perceptual reactions which appear due to maturation rather than learning. For example, Gibson and Walk[98] have recently shown that rats, cats, goats and infants show avoidance motions to visual perception of non-support. These reactions were displayed by infant animals without prior experience in the situation when they were placed on a clear glass surface above the floor. Other specific space-organized motions which have been shown to be maturational in character are migratory patterns in turtles,[60] righting reactions in cats and rabbits,[312] placing, hopping, and optokinetic reactions in cats,[313] eye movements in infants,[182] and postural and locomotor patterns in infants.[96] Observations such as these have been numerous and conclusive enough to convince us that the major space-organized response patterns of the animal system — postural control, transport of the limbs, head movements, all the forms of eye movement, grasping, the patterns of locomotion — appear as integrated patterns of response in the normal development of the behaving system.

Conditions of Normal Development

Although it appears that no specific learning or practice is required for the differentiation of the basic perceptual-motor patterns, it is true that in some cases, at least, these patterns cannot de-velop in a behavior vacuum. The question is whether some sensorimotor experience is necessary for normal development of motion, and how specific the sensorimotor conditions must be. Experimental results here are somewhat contradictory.

In an early study, Harrison[110] anesthetized tadpoles, and observed that this restriction on behavior apparently had no effect on motor development. Similar results were found on larval salamanders by Matthews and Detwiler[178] and Carmichael.[38] Temporary anesthesia produced no delay in the development of swimming movements. Along another line, Lashley and Russell[157] found that young rats reared in the dark from birth could jump from a stand to a feeding station when put in a visual environment just about as well as rats reared normally in the light.

Quite different results have been reported more recently on the effects of restriction of perceptual-motor activity. Newborn kittens reared in the dark for four weeks after birth (about two weeks past the time when their eyes normally open) took about a week to recover to normal level in visually-guided motion.[98] Riesen[221] studied the effects of visual restriction in infant chimpanzees, comparing different periods of restriction (up to 16 months), complete restriction with restriction of pattern vision only, and complete restriction with restriction for all but 1½ hours a day. The animal given normal vision for 1½ hours daily showed no ill effects, but all other animals, including the animal which had received light stimulation through translucent goggles, were gravely deficient in visual coordinations. Although their eyes were sensitive to light, their visually-guided locomotion, object manipulation, reaction to moving objects, and pattern vision were greatly impaired. Hundreds of hours were needed for these perceptually organized activities to approach normal efficiency.

Similar retardation in visually-controlled behavior is seen in children who have been blind from birth and then acquire sight after removal of cataracts.[235] Deficiencies in manipulation were found in young chimpanzees who had been reared for a period of time with their hands enclosed in restricting containers.[202] In all of these situations, the development of motion patterns was seriously retarded, or even permanently impaired, by gross restriction of perceptual-motor activity.

In some cases, the appearance of space-structured motions requires fairly specific sensorimotor conditions. The phenomenon which has been called "imprinting" describes the onset of following behavior in certain newly hatched ground-nesting birds.[169] A duckling, for example, typically follows its mother consistently. However, it will follow the first large moving object it sees during the first few days after hatching. Chicks can be made to follow moving geometrical forms that are presented during the "critical period" after hatching.[120, 141, 142] Here the development of an organized perceptual-motor pattern depends on the appearance of a fairly specific visual stimulus during a critical period of time. A similar situation was reported by Daniel and Smith,[60] who observed that in young sea turtles there is a critical period of about seven days after hatching during which light stimulation will release light-following reactions. This concept of a critical period during which time appropriate external conditions can initiate a genetically defined motion pattern probably has general significance in development. Certainly the gross restriction studies suggest that motor deficiencies occurred because of sensory restriction during early life. In contrast, temporary periods of restriction later in life, e.g., blindness, have less serious effects.

It is not entirely clear why the earlier experiments on rats reared in darkness found no effects comparable to those reported in the later restriction studies. As far as the anesthetized amphibians are concerned, it seems credible that their activity was not retarded to any great extent because the swimming pattern is not highly articulated with respect to variations in the environment. The degree of precise visual organization may also account for the differences between the rats and the chimpanzees, i.e., the rats may have suffered less from early blindness than did the higher animals because the rodent visual system is not as highly organized. Only tentative conclusions can be reached on some of these points until more evidence is available.

Although a certain amount of sensorimotor experience during a critical period in early life apparently is necessary for the normal development of the basic perceptual-motor patterns, these patterns are not organized according to specific learning or conditioning procedures. Rather, the organization of motion in the animal system is genetically determined and only incidentally modified by specific learning. The duckling's pattern of following an object is genetically organized; only the object is subject to the chance of the moment. A striking demonstration of the genetic determination of motion patterns has been afforded by experiments, usually with amphibians, involving the transplantation of limbs or sense organs to abnormal or displaced positions, with subsequent regeneration of the nerve supply.[286, 288, 321] The general result of these studies is that stimulus-released motion involving a transplanted or displaced organ is likewise specifically displaced or disoriented with respect to the stimulus. The geometric relationship between the stimulus and response is determined by the anatomy of the nervous system. We will discuss more of this later.

ANALYSIS OF MOVEMENT ORGANIZATION

Heretofore the scientific problems of motion organization have been dealt with outside the mainstream of behavior science. Although we have some detailed analyses of the mechanisms and functional structures of specific movement systems, such as locomotion, speech, and eye movements, this knowledge has had little effect on the course and theories of psychology and physiology.

There is one area of the study of motion patterns — the organization of manual movements — which has remained elusive. The hand and its ways have resisted scientific analysis. We are beginning to understand that the key to understanding manual movements lies in the primary function of the human hand as a tool-using mechanism. This fundamental adaptive use of the hand evolved concurrently with the evolution of man, as a critical aspect of that evolution. Thus, any scientific analysis of the movement organization of the hand is tied in with the subject of work, with the use of tools and machines, and with the "human engineering" problems of behavior. Accordingly, we divide our survey of the study of movement organization into two parts: the analysis of unaided movements of the locomotor, ocular, and speech systems, and the use of the body as a control mechanism in work and machine operation. This second area will be described in the next chapter in relation to development of the psychological testing of perceptual-motor activities and of the human engineering and cybernetic approaches to the science of human motion.

Human Gait

In the first systematic studies of human gait, Borelli[29] attempted to formulate a mechanical theory of locomotion.

The next notable advance in the field was made 150 years later, when Marey[173] developed the first two scientific methods for studying gait — the basographic and the photographic methods. In his first studies, he used pneumatic devices built into the base of shoes, and recorded on a moving kymograph paper the changes of pressure induced by walking (Fig. 2-3). Marey[174] later adopted a suggestion of an astronomer, Janssen,[140] for making a rotating photographic device to take sequential pictures. With this device, which was known as the Marey wheel, he was able to record and time the movements of human gait. Marey's method of studying motion was a milestone in the development of motion-picture photography.

Two further advances in photographic methods of studying gait were made. The artist Muybridge[196] improved the multiple exposure method of photography and applied his techniques to detailed studies of the clothed and unclothed human body in action and work. Muybridge's photographic studies of man in motion rank with the graphic studies of Leonardo both as an artistic and a scientific innovation, and were definitive in shaping the course of both motion study and graphic art in the twentieth century. Braune and Fischer[30] used what is known as multiple image or stroboscopic photography. They attached eleven neon-like tubes (Geissler tubes) to different positions on the human body and photographed the intermittent lights from different angles during locomotion (Fig. 2-6). They then made a careful analysis of the timing and forces involved in the movements of locomotion.

Although these photographic techniques have yielded precise information about patterns of locomotion, there are certain advantages in recording from the soles of the feet. All of the actions and interactions of the body in walking — landing, stride, take-off, postural bal-

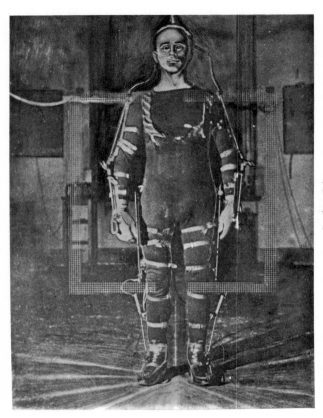

Figure 2-6. The multiple-image photographic method of Braune and Fischer used to study human motion. The straight tubes alongside the torso and body members are Geissler tubes. (Braune and Fischer.[30])

ance, and direction of gait — are reflected in the many articulations of the base of the foot in relation to the substrate.[228] In recent years there have been two refinements in Marey's basographic method. In the first, Schwartz, Heath, and Wright[230] recorded gait by means of a polygraph from electrical contact devices built into the sole of the shoe at the point of the big toe, the fifth metatarsal joint, and the heel. Their later detailed analysis of the kinetics of locomotion had certain practical applications, as, for example, in designing shoes for crippled gait.[229] Second, we have used an electronic motion analyzer to time precisely the movements of the shod or unshod foot in many forms of locomotion — walking, running, stair climbing, hopping, and skipping.[267] As

described in Chapter 1, this method (Fig. 2-7) involves passing a very small electric current through the body of the subject and the runway. Contact of the foot with the runway completes a circuit through a relay unit which activates a time clock, and breaking contact activates a second clock. Thus, separate measures of contact and stride time are obtained. Contacts of different parts of the foot are timed separately by attaching leads at different points on the sole.

Modern electrical methods of analyzing muscular activity had their origin in the first recordings of electrical currents in muscles by Galvani in 1791 and later by Matteucci and duBois-Reymond.[183] With the development of present-day amplifying and recording systems, it has been possible to relate photographic and

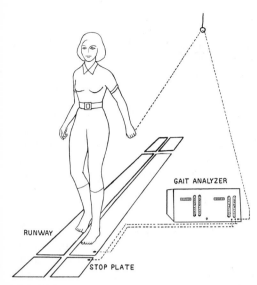

GAIT ANALYZER

RUNWAY

STOP PLATE

Figure 2-7. The electronic basometer. A sub-threshold current is passed through the body and through the runway. Separate measures of contact and stride time can be obtained.

basographic indices of gait with the recorded electrical activity of particular muscle systems. These recording methods were perfected some 30 years ago by Stetson and Bouman,[292] and the most thorough of these comparative analyses were made by Stetson and his students.[280, 291] Stetson described the two types of movement involved in gait — as well as in other motion — as ballistic movements, which throw the limb or part of the foot in a free-swinging arc, and tense movements, which fixate a particular part of the body or regulate its course of action throughout relatively slow pursuit or travel.

Historically, there have been two distinct points of view about the organization and control of gait. The pendulum concept is a prescientific notion that the limbs in walking and running act according to a relatively simple rule approximating the law of the pendulum. The second notion, the mechanical-reflex theory, described locomotion as

a complex combination of reflexes related to regulation of the center of gravity of the body while in motion. This description of gait is inadequate from either a physiological or a behavioral point of view. It accounts neither for the differentiation of patterns of locomotion from generalized body motion during the course of development, nor for the highly organized nature of locomotor patterns throughout life.

We describe human gait in terms of perceptual-motor interaction at three levels of movement.[267] The three component movements involved are postural movements, transport movements, and manipulative or articulatory contact movements of the foot. Postural movements are organized in relation to gravity, and control the center of gravity of the body. Transport or stride movements are organized in terms of action in free space, and are specifically regulated in terms of differences in stimulation on the two sides of the body, or between different segments of the same side of the body. The articulatory movements of the foot are space-organized in terms of the properties of the hard matter of the walking surface. Gait is thus the resulting integration of three levels of perceptual-motor activity, which maintain the center of gravity, drive the leg in the stride, and articulate the force and direction of the movements of the foot.

Eye Movements

The first successful recordings of eye movements are usually credited to Högyes[126] who thrust a needle into the eye of animals and allowed it to operate against an air capsule. Delabarre[64] made an early attempt to record human eye movements mechanically. He inserted a plaster of paris contact plate over the cornea of his own eye and led an attached thread to a recording lever.

Photographic methods for recording eye movements were developed by

Dodge[66] before the motion-picture camera was highly perfected. Dodge's analysis of the different patterns of eye movements, such as pursuit, reading movements, nystagmus, and visual exploration, was an extraordinary contribution to the science of motion. He defined the basic components of these patterns as the fixation, pursuit, and saccadic (equivalent to Stetson's ballistic) movements. Dodge's work on eye movements led to development of the eye-movement motion-picture camera that photographs a point of light reflected from the cornea (Fig. 2-8, A). This camera has been used to record movements of the eyes in reading, during rotation and acceleration of the body, and in other situations. Stroboscopic photography also has been used to record eye movements.

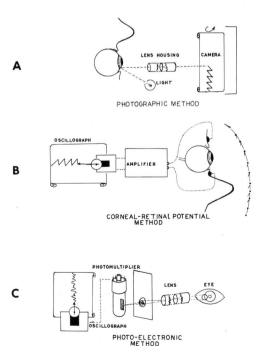

Figure 2-8. Techniques of recording eye movements. A. Photographic method. B. Corneo-retinal potential method. C. Photo-electronic method.

Another method for recording eye movements is based on a standing electrical potential difference between the front and back of the eye, which was first described by duBois-Reymond.[69] If electrodes are placed beside the eyes, the potential difference between them, due to the corneo-retinal potential, varies as the eyes are moved laterally. The sign of the potential gives the direction of rotation; the degree of the potential gives the magnitude of rotation. Thus, change in sign and magnitude of the potential can be amplified and recorded on an oscilloscope (Fig. 2-8, B).[83, 183, 194, 266]

The most recent innovation in recording and analyzing eye movements is shown in Figure 2-8, C. In this system, an image of a portion of the iris and sclera is focused on a surface containing a small slit. The total amount of light passing through the slit is picked up and amplified by a photomultiplier tube. Because the amount of light passing through the slit varies directly with the angular position of the eye, the recorded signal from the tube gives a record of eye movements. This system was used to great advantage by coupling it with a system for recording an electrical signal proportional to the movement of a visual stimulus presented to the subject.[272] Thus a simultaneous recording of stimulus movements and correlated tracking movements of the eye could be obtained.

Some of the basic spatially organized patterns of coordinate eye movements are diagrammed in Figure 2-9. These diagrams simulate electrical records that might be made by registering changes in the corneo-retinal potential on an oscillograph. Vertical lines represent fixations; diagonal lines, pursuit movements; and nearly horizontal lines, saccadic jerks. Although these patterns of movement have been known for many years, no systematic theory has been formulated to account for their organi-

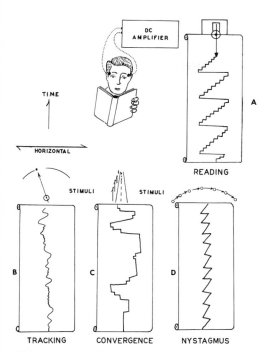

Figure 2-9. Different patterns of eye movements. A. Reading, consisting of fixations and lateral saccadic movements. B. Tracking. C. Convergence. D. Nystagmus.

zation and control. We recognize some principles of the evolution of these different movements, and can describe some of the specific conditions of spatial stimulation with which the different patterns are correlated. Certain applications of our own theory of motion to eye movements will be described later.

Movements of Speech

Most analyses of speech have been concerned with its acoustic properties, rather than with the motion patterns which produce the sounds. This preoccupation with speech sounds has focused attention on the larynx, which is commonly thought of as the organ of speech. As a matter of fact, the larynx is not a necessary part of the basic motion system which produces speech. Speech behavior involves integrated action of muscles of the abdomen, diaphragm, chest, neck, throat, jaw, lips, and tongue. Vibrations of the vocal cords add acoustically to speech, but are not an essential component of the movement patterns.

The first recordings of speech movements were obtained by Rosapelly[224] while working in Marey's laboratory. He recorded simultaneously speech breathing movements, vibrations of the larynx, movements of the lips in articulation, and air pressure from the mouth and nose. Rousselot[225] extended Rosapelly's techniques and developed the basic methods of experimental phonetics. By far the most systematic analyses of the motion system of speech were made by Stetson,[291] whose first studies in phonetics used refined kymographic techniques to record movements of the abdomen, chest, jaw, lip, and tongue. Later, in collaboration with Snodgrass, Hudgins, and Bouman, he perfected electronic methods for recording action potentials of these different muscle systems. He and Hudgins also used a sound spectograph to obtain visible records of speech sounds. Simultaneous recordings of visible speech, acoustic intensities, movements of lips, tongue, jaw, chest, and abdomen, and air pressure in the mouth permitted a careful analysis of the organization of this action system in relation to its acoustic output (Fig. 2-10).

Stetson described the patterns of speech in terms of the movements which produce them. The basic unit of speech is the syllable – a pulse initiated by muscles between the ribs, and arrested either by opposing rib muscles or by a partial or complete closure of the throat or mouth. The characteristic cadence and rhythms of speech are organized and sustained by larger movements of the diaphragm and abdomen. Children learning to speak learn these larger movement patterns first, their phrasing and inflection may communicate their meanings even though their articula-

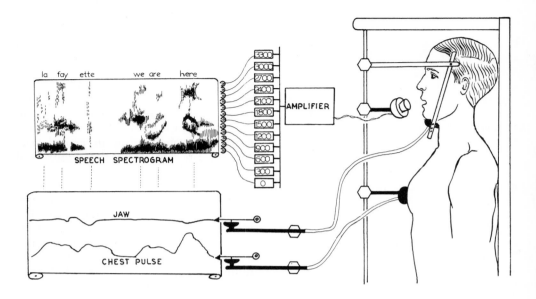

Figure 2-10. Stetson's method of recording simultaneously the sound spectrograph of speech in relation to different movements of the speech mechanism. (Spectrogram from Stetson.[291])

tions are not precise. The finer articulatory movements of the throat, jaw, and mouth define both the vowel quality and the consonants of speech. Vowels are differentiated by the size and shape of the resonating chambers above the larynx, while consonants represent partial or complete closures of the vocal canal, either at the beginning or end of a syllable. Vibration of the vocal cords adds tone to the voice, but is not necessary for intelligible speech; whispering is speech without tone.

By defining speech in terms of its movement systems, Stetson's work discredits traditional interpretations that regard speech as primarily a mental or psychic phenomenon. However, as yet we know very little of the neurophysiological basis for controlling and regulating the integrated patterns which Stetson described. Our knowledge of the motor centers of speech in the cortex does not extend to related mechanisms which interrelate auditory and kinesthetic feedback with the speech movement pattern.[320] The basic question of the organization of speech motions is equivalent to the general problem formulated in this book, i.e., how the pattern of motion (of talking) is integrated with the pattern of stimulation (of sounds and kinesthetic feedback of speech). The importance of this interplay between perception and motion is evidenced by recent experimentation on the effect upon speech of delayed auditory feedback. Marked disturbances of the speech pattern occur if the sounds of a person's voice are delayed before being presented to his ear.[160] In common with all motion patterns, organized speech patterns are regulated by continuous interplay between patterns of stimulation and the movements in progress.

SUMMARY

1. The analysis of motion has always been motivated by practical problems related to work, and artistic interest, as well as by scientific curiosity. The first careful studies of movement patterns in relation to the anatomy and functions of the body and the design and operation of machines were made by Leonardo da Vinci in the late fifteenth and early sixteenth centuries.

2. Borelli identified the nerves as conductors to the muscles, and Descartes recognized the importance of the brain as a conductor.

3. The concept that the brain is an integrative system as contrasted with a conductive system, is a relatively modern idea based on neurosurgical extirpation experiments in animals. Observed changes in behavior due to removal of higher brain centers led to theoretical distinctions between reflex action and voluntary behavior, as well as to Sherrington's scientific study of the integrative mechanisms of reflex activities in the lower brain centers. Thus, the notion of neural integration was differentiated to cover both the simpler reflex movements and complex motions involving perception and "voluntary" control.

4. Pavlov's studies of conditioning resolved, for some, the theoretical problem of neural integration of complex motor activities by interpreting all forms of behavior in terms of temporally-chained reflexes. The phenomena of conditioning have played a major role in defining current learning and reinforcement theory in psychology. Although such doctrine is commonly applied to many diverse events in behavior, it provides no general answer to the problems of neural integration and the organization of motion. The notion that organized movements can come about as a result of sequential chaining of unit reactions cannot be substantiated. The development of motion patterns in the young, and in different animals indicates that the primary integrative mechanisms are genetically determined.

5. Developmental studies of motion in the human infant show a progression from generalized movements to more specific, more finely articulated movements. Studies of young animals and children alike have shown that many specific patterns of motion emerge as a result of maturation, and are only incidentally modified by learning. However, gross restriction of perceptual activity may interfere with the normal development of perceptual-motor patterns. It appears that in many cases there is a critical period during early life when adequate conditions of stimulation are needed for the development of a genetically defined pattern of behavior.

6. The analysis of motion organization in the individual can be divided into two areas. The study of manual movements has inevitably been tied in with problems of tool using and work. The unaided motion patterns which have been studied most extensively are locomotion, ocular movements, and speech.

7. Human gait has been studied and analyzed by photographic methods (motion pictures and stroboscopic photography) and by basographic methods, or analysis of the action of the foot against the substrate. Among the latter are pneumatic, electrical, and electronic techniques. Recordings of action currents from muscle systems have been correlated with basographic records. Human gait is an integrated pattern of postural, transport, and manipulative (contact) movements.

8. Eye movements have been recorded photographically; electrically, from the corneal-retinal potential; photoelectrically; and by recording the amount of light reflected from a small area of the curved surface of the eye, which varies as the eye moves. Different patterns of eye movements are made up of fixations,

tense pursuit movements, and saccadic jerks.

9. Stetson's analysis of the movements of speech describes integrated patterns of activity involving the abdomen and diaphragm for breath control, muscles between the ribs to produce the syllable units, and articulatory movements of the throat and mouth to give vowel and consonant quality. Vibration of the vocal cords supplies tone. Thus, speech can be described as a motion system, but we know very little of the neural integrative mechanisms which regulate it in terms of auditory and kinesthetic feedback.

CHAPTER 3

MOTION, WORK, AND MACHINES

In the evolution of man from sub-human forms, the critical factor in the differentiation of the human species was consistent tool-using behavior.[61, 131, 159] The use, retention, and manufacture of tools to aid almost all kinds of activity has been a feature of the behavior of all strains of prehistoric and modern man. The organized patterns of perceptual-motor behavior which are uniquely human cannot be separated from the tools which so often structure that behavior. Thus, any study of man's adaptation to his world is concerned more often than not with aspects of tool using.

This relationship between tool-using behavior and human biological adaptation is most explicitly stated in studies of human motion in work. Scientific in-terest in this area is relatively new, but has been intensified in recent years because of rapid changes in technology. Modern machines have become so complicated that the human factor in their design and use has gradually become recognized as of primary importance. That which began with some simple time and motion studies has burgeoned into the present-day science of human engineering and ergonomics, a field with many ramifications. In outlining this development, we shall consider attempts to type or classify work motions, psychometric measurement of motions and motor capacity, analyses of motion efficiency, analyses of tracking and steering behavior, and studies of interactions between behavior and machine systems organization.

TYPES AND CLASSIFICATIONS OF MOTIONS

The earliest sustained interest in motion typology originated with the desire of industrial management for worker efficiency. In the late nineteenth century the mushrooming expansion of industrial technology and organization led to increased efforts to control the worker and his production. These efforts, aided by the new techniques of recording and measurement then being developed, gave birth to the era of "scientific management."

Time and Motion Study

The first efforts to analyze work patterns were the beginnings of what we call time and motion study — the specification of work patterns in terms of durations of component movements. Taylor[300] is generally credited with making the first measurements, starting in 1878 and continuing for more than 20 years. In his early studies he was attempting to specify working roles in the steel industry, and to speed up the handling of materials. He used a stop watch for measurement and he tried to speed up workers by social pressure and promises of material reward. Later, Taylor developed an operational approach to problems of productivity. He accomplished one of the first systematic studies on tool design, i.e., adapting the design of shovels to the weight of materials to be lifted.

The best known name in time and motion study is that of Gilbreth.[100, 101] Early in his career he took a direct cue from Muybridge's[196] motion-picture study of bricklaying and applied more advanced film techniques to analysis of the motions of this trade. Gilbreth formulated the concept of elemental motions and operations which he thought could be used to specify all work. His elemental motions — such as grasp, turn, lift, release, select — were called therbligs, a neologism derived from his own name spelled backward. The 17 basic therbligs are shown in Figure 3-1. Using this motion classification, he developed a highly arbitrary but comprehensive system of work specification by means of

which work patterns were to be standardized and thus controlled more effectively. Standardization meant, to Gilbreth, simplification of the work pattern to the best and most economical (fastest) method of doing it.

Gilbreth's whole system was based on the idea that work can be broken down into elemental motions, with no variation in the motion units except the frequency of their occurrence. The therblig structure of a task is sequential, and can be described by a process chart. There is assumed to be a "true" time for each therblig, i.e., ideally, the time required to carry out an elemental motion is assumed to be invariable. Therefore, in order to set time standards of performance for particular jobs, one needs only to discover the "one best way" of doing the job, described in terms of the therbligs used, and then add up the therblig times.

These off-the-cuff assumptions about movement organization have served as the basis of industrial time study for many years. Although various procedural modifications have been devised to make Gilbreth's ideas "fit" the practical applications more readily, the theory itself has not usually been questioned seriously by time-study engineers.

The earliest general method of time and motion study in industry was to break down a job into elements, and then time these elements separately. To revise the job or specify standards for it, the best or simplest combination of elemental movements was chosen according to certain principles of motion economy, which were originally formulated by Münsterberg[195] on the basis of the suggestive ideas contained in Gilbreth's bricklaying study. Because the time measurements were often based on the work of a single operator (or at most two or three operators), it was found necessary to correct or "normalize" the obtained time data. Thus, an arbitrary performance rating was superimposed

Figure 3-1. Gilbreth's[101] "therbligs." The symbol used for each therblig on process charts of work motions is indicated above the name.

upon the time study. The skill and effort of the worker who was timed were compared to what the engineer considered normal, and a quantitative rating factor was computed by means of which to "level" or "normalize" the performance times secured from this particular worker. This leveled or corrected time value

plus a standard time allowance for rest and personal needs was used to set a job standard.

These procedures of measurement and rating have never been demonstrated to be either reliable or valid, and have always been suspect in some measure among trained engineers themselves.

One effort in industry to revise the procedures, with the main objective of eliminating the performance rating, has been the development of so-called synthetic or standard data systems.[13] In these systems the times for selected therbligs are determined from a limited number of jobs, and thereafter tabulated and used as "standard data" to compute time standards for other jobs. The engineer determines what therbligs are involved in a given operation, reads off the times for them from his standard data table, and computes a standard for the job without the necessity of going near the worker.

A further modification of the standard data systems has been to allow some variation in therblig times by applying methods factors or work factors. These factors represent performance variables such as the distance of a movement, force exerted, complexity of perception, and precision of movement required. As the importance of such variables in influencing performance has been brought out in motion research over the past 30 years, the time-study engineers using synthetic data systems have tried to modify their systems accordingly. Different therblig times are given for different conditions of distance, precision, force, and complexity of perception. With three to six or seven values for each factor, the therblig is no longer as invariable as Gilbreth suggested. There are a number of these modified standard data systems on the market, which are said to be more scientific than the factory procedures because they have eliminated the need for performance rating. Needless to say, the different systems are highly variable among themselves and subject to still more variation when applied by particular practitioners.[51, 167]

The principles of establishing work standards have recently been extended to more complex motion operations in industry under such names as work standardization, work sampling, ratio sampling, operations analysis and systems analysis. The objective is to measure and standardize relatively long-term motion sequences and operations, as in clerical, maintenance, inspection, shipping, handling, transport, and other so-called "nonproductive" or "indirect" jobs.[13]

A recent trend in time and motion study is toward using semi-automatic methods of recording times, and computer procedures to compute work standards. In one recently developed automatic production-recording method, the time and motion study analyst punches a timing keyboard instead of a stopwatch, and the duration values of therbligs are registered automatically on a punched tape which can be used to punch computer cards.[156] From this point on, the data can be processed by appropriate computer programming.[192] It is perhaps an example of roundhouse justice that the process of timing industrial operations can be more or less completely automated, thus eliminating the time-study analyst in the factory.[77]

Our primary interest in describing the methods of time study is to assess the validity of the concepts of motion organization on which they are based. The critical evaluative literature in this field is very limited. We would like to say in advance of reviewing it that the basic assumption that motion in man can be dissected into independent, noninteracting elements which can then be added, subtracted, and leveled like so many separate marbles in a pile has never been and cannot now be verified. In view of the application of time-study concepts to the central life activity of millions of people, it is difficult to see how they have escaped exhaustive critical examination and repeated experimental analysis. It is of no credit to behavior science in the first decades of this century that more probing and theorizing were directed toward the caged white rat and the restrained dog than to the psychological theory and practice of setting work standards in industry. It is unfortunate that in the more traditional areas of science the study of work as an adaptive activity has never been accepted as quite respectable or as "basic" in nature.

Evaluation of Industrial Motion Study

In the early days of industrial motion study some attempts were made to check the validity of the procedures used by means of fast motion pictures of the motions to be analyzed. This method was so cumbersome and so uneconomical in time and money that it was rarely used as a systematic assessment procedure. Gilbreth and his behavioral concepts were accepted originally at face value by some industrial psychologists,[197, 210, 310] and no meaningful steps toward assessing them were made in psychology until recent years. Barnes[13] began such an evaluation in the 1930's, but his methods and scope of critical analysis were limited. A more promising approach has been made possible in recent years by development of electronic methods of motion study. With these techniques the industrial time-study procedures can be investigated more critically than heretofore.

Nadler and Goldman[199, 200] have developed an electronic motion recorder which broadcasts a high frequency signal from a moving member and picks up the Doppler effect of this signal by means of an acoustic recording system. As shown in Figure 3-2, a small unit mounted on the wrist of the subject broadcasts a high-frequency signal. Acoustic pickups are located in three planes to record separately effects due to movement in three dimensions. As movement in a given plane produces variations in pitch and intensity of the sound (the Doppler effect), a graphic

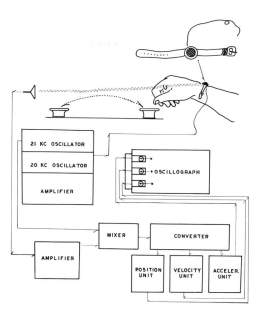

Figure 3-2. The electronic components and mode of action of a single channel of the universal operator performance analyzer and recorder (Unopar). This motion-recording system registers the Doppler effect produced by movements of a high-frequency sound generator carried on the moving hand. (Based on Nadler and Goldman.[200])

record is made of the changes. The record can be calibrated to represent the velocity and acceleration of movement in that plane.

We have used our own electronic motion analyzers to study many kinds of motion patterns.[270] One analyzer that has been used with complex operations such as assembly work is shown in Figure 3-3. This is a four-channel timing unit, composed of two interlocked flip-flop circuits, both of which pass a sub-threshold current through the subject, and four time clocks. For the first circuit, the keying subthreshold current is passed through the subject and the assembly bins. For the second circuit, the current is passed through the subject and the assembly plate. With this analyzer it is possible to record separately the times needed for grasping

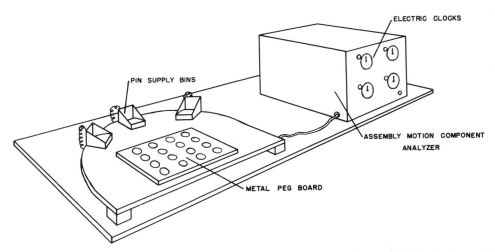

Figure 3-3. Electronic assembly motion analyzer. This analyzer utilizes a double relay system of two pairs of recording amplifier relay units and clocks. One pair registers the time of the grasp and loaded transport movements, and the other the time of the assemble and empty transport movements. The task shown is to assemble pins in a plate.

(contact with parts in the assembly bin), loaded transport (travel between assembly bin and assembly plate), assembling (contact with the assembly plate), and free transport (travel back to the assembly bin). Each clock times one phase of this assembly cycle and summates the times from successive cycles until a stop plate is touched to stop all timing.

Electronic techniques such as these can be used to obtain systematic data on motion study in situations in which motion-picture photography or graphic recording would be out of the question. A routine experiment with an electronic motion analyzer might, for example, train 48 subjects for one hour per day for 20 days to stabilize their work motions. To time these motions by means of speeded up motion-picture photography would take millions of feet of film. Some of the tool-using operations which have been analyzed electronically are panel control operations,[270, 319] dial setting and scale setting movements,[108, 109] assembly operations[241, 249] and handwriting.[261] In general, such studies have indicated that component movements of

a task interact within a motion pattern to affect movement times, are affected differentially by many variables, and, thus, do not conform consistently to standard time data.

One study[112] designed to measure movement interaction in compound motion is illustrated in Figure 3-4. The experimental set-up consisted of two work panels, each containing four types of manipulative devices. Subjects were required to perform manipulations on the left and right panels alternately. Eight sets of these panels were prepared in order to vary the pattern of manipulative motions for different subjects. The eight manipulations used were right and left switch turning, linear up-down and right-left manipulations, dial setting, pressing together, pushing a button, and a pulling motion. The primary object of the experiment was to time the transport or travel movements between successive manipulations in order to determine whether travel time varied as a function of the pattern of manipulation. Although the distance covered by the travel movements was constant, it was

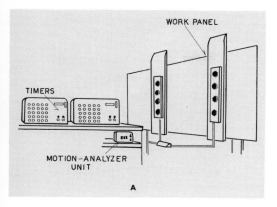

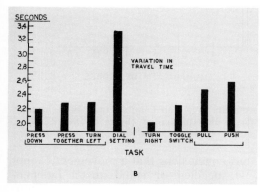

Figure 3-4. Motion analysis instrumentation and results of a study of the degree of interaction of movement components in panel-control motions. A. Motion-analyzer unit and panel control board. B. Mean durations of travel movements of fixed distance with different patterns of manipulation.

found that their duration varied greatly, up to 50 per cent of the fastest time. In other words, the pattern of manipulation required of the subject influenced the time of his transport movements between manipulations, slowing down this movement in some cases by as much as half its base (fastest) value. In industrial time study, this variation would appear as outright error in estimating a standard time, and it would not be eliminated by use of work-factor or method-factor corrections. The variation in travel time was due to interaction of the travel movement with other components of the

pattern, a situation which is not handled by time-study concepts. These results confirm Nadler's[198] findings that adding new therbligs to a task alters the basic configuration of the motions in it. Buffa's[34, 35] studies, showing that minor alterations in a work cycle changed the time of the total cycle only slightly, apparently were too limited in design to disclose the major variations in movement time that can occur in complex tasks.

A more complex problem than that of direct movement interaction is to determine the effect on different movements of psychological dimensions such as learning, perception, motivation, task rewards, stress, and social pressures. We have some quantitative measurements of movement times, as a function of variable conditions of learning,[226, 227, 319] motivation,[107, 271] and perception,[134, 240, 241] that show that movements in common tasks such as assembly, panel control operations, object manipulation, and handwriting are affected quite differently by these psychological variables. Thus, we believe that the time-study procedure of rating level of learning, fatigue, amount of perception, and level of effort, and using this rating as a constant factor without regard to the nature of the operation, is invalid. The influence of these various psychological or performance variables must be determined specifically for each component in a task.

The variable effect of learning on the durations of specific movements in a task is shown in Figure 3-5. Here are shown the learning curves for the turning movement and the transport movement of a panel control task. While the transport movement time remained constant during the course of practice, the manipulative movement time continued to change throughout the entire period. These results show the fallacy of assuming a constant learning factor and applying it to different types of operations.

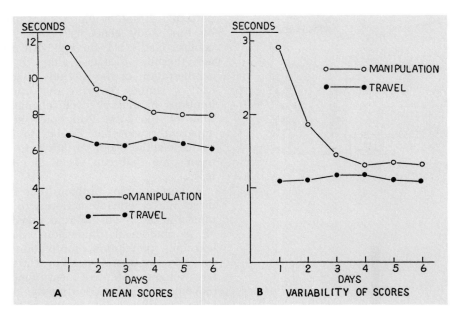

Figure 3-5. Learning curves of component movements in a panel-control task. Both mean durations (A) and variability measures (B) indicate the differential effects of practice on travel and manipulative movements.

Finally, what do we know of the effects of various physical variables — the methods factors and work factors — on movement patterns? Do significant interactions occur between such physical variables as weight moved, distance traveled, size of work object, and relative timing of components within the task, and specific therbligs such as grasp, turn, or move? The standard data tables imply that the effect of the physical variables can be specified for each movement independently of its actual occurrence in a movement pattern. However, a number of specific studies show that nothing could be further from the truth.[63, 227, 241, 261, 311, 319] The duration of a single movement depends on the configuration of physical conditions in which it occurs, as well as on its position within a motion sequence. Many configurational effects are significant, with travel-distance and movement-timing interactions especially so. The experimental results confirm our previ-

ous conclusions that a movement cannot be specified or standardized independently of its integrative relationships with other movements and other variables. Work-factor and methods-factor systems of work specification have fundamental defects which cannot be adjusted out by any number of correction tables.

Scientific Motion Analysis

The basic problem posed by Gilbreth's system is whether or not his motion typology is scientifically valid. Unfortunately, scientifically oriented efforts to analyze motion into its basic components have for the most part ignored the therblig-oriented technological systems, and vice versa. Most of the basic scientific concepts concerning the organization of motion have been touched on in the last chapter. We shall examine these various ideas again from the point of view of motion typology, and in relation to the time-study concepts of independent movement elements.

Throughout the period of modern physiology and psychology, one school of thought has held that all motion develops from basic reflex movements. Traditional reflex doctrine has emphasized research in two main areas: (1) exploring the properties of the conduction system — such as inhibition, summation, and fatigue — and (2), extending the experimental facts of conditioning or reinforcement learning to account for all learned behavior. In this view, motion is made up of sequentially linked primary reflex units, with the probability of occurrence of the units defined by the properties of retention, strength, generalization, inhibition, summation, and so on. In other words, motion can be specified in terms of reflexes or learned reflex or response patterns and their quantitative properties.[247]

Another approach to movement classification has been to analyze various patterns of muscular response. With recognition late in the nineteenth century of the reciprocal nature of muscular movements came the realization that different types of movement patterns could be distinguished.[16, 219] In general, three types of muscular contraction have been described: a thrown reciprocal movement, a tense movement in which opposing muscular contractions balance each other, and a tense movement in which one muscle contracts while the antagonist is partly contracted. Huey[133] and Dodge[66] applied this type of analysis to the different types of eye movements, and Dodge described them in terms we still use today: saccadic jerks, pursuit or moving fixations, and fixations.

A similar classification was proposed by Stetson and his co-workers,[132, 290-293] who in their later work obtained simultaneous recordings of action currents in the muscles and movements of parts of the body (see p. 31). Stetson's revised classification of movements described two main types: tense and ballistic, each with two subtypes. Slow tension movements are either fixations, which result in no displacement, or moving fixations. Ballistic or free-thrown movements include completely free movements, in which only one muscle of a pair contracts, and stiff movements thrown by a rapid muscular contraction of one muscle superimposed upon tension of both members of the antagonistic pair. Records of walking,[132] arm movements,[280, 292] and speech[291] all show the differential role of these ballistic and tense movements in determining the coordinations observed.

Although these analyses have established the fact that different patterns of muscular action are involved in motion, they have not defined the perceptual-motor or neuromotor mechanisms involved in their control. Studies of optical pursuit movements in animals have indicated that distinctive neural mechanisms regulate different types of eye movements, and that the patterns vary according to various levels of perceptual-motor integration.[250, 254, 262, 266, 269, 298, 301] The problem of differentiating the neural mechanisms which regulate ballistic movements and continuously controlled tense movements remains unresolved. Our own theory of motion (see p. 6ff.) proposes three basic movement components — postural, transport, and manipulative movements — which are integrated at different levels of the nervous system. While this classification and Stetson's are not equivalent, they are not contradictory.

At least two practical applications of these scientific classifications of movements have been proposed. One is to analyze defective motion patterns, as in reading, speech, and athletic performance, in terms of the types of movements used. The other is to develop rules of motion efficiency and economy, equivalent to or in addition to those originally proposed by Gilbreth.[111] Such rules are essentially a practical guide for using knowledge of movement types in coaching or in self-improvement. Few controlled studies have been carried out to determine whether these rules can be applied successfully to skilled performance, or what the limitations of their application might be.

Factor Analysis of Motion

The origin of the factor analytical approach to motion typology was twofold: in the early work of psychometricians in testing perceptual-motor phenomena such as reaction time, target pursuit, tapping, and the like,[42, 135, 195, 310] and in the development of the statistical procedures of factor analysis. During the 1930's, it was hoped that the statistical tools of correlational analysis would disclose the fundamental dimensions of human psychomotor skills and abilities.[37, 233, 234] The general method of investigation was to canvass variations in psychomotor ability in relatively large populations by means of different psychomotor tests, to intercorrelate the scores of these tests, and then to determine statistically how many behavioral factors must be assumed in order to account for the variance in the table of intercorrelations. In view of the optimism with which these studies were launched, the results have proved disappointing. In the first systematic studies, the number of factors extracted from different series of tests equalled the number of types of tests used. The elaborate statistical procedures did little more than identify the obviously different patterns of behavior characteristic of the parts of the test battery.

More recently, this problem has been approached anew, by using a larger number of tests which emphasize more specific motor functions such as coordination, dexterity and the like.[88] In one study in which tests of ability in bal-

ance, reaction time, coordination, posture, pursuit of target, manual control, steadiness, tracing, tapping, and aiming were administered to several hundred young men, it was concluded that ten factors could account for the tables of intercorrelations.[89] However, the factors identified — such as reaction time, manual dexterity, coordination, aiming, and rate of arm movement — are characteristics of motion which might be identified from direct observation of the performances involved. In other words, the statistical procedures do not extract much more information about movement organization than one might get from superficial examination.

In general, factor analyses of motion have added little more to the theoretical understanding of motion organization than did Gilbreth's therblig classification. Such systems may have some practical value in describing tasks or devising tests, but have little scientific significance. The specificity of movements is such that they resist classification except in the most general terms.

MOTION EFFICIENCY

One of the earliest interests in the science of motion was in motion efficiency, and fatigue, from both scientific and practical points of view. The first systematic studies were carried out by Marey[173] and Mosso[191] in the last century. Using his original myographic methods, Marey demonstrated the occurrence of work decrement in repeated contractions of frog muscle. Somewhat later, Mosso used a finger ergograph to record the decrement in repetitious human work, and developed a biochemical theory of neural fatigue to explain decreased efficiency. Since these early studies, the problems of fatigue and motion economy have been studied in research laboratories and in industry, in relation to both behavioral and physiological events. Curiously enough, very little progress has been made in defining the critical factors involved.

Psychological Study of Fatigue

Systematic descriptive studies of work decrement have been extended to many different patterns of behavior.[4, 8, 18–20, 335] The general conclusion to be drawn is that every complex motion pattern and condition of work in man has its own distinctive work decrement and fatigue-recovery characteristics. It has been demonstrated that verbal work, such as that involved in mental multiplication, shows only the most limited decrement,[4, 17, 304] and that prolonged visuo-motor behaviors, such as reading and specific psychomotor activities, typically are subject to decreased alertness and vigilance in observation.[41] As Münsterberg[195] originally pointed out, more marked decrement generally occurs in work involving the larger muscular masses than when finer movements are required. Current systematic efforts in psychology to interpret behavioral fatigue[14] have been almost as much of a conceptual hodge-podge as the behavioral theories of learning.

Physiological Study of Motion Efficiency

For many years, Hill[123, 124] has studied the problems of fatigue and efficiency in muscular reaction. Some of his early work, carried out with nerve-muscle preparations of the frog, was concerned with heat production in muscle activity. Later he tried to define the critical conditions of efficiency and fatigue by analyzing running in man. Hill thought that a fixed constant of efficiency (energy output in work divided by energy input) could be established for particular types of work and motion, and that variations in this constant for different types of activities were due entirely to variation in time of onset of fatigue. He speculated that the limits of efficiency in muscular work were determined by the viscosity of the muscle itself.

Fenn[81, 82] explored this problem of maximal efficiency of motion by means of motion-picture analyses of running. His actual procedures involved attempts to calculate the effects on energy expenditure of acceleration and deceleration of the limbs and control of the center of gravity of the body, and to compute the percentage efficiency of muscle contraction involved in the activity. In making his calculations, Fenn assumed that the muscles used in running were all acting in a uniform way, i.e., under continued tension during the course of contraction. His results showed a higher figure for muscle efficiency than Hill had found, a difference which he attempted to explain by saying that Hill had overestimated the effects of muscle viscosity on efficiency of contraction. However, the differences in results between these two major investigations were never fully explained by Fenn.

Other analyses have suggested reasons for the discrepancies which can occur in computing muscle efficiency. It has become clear that differences in motion efficiency depend in part on variations in the motion pattern. Lehmann[163] recognized this fact when he measured the incidence of fatigue in lifting a weight and in holding it in position. He found that fatigue from static work was three to six times as great as from the lifting action, but gave no physiological explanation of the difference. One of the answers is that the energy expended by the muscles is not necessarily a function of the amount of work accomplished by a movement. The assumption made by Fenn and others that muscles involved in motion are under continuous tension is unwarranted. As Stetson[291] has shown, one member of a pair of antagonists may be relaxed during the course of a ballistic movement, although both members of the pair are contracted during a tense movement. Thus, the amount of muscular energy expended in lifting a weight, for example, would depend in part on whether a free-thrown or tense movement were used.

A second factor to be considered in computing motion efficiency is the discovery that the actual utilization of chemically free energy by the muscles is determined by the nature of the motion. That is, there is an intricate feedback relationship between the biochemical processes involved in muscular contraction and the pattern of the contraction. This conclusion is based on recent investigations of Hill,[125] who observed that net energy expenditure during work is very different depending on whether the muscle is stretched or shortened. When the muscle is stretched during the process of contraction, the biochemical process of utilizing chemical energy is reversed so that the muscle actually replaces the energy utilized. Thus, the muscle performing work while undergoing stretch may act with nearly 100 per cent efficiency. On the other hand, a muscle performing work while shortened operates with decreasing efficiency leading to fatigue (Fig. 3-6).

Hill arranged a striking demonstration of these "positive" and "negative" motions in work and the variation of efficiency involved in them. A tandem bicycle with a common chain linking the two sets of pedals, and no brakes, was fixed with the drive wheel elevated off the ground. A sturdy young man sat in front pedaling forward, i.e., doing positive work. A petite young woman sat on the second bicycle and opposed the driving action of the man by trying to pedal backward (negative work). If the efficiency factors in movement were the

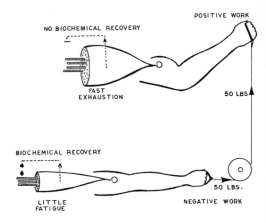

Figure 3-6. The difference between "positive" and "negative" work. A muscle system that must continually shorten during contraction to do work fatigues much faster than a muscle system that is stretched while in the process of doing an equal amount of work in overcoming a tension imposed upon it.

same for all types of motion, the two riders would exhaust at a rate corresponding to their particular physiological capacity. Thus, the girl, having more limited muscular resources, would tire first. In actual fact, she remained fresh while reducing the man to exhaustion, proving that the form of motion affects the utilization of energy by the muscles. This conclusion was supported by analyses of heat production in muscle when subjected to isotonic contraction and other forms of "negative" work in which the muscle is stretched during contraction.

These observations on the reciprocal relationships between energy expenditure and pattern of motion may clear up some major questions about efficiency and fatigue in human work, such as the long-term stamina and freedom from fatigue displayed by long-distance runners and swimmers, the effects of emotional tension on work and fatigue, and the effects of massage and activity in inducing muscular relaxation. To define the efficiency of motion, we must understand the partly self-regulating interactions between muscular contractions and biochemical processes, and between muscular contractions and the pattern of motion. The energetics of motion cannot be reduced to some single fixed constant of efficiency as was once assumed.

Principles of Motion Economy

The study of motion organization in industry has inevitably been concerned with questions of motion efficiency and economy in specific work tasks. Early in the century, Münsterberg[195] formulated a set of rules of motion economy based on Gilbreth's[100] limited work on bricklaying. These principles were accepted almost without question, both by industrial engineers[13, 101, 171] and psychologists,[197, 310] and were used widely as guides in designing work patterns and in specifying work standards.

Münsterberg's principles of motion economy were formulated as energy-saving rules. He stated that a motion is more efficient, i.e., less fatiguing, if: (a) it is in the direction of gravitational force; (b) both hands act simultaneously; (c) the distance of movement travel is reduced to a minimum; (d) it is practiced in its final preferred form from the outset; and (e) it is composed of smooth, uninterrupted rather than jerky movements. Later, rules of "tool economy" and "machine economy" were added to these first principles of motion economy. In the course of time, the published lists of these rules were altered both by psychologists[197] and engineers.[171]

Although the implication in Münsterberg's rules is that efficient motions are less fatiguing in a physiological sense, in practice industrial engineers have turned to the rate or time of a complex motion pattern as the index of efficiency. Following Gilbreth and Gilbreth,[101] they have assumed that the most efficient operation is the simplest, and, hence, the fastest pattern of motion that can be found for the job. Accordingly, "work simplification" has been the indispensable principle followed in designing industrial operations and setting work standards.[198] Neither Münsterberg's rules nor related principles of work simplification have ever been systematically assessed by scientific procedures. To do so, one would need an organic criterion of fatigue or energy expenditure in work, as well as a behavioral criterion.

INDICES OF ENERGY EXPENDITURE. There have been many attempts to define energy output in a work situation in terms of some metabolic index. Differences in oxygen consumption, respiration, and heart rate in different types of work have all been investigated,[17–20] but none of these metabolic indices has ever been found to correlate systematically with fatigue in verbal or psychomotor work.[210] Significant and reliable changes in pulse and oxygen consumption are found only with marked change in rate of work, or with heavy muscular labor. We have reason to believe that measurable metabolic change may indicate extreme stress on the system, but provides no basis for comparing different methods of motion organization in work.[107] When there is a need to establish limits for heavy labor or physical exertion, a metabolic index can be used. Portable heart rate (photometric) recorders and respirometers have been developed and used successfully in heavy industry.[238]

Another approach to the problem of assessing energy expenditure in work is the search for an indirect behavioral index. The assumption has been that metabolic changes related to fatigue occur at the neural level and lead to corresponding changes in such behavioral functions as reaction time or flicker-fusion frequency in vision.[102, 244, 245] As yet, these behavioral measures have provided no basic index of motion efficiency in work.

A more promising attack on the problem of assessing motion efficiency is based on the idea that relatively complete measurement of the forces exerted by the body in movement will provide a meaningful and reliable index of the energy exerted in common tasks. Lauru[158] has designed an interesting stabilometer method for this purpose. The Lauru platform (Fig. 3-7) consists of a triangular table supported on three piezo-electric crystals. Such crystals generate a small electric current with minute degrees of deformation due to pressure exerted on them. The performer, working on the platform, exerts differential pressure on the three crystals depending on the externalized force of the different movements involved in a given work pattern, and the resulting electrical signals generated by the crystals are amplified, recorded, and integrated.

Results with this platform are of interest in assessing ordinary conditions of work. For example, Lauru showed that

Figure 3-7.   The Lauru[158] platform. This platform records the externalized force of motion patterns by means of electrical signals generated by piezo-electric crystals supporting the three corners. (Based on photograph, courtesy of the Haskell Laboratory.)

Gilbreth's recommended method for bricklaying requires less dynamic effort to take mortar and brick than other methods, but demands greater postural effort. Other studies with the Lauru platform indicate that each pattern of motion and work can be analyzed in terms of the variations in pressure recorded on the platform, and that these variations can be related to the effort and fatigue associated with the method of performance. The method promises to provide a means for estimating energy equivalents of the critical static (postural) and dynamic (transport) activities in work.

TIME AS AN INDEX OF MOTION ECONOMY. Although we have as yet no general index of energy expenditure which can be used to compare the efficiency of different work patterns, the industrial engineer's criterion of motion time permits a limited judgment of efficiency, and can be used to check the validity of Münsterberg's principles of motion economy. These general rules of motion organization are assumed to define the "best", fastest, and least fatiguing way of performing a task, an assumption that has not been confirmed by experimental analyses.

In recent studies, Block[27, 28] has analyzed the old principle that two hands should be used simultaneously in motion. Careful measurement showed that symmetrical two-handed cycles of motion required more time per cycle (not necessarily more time per unit of work output) than an equivalent one-handed cycle. Also, the percentage increase in time of two-handed cycles was dependent on the complexity of the motions. The task in this study was to grasp pegs from two bins and insert them into holes. When the task conditions were varied in such ways as changing the manner of dispensing the pegs, or increasing the travel distance for the two hands, the time needed for simultaneous two-handed assembly was greatly increased. No such effect was found for one-handed assembly. Screening the bins holding the pegs caused marked increases in time for two-handed assembly, but not for one-handed. It was found that the main factor involved in the time increases was the relative difficulty of surveying the performance field visually. The speed of one-handed assembly remained fairly constant because the restricted field of operation could be perceived easily. Thus, the rule that two-handed motions are more efficient cannot be accepted as generally true, but must be tested for each different task and each situation.

We have used our electronic methods of motion analysis to evaluate some of the original rules of motion economy in terms of durations of component movements. Figure 3-8 illustrates a controlled panel system used for a number of these studies. An early experiment was designed to test the assumption implicit in Gilbreth's principle of work simplification, that time per movement is less in simpler motion patterns.[227] Actually, neither manipulative nor travel-movement times varied according to the complexity of the task. That is, the duration of a movement is not necessarily decreased by reducing the number of possible movements in the overall task pattern.

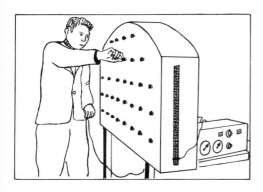

Figure 3-8. A universal panel motion analyzer used to time movement components of different motion patterns.

In another study of panel operations, we examined Münsterberg's rule that movements in the direction of gravity are more efficient.[311] The task in this experiment involved a series of manipulations on the panel proceeding either in an upward or downward direction. When the mean durations of manipulative and travel movements were compared, it was found that the manipulative movements in the task were significantly slower in the downward series, whereas downward travel movements were faster than upward travel movements. For the complete motion pattern, there were no differences in duration related to direction of movement.

These two experiments and others[108, 249, 261, 267, 319] confirm our belief that the principles of motion economy have no general validity. While these rules may apply in some cases — usually with very simple motion patterns — they are not true of organized motions in general. When a motion pattern is complex, and especially when the perceptual requirements of a task are complicated, Münsterberg's and Gilbreth's principles break down.

The simplified rules of motion economy are particularly inadequate when one is concerned with the interaction between a motion and the design of a machine or system of operations in which the motion must be performed. There is no simple rule specifying accuracy and economy of motion in activities involving machines. Valid rules of tool economy — of finding the best tool for the job — are not self-evident but demand painstaking psychological and engineering research on operational and systems relationships. The interdependence of motion organization and machine design is particularly evident in the use of complex control mechanisms, steering and tracking devices, and other guidance systems for human use.[86, 299] In using these machines, where accuracy of control is the prime requirement of motion, the original laws of motion economy mean little. The simplest type of movement may be the worst type of control on some machines. Substituting aids for part of the motions in the task, according to the rules of tool economy, may actually hinder rather than aid the operator, as has been shown for aided-tracking devices.[168]

These considerations lead us into the next and most recent chapter in the science of motion: the field of human engineering, which is concerned with systematic analyses of the operational factors of behavior organization in relation to machine design. We do not subscribe to the point of view proposed by some that human engineering is simply an extension of established methods of time and motion study.[180] We believe that the older atomistic and linear concepts of behavior organization are inadequate in dealing with either unaided or aided motion, and that the complex motion-machine problems posed by modern technology point up the need for a new theoretical orientation.

MOTIONS AND MACHINES

Ever since man designed tools for his own use, he has been faced with the basic problem of human engineering — that of fitting the tool to the motion system of its operator. However, until recently this problem, while real, was given no formal recognition. The great impetus for the acknowledged study of human engineering was the development during World War II of highly technical devices for gun laying, high-speed aircraft, detection (radar, sonar), and communication. Such technological marvels were successful only insofar as they could be operated by man, equipped with human perceptual-motor skills. Thus, the contemporary field of human engineering, also called human

factors engineering, ergonomics, and systems analysis, is generally agreed to have originated some twenty years ago with those psychologists who studied the human factors involved in operating military machines.[181]

The general effort in the field of human engineering is to analyze the basic mechanisms and interactions of human motion and perception in relation to machines and machine systems. At least three lines of effort have emerged: (a) analyses of human control, as in tracking and steering; (b) studies of integration of perceptual information for motor control; and (c) research on the space and time relations between perception and motion — the problem of central concern in this book. The common feature in all of this research effort is the attempt to measure operational factors relating motion, perception, and machine design.

Motions in Tracking

Tracking, steering, or controlled pursuit and guidance are continuously controlled motions such as the action of the eye in following a moving target or of the hands in steering a vehicle. Systematic study of this type of behavior began with the development of psychomotor tests of tracing and pursuit-rotor tests,[232] and increased greatly during World War II.[57, 117, 118, 121, 309]

Figure 3-9 illustrates one technique for studying tracking behavior. A target generator system is used to induce motion of a target, which the subject follows with an indicator controlled by a handwheel. The characteristics of the actual movement of the indicator are recorded, as well as the relative difference in position of target and indicator, representing an error record. The movement record permits analysis of such properties of control as reaction time, velocity, and acceleration of motion. With the error record, one can deter-

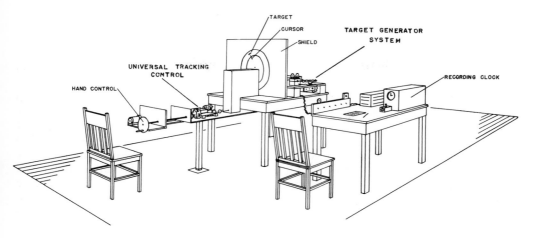

Figure 3-9. A controlled tracking device. The tracker uses a handwheel in order to make a cursor follow a moving target. Both actual movement of the cursor and the error in alignment are recorded graphically. Different motor controls can change the system to "velocity" and "aided" tracking.

mine the relative frequency and magnitude of different types of adjustments, and the accuracy of these adjustments in relation to the characteristics of the target display and other features of the tracking system.

A tracking task can be instrumented in several ways to require different patterns of control. The basic forms of tracking are shown in Figure 3-10. In *direct tracking*, every movement of the subject produces an immediate corresponding movement of the cursor in the same direction. There are other tracking systems, partially automated, in which the indicator is controlled only indirectly by the subject's movements. In *velocity tracking*, movements of the tracker generate a direction and rate of movement of the indicator by means of an intermediate motor output. That is, the subject controls the motor output, which in turn controls the indicator. This type of control is very unstable. In so-called *aided tracking*, the operator's movement positions the indicator directly, but an intermediate motor and differential system also generates a *rate* of movement in the indicator, according

to how much the handwheel has been moved.

In addition to these different types of control, tracking tasks may vary according to the nature of the display. In *pursuit tracking*, the tracker follows a moving target, while in *compensatory tracking*, the tracker adjusts his indicator to try to keep it fixed on a zero position. *Intermittency tracking* refers to a target which is presented intermittently instead of continuously on the display.

One of the controversial questions in tracking research has been concerned with the relative accuracy of direct, velocity and aided tracking. During and after World War II, it was recognized by military engineers that velocity tracking gave poor results, but they believed that aided tracking was superior to direct tracking. This belief guided the design of aircraft, radar, and gun systems for years, and is still generally accepted. The first to question seriously the superiority of aided tracking were Lincoln and Smith,[168] who carried out a study comparing relative accuracy in the three different tracking systems. According to their results, which are summarized in

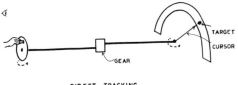

DIRECT TRACKING

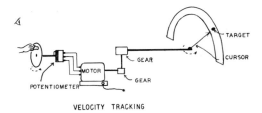

VELOCITY TRACKING

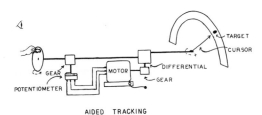

AIDED TRACKING

Figure 3-10. Different forms of tracking control. In direct tracking the tracker controls the motion of the cursor directly. In velocity tracking, the tracker generates a rate of movement of the cursor by means of an intermediate motor system. In aided tracking, movements of the tracker position the cursor directly, but also generate a rate of movement of the cursor.

Figure 3-11, tracking difficult and variable target courses is not helped but rather is hampered by the "aiding" systems of tracking control. These experimental results were confirmed by later investigations.[48, 49, 53] The critical factor defining the relative efficiency of direct and aided tracking appears to be the delay in sensory feedback which occurs in the automated systems. As we shall show in a later chapter, feedback delay almost invariably reduces accuracy and efficiency of motion.

Although extensive literature is available in tracking research, there is no generally accepted theory of the perceptual-motor integrations involved in this

behavior. We can differentiate three theoretical approaches to the problems of tracking. The first point of view is that a general quantitative formula can be derived to define both the precision of the operator and his characteristic functions of perception and motion in tracking or vehicular steering (Fig. 3-12). In this view, perception is conceived of as a feedback process related to some desired state or output function. The nervous system acts as an amplifier and integrator, and the muscle system as a motor generator for directing a vehicle or pointer. Error is the difference between perception and the desired state or condition. Some treatments within this framework describe tracking as a linear function,[56, 72] although other treatments recognize that tracking cannot be described so simply.[166] In general, servosystem analogies do not specify the various features of behavior involved in tracking, and do not allow for human flexibility.

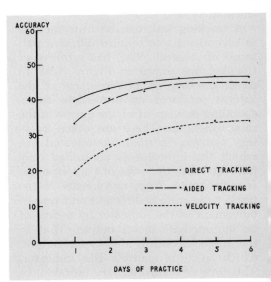

Figure 3-11. Relative accuracy of direct, aided, and velocity tracking. With complex or high-speed target courses, "aided" tracking is consistently less accurate than direct pursuit tracking.

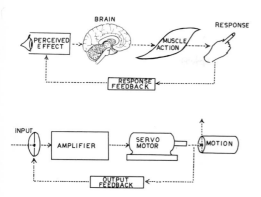

Figure 3-12. Tracking conceived of in terms of a servosystem analogy. Perception is thought of as an input-feedback process, the nervous system as an integrator-amplifier, and the muscle system as a motor generator for directing action.

A second point of view is that the characteristics of tracking and the instrumentation for its control can be defined in terms of some generalized psychological function. Mechler, Russell, and Preston,[185] for example, have tried to account for the properties of tracking in terms of reaction time in perceiving the alignment of target and pointer. Searle[231] and Vince[308] have described tracking in terms of intermittency of perception in control of the pointer. Birmingham and Taylor[23] and Fitts[86] reduce most of the problems of error to time lag in physical systems of control in supplying an operator with information about the accuracy of his own movements. Recognition of the importance of this factor of time lag in tracking accuracy has led to practical improvements in instrument design.

Our own approach toward an understanding of tracking behavior is to describe the basic reactions and the systems interactions in it in terms of integrated, space-structured motions with postural, transport, and manipulative components.[168, 206, 242] If the requirements for the perceptual-motor integration of these three movement compo-

nents are not met, the addition of so-called aiding devices cannot improve the accuracy of human control. Although it may be possible to describe tracking behavior in terms of a mathematical function or a single psychological dimension, such formulations are either too broad to be meaningful or too specific to the particular conditions from which they are derived. Tracking behavior is a complex motion pattern structured by a number of spatial and temporal variables and involving several levels of neuromotor integration. Its basic problems are not likely to be resolved by generalized mathematical formulations or machine analogies.[15]

Integrating Perceptual Information

Human engineering research has emphasized more than any other field the significance of perceptual detection, discrimination, and orientation as operational interactions. It is not enough to know whether a scale or dial is read accurately under some general condition, but whether it is read accurately in the particular operating circumstances in which it will be used. Thus, in this field the problems of perception have been dealt with not as exercises in the abstractions of psychophysics, but as operational questions concerning the organization of perceptual-motor behavior.

Three types of research on perceptual displays are noteworthy. First there are studies dealing with the effectiveness of various types of auditory, visual, and tactual display of information.[92, 143] A second concern is with the requirements of arrangement and design of particular kinds of dials, scales, and indicators used for perceptual-motor control.[104, 146, 170] Third, the techniques of integrating various types of perceptual information through principles of simplification and systematization have been explored.

One technique of perceptual simpli-

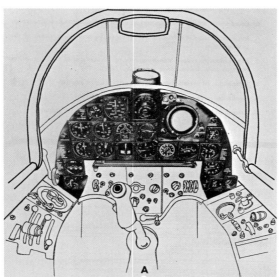

Figure 3-13. Techniques of perceptual simplification in aircraft control. (From Douglas Aircraft Co.[68])

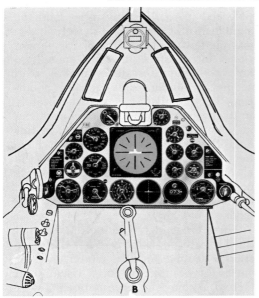

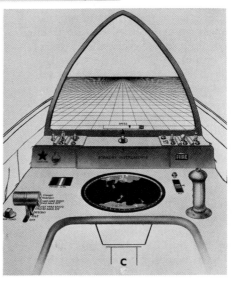

fication in aircraft[68] is illustrated in Figure 3-13. The first drawing shows the cockpit controls of a fighter aircraft of an old type. The second drawing shows a revised type of cockpit control panel in which the number of dials has been reduced and reordered. To accomplish this effect, data for different aspects of the aircraft's action have been combined and integrated into single displays, using special computing devices to achieve the integration. The integrated data are then presented on a single dial or a limited number of dials which show direction as well as general level of functioning of particular parts of the aircraft.

Spatial Correspondence of Perception and Motion

The accuracy with which a human operator can reproduce in motion the spatial patterns of his perceived environment is a critical problem in the study of perception and in the human engineering field. In a number of situations, serious discrepancies in spatial control have been observed. One source of inaccuracy is the disorientation and loss of perception of the vertical experienced by aircraft pilots during acceleration and deceleration.[184, 190, 211] Another source of error lies in the directional characteristics of motion. Movements in some directions are intrinsically more accurate than in other directions.[87, 189, 308, 309, 314] For example, manual motions performed in the mesial plane are more accurate than sidewise motions. Also, the direction of motion relative to the movement of an indicator or pointer must be considered. If a control mechanism is such that the operator must move to the left in order to move the pointer to the right, his control is less accurate than when his movement moves the pointer in the same direction. Finally, accuracy is affected by parallax factors between the operator's eyes and the direction of movement of a device. An operator inside a vehicle can steer it much more accurately than he can with remote control, i.e., his control is more accurate if he is located so that his mesial plane corresponds with the line of movement of the vehicle.

Whereas only gross discrepancies between perception and movement were once recognized, it is now known that very subtle relationships influence the accuracy of spatial control. For example, the problems of unifying display and control systems must take into consideration not only the similarities of viewing conditions at two or more control points, but also uniformity of interaction and perceptual feedback between display and control at these points. This idea is illustrated in Figure 3-14, which shows the presentation of uniform perceptual displays to the pilot in a plane and to a controller on the ground. In such a system, both perceptual display and steering devices should correspond if comparable control actions are to be expected.

Although these ideas of perceptual-motor integration in systems control are relatively new, they present significant problems in aircraft research. We believe that the critical factors which must be defined are the relative space and time displacements between perception and motion at the different control points. However, in systematic accounts in human engineering literature of the problems of perceptual-motor correspondence, the relevance of the experimental studies of displaced vision has

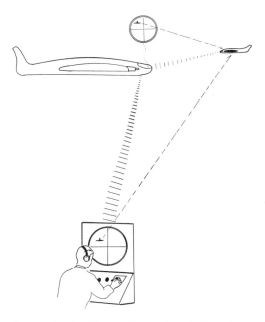

Figure 3-14. The problem of unified and integrated visual feedback and control. The remote controller on the ground should have the same view of the steering field as that of the pilot in the plane, if he is to control the plane in the same way as the pilot.

been overlooked.[86, 299] Yet, experimental inversion, reversal, and other displacements of the visual field, as studied by Stratton,[295-297] Wooster,[334] Brown,[32] Ewert,[74] and others, differ only in degree from the sort of visual displacement imposed routinely by the display-control arrangements of many machines. The problems posed by experimental visual displacement and by the practical need to design machines for accurate human control are interrelated, and present a challenge to describe them and understand them in terms of a uniform theory of motion. We believe that nearly all of the theoretical problems of human engineering and of the organization of operational behavior can be described in terms of spatially and temporally displaced perception and motion.

In succeeding chapters, we propose to review the problems of displaced perception and motion from both practical and theoretical points of view. The various experimental methods which have been used to analyze displaced vision will be described, and different theoretical approaches to these problems will be presented in some detail.

SUMMARY

1. Although tool using has been a crucial feature of human evolution and adaptation, it has become a subject of systematic research relatively recently.

2. So-called scientific management grew out of industrial pressures toward worker efficiency. Time and motion studies were begun by Taylor and expanded by Gilbreth.

3. Gilbreth classified work motions into 17 elemental "therbligs," which were assumed to have standard durations. Industrial engineers have worked out a number of systems of computing time standards for jobs in terms of therblig times, modified by performance ratings and performance variables.

4. There are few critical evaluative studies of time-study methods. Motion-picture studies are expensive and time-consuming. More promising are electronic methods of motion analysis, which have shown in controlled studies that component movements of a task cannot be standardized because they interact to affect movement times and are affected differentially by many physical and psychological variables.

5. Scientific studies have classified motions into a few general types, such as fixation, tense, and ballistic movements, or postural, transport, and manipulative movements.

6. Fatigue is difficult to define in either behavioral or physiological terms. Work decrement is subject to many variables, particularly in relation to patterns of motion and muscular contraction.

7. Münsterberg's rules of motion economy are not easily assessed in the absence of a good criterion of fatigue or energy expenditure. When tested in terms of movement time, these rules are not generally valid.

8. Human engineering is concerned with rules of tool economy — with fitting the tool to the job. Research is aimed toward measuring operational factors relating motion, perception, and machine design. Three areas are studies of human control of machine systems, studies of integration of perceptual information, and studies of spatial correspondence of perception and motion.

9. In tracking systems, partial automation has been assumed to be helpful to the tracker; comparative studies have shown that direct tracking is more accurate, apparently because of the delay in sensory feedback caused by automated systems.

10. Relevant to the problems of spatial correspondence of perception and motion in machine operation are studies of displaced vision, both spatial and temporal. This area will be reviewed in this book.

CHAPTER 4

EARLY EXPERIMENTS ON THE SPATIAL PROBLEMS OF BEHAVIOR

The problem of the geometric correspondence of motion patterns with the spatial patterns of the stimulus field was first formulated in science as a problem of perception — the perception of space. The specific question that intrigued some of the early sensory physiologists and psychologists — and which is no less intriguing today — had to do with the retinal image: What is the significance of the inverted retinal image in our perception of an upright world? This question and a proposed theory to answer it were first stated clearly by Helmholtz,[116] and have since given rise to an important series of investigations of experimentally inverted and otherwise displaced vision, begun by Stratton[295-297] and extending to the present day. These studies have been referred to again and again in psychological literature, yet a careful survey of their methods, their results, and their significance to behavioral science has never been made. In this chapter and the next, we shall present such a survey, in the belief that the phenomena of displaced vision are critical in defining the nature of perceptual-motor integration and its neural mechanisms. In this chapter, dealing with investigations up to the mid-1930's, we shall draw heavily on original sources, in order to present the investigators' points of view and important results in their own words.

HELMHOLTZ'S DEFINITION OF THE PROBLEM

Interest in retinal inversion in relation to human perception and motion coincided with the development of the sciences of optics and physiological psychology. The first systematic observations were probably those of Leonardo, who made extensive graphic studies of the visual system and its relation to the brain, and of optical devices for human use.[5] Leonardo thought that the rays of light which enter the eye cross twice in their path, once at the pupil (as in the camera obscura) and once in the vitreous humor, so that a "correct" or upright image is at last imposed on the retina. A century or more later, in the early seventeenth century, Kepler corrected Leonardo's mistaken assumption by describing how light rays from an object source cross in the lens and thus produce an inverted image of the object on the retina.[5] In the second half of the nineteenth century, Helmholtz[116] gave systematic consideration to the problems of the inverted retinal image and the perception of direction in space, and formulated what is known today as the empirical or experiential theory of space perception.

The Helmholtz doctrine of space perception, presented in his extensive writings on physiological optics, was one of the best known scientific theories of his time. As a foretaste of modern learning theory, it was in direct conflict with the then prevailing theories of space perception, including Kant's theory of innate dimensions of space, and the sensationalist view, based on concepts of local sign, that space direction is perceived in terms of the addition of numerous individual sensations which bear a point-to-point projectional relation with physical space. Helmholtz proposed, essentially, that space perception is learned. The world is perceived as upright because we learn that it *is* upright, and, from that point of view the orientation of the retinal image is of no particular significance.

Having no direct experimental evidence to apply to these assumptions, Helmholtz sought relevant data elsewhere. He was particularly interested in observations on children who are born blind because of congenital cataracts, and then are given their sight by surgical removal of the cataracts. These children show marked defects in visual behavior after the operation, and achieve normal vision only after a long period of adjustment. Helmholtz felt that these facts strongly supported his learning theory of perceptual development. Instead of quoting directly from Helmholtz's rather involved discussions, we shall present a summary of some of his ideas in the words of von Kries, a younger contemporary who wrote the following passages after Helmholtz's death:[116]

"The next subject we have to consider is how persons who are born blind can learn to see after having undergone an operation. We can dispose of it rather briefly, because, while quite a number of new cases have been reported, there is not much more to be learned from them than was contained in the earlier accounts that have been fully discussed by Helmholtz in the text. . . . All the observations tend to show that an optical recognition of definite *objects* that are otherwise familiar is impossible at first and is acquired only very gradually in the course of weeks. (Perhaps this is the main reason why vision is so extremely imperfect just after the operation has been performed.) This is a fact which doubtless is principally of psychological importance, inasmuch as it indicates that here, as everywhere, the retention in the memory of compound impressions comprising a lot of details is a matter of repeated perception and of an acquisition depending thereon. With respect to what may be considered as primitive space-determinations undeveloped by any experience, the fact is not without interest that even quite simple forms are not recognized at first. (See, for instance, Uhthoff, *Zft. f. Psychol.*, XIV. p. 209.)

"The most interesting fact of all from the optical point of view is the great uncertainty about perception of distance. (The boy examined by Uhthoff two months after the operation tried to reach out his hands and take hold of an object 1.5 metres away.) The other thing (undoubtedly connected with the first) is the corresponding uncertainty about judgment of size. These facts bring out very clearly the great role played by experience in regard to these matters. It is especially remarkable that the wholly peculiar relations between size and arrangement, the way in which they depend on the distances being unequal, the occlusion of a (farther) larger object by a smaller near one – all have to be learned over again. – A brief reference should be included here to another class of phenomena with which we have become acquainted in recent years, and which in many ways are similar to the cases of which we have just been speaking – namely, the phenomena of *forgetting how to see* resulting from long disuse of vision. For instance, if a child's eyes have not been functioning for years as the result of what is known as blepharospasm, vision has to be acquired anew to a certain extent after that condition has been cured, and the phenomena observed in such circumstances are very analogous to those which are noticed in the case of a patient who, being blind from birth, has undergone an operation to enable him to see."

Von Kries further discussed Helmholtz's original doctrine of the learning basis of perceptual localization in relation to observations subsequent to Helmholtz's time about the condition of strabismus – the abnormal deviation of one or both eyes – which can be modified by special treatment and training of the child early in life. Von Kries felt that, although Helmholtz's ideas might be modified somewhat in favor of attributing more importance to innate factors, on the whole the empirical theory was strongly corroborated by the new facts.

"Concerning the real crux of Helmholtz's doctrine, the matter of localization, it must be granted, I think, that the facts by which this question has to be decided at present are on the whole practically the same as those which were known forty years ago and which Helmholtz made the foundation of his argument. Since then no positive facts have been brought to light that could tend to upset the main features of this theory or modify them essentially. The fact is, rather, that certain special observations, for instance new data about strabismic vision, together also with some mod-

ifications in general points of view, have tended to support the empirical theory in a remarkable way and to put it on a broader and firmer foundation. Thus, while we have been compelled to differ with Helmholtz's theory about some matters of principle in regard to the psychology of the idea of space, the trend of our discussion, as has been shown repeatedly, has been essentially in agreement with this theory as to the main question of localization. Moreover, the result of our studies of this question has been to show that experience and training were of fundamental importance in this connection. In the main it is the facts bearing on this subject which Helmholtz has presented and discussed that enable and indeed compel us to assert today that localization is a development through experience. "Those points in regard to localization where we have been obliged to differ with Helmholtz (or rather – strictly speaking – where it was found necessary to develop his theory further) are only of secondary importance after all, no matter how much weight may be attached to them. What they amounted to was that, in the first place, more significance must be allowed to congenital substructures of localization (particularly by assuming that there are such bases for the associations between the two eyes); and, secondly, the processes of learning must be regarded from the point of view of a physiological development, which necessitates some modifications of the theory, partly on account of these processes themselves and partly also with reference to the substructures that are needed for them. In order to obtain a proper appreciation of these modifications, it should be borne in mind that, positively convinced as Helmholtz was of the fundamental significance of learning for localization, he would certainly have been the last person to maintain that he or anybody else at that time was in a position to give a complete and thoroughly satisfactory picture of the nature of the processes of localization or of the innate predispositions that must be connected with learning. On the contrary, he was careful to state again and again that for reasons of methodology he preferred above all to employ a principle of interpretation of the facts, which was recognized to be correct and indispensable, in order to see how far he could get with it, so to speak. While this mode of treating the subject may have involved his relegating other possible explanations to the second place, there was no implication that these possibilities were denied or disputed; it simply meant that he considered that they belonged in another field of inquiry which was not thoroughly developed at the time, and that for this reason he thought it best to keep them carefully in the background. It would be, therefore, a complete misapprehension of Helmholtz's views to suppose (as has been intimated sometimes) that he meant to deny altogether the participation of innate factors in the case of localization. The truth is, rather, that Helmholtz was disposed to think that from his point of view it was extremely probable that there was some kind of cooperation such as we have deemed likely; that is, with respect to the relationship existing between the visual direction and the location on the retina, although he doubted whether such an assumption could be absolutely verified. The fact that modern investigations of strabismus have enabled us to develop still further assumptions of this sort need not imply that any fundamental modification has to be made in Helmholtz's theory.

"It is necessary to put special emphasis on this, because some of the writers mentioned above have taken the position that these new observations have upset the empirical theory or shown that it was not correct. To express such an opinion as this amounts to placing secondary considerations on a par with fundamental ones in a more than arbitrary fashion, it seems to me. Modern observations tend to show that the secondary correspondence is not so precise or so efficient as the primary correspondence, indicating therefore the probability of an innate predisposition in favour of the latter; but this is an idea of exactly the same kind as was advocated by Helmholtz himself in regard to the arrangement of direction within the field of view. Had the facts now known been current forty years ago, Helmholtz doubtless would have deduced from them a closer connection between the local signs of corresponding pairs of retinal points, which was an assumption which he considered then as superfluous.

"But the main thing to be remembered is that to a great extent these modern investigations have *corroborated* in a very positive manner inferences that Helmholtz had already made from the scant material at his disposal at that time. The main conclusions which he reached have been shown to be absolutely probable. One instance is the *modification in the relation of visual directions* (or the anomalous association of visual directions, as Tschermak expresses it). As has been already said, this one fact brings out in a particularly striking way the circumstance that what is called visual direction is not something given and fixed by the retinal place itself, but is a complicated result, which for that reason is capable of being modified, and which depends on the cooperation of the adjustment-factor. Undoubtedly, these new facts do enable us to appreciate the profound modifications of the

mode of vision in strabismus, and they show especially the development of an anomalous relation of visual direction. But granting all this, I am convinced that, . . . in regard to the most important and decisive matters, the facts tend to support the fundamental conceptions of an empirical theory to a remarkable degree, although perhaps not altogether to the extent that Helmholtz supposed. It would be turning things upside down, it seems to me, to regard these new facts as a corroboration of the points of view of the intuition theory. They are certainly the opposite of what might be anticipated on the basis of those conceptions."

STRATTON'S STUDIES

Stratton[295-297] performed the first systematic experiments on displaced vision, using himself as subject. He originated optical methods of inverting and reversing the visual field, and devised the first mirror apparatus which could be worn on the head in order to displace the visual field. In addition, Stratton's observations on the effects of displaced vision on different types of motions were important in emphasizing the motion aspects of the displaced vision problem in addition to the more ambiguous perceptual effects.

First Inversion Experiment

Stratton[295] planned his first study of visual inversion as a specific test of then current theories of space perception which postulated that inverted retinal images are necessary for normal upright vision. The projection theory of space perception was the precursor of local sign theory. It stated that objects are projected back into space in the direction in which the rays of light fall upon the retina; the crossing of these lines in the lens requires that if an object is to be projected right side up, the image on the retina must be turned upside down. The eye movement theory asserted that perception of eye movements and of their direction constitutes the mechanism by means of which we perceive the space relations of visual objects. This theory also required that if objects are to be seen upright, their image must be inverted on the retina.

Stratton devised light telescopes with double convex lenses at each end that inverted and reversed the visual field. These short, adjustable tubes were formed at one end to fit snugly around the eyes, and could be attached firmly to the head. They gave a clear field of vision, 45 degrees in extent. Stratton had hoped to wear them both for binocular vision, but the strain on his eyes was too great because of the interference with convergence movements. Accordingly, he discarded one tube, covered his left eye with a blindfold and carried out his experiment with monocular vision.

Stratton's regular procedure was to wear his optical devices continuously during daily periods, and to blindfold himself at all other times. On the first day he wore the telescope from 3:00 P.M. to 10:00 P.M.; on the second day, from 9:30 A.M. to 10:00 P.M.; and on the third day, from 10:00 A.M. until noon, for a total of 21.5 hours of inverted-reversed vision. All of this time was spent indoors.

Stratton described his experience as one of "undoing" a lifelong habit of interpreting visual signs. "All images at first appeared to be inverted; the room and all in it seemed upside down." Yet, although all these images were clear and definite, they did not seem to represent real things at first; they seemed to be misplaced, false, or illusory images between Stratton and the objects themselves.

"For the memory-images brought over from normal vision still continued to be the standard and criterion of reality. Things were thus seen in one way and thought of in a far different way. This held true also of my body. For the parts of my body were felt to be where they would have appeared had the instrument been removed; they were seen to be in another position. But the older tactual and visual localization was still the real localization."

Movements were awkward and surprising, frequently in error, and required correction until the limb was brought into the required position in the visual field. The affected limb usually started in the wrong direction from the one desired, or the wrong hand would be used in grasping objects.

"As I moved about in the room, the movement of the visual images of my hands or feet were at first not used, as in normal vision, to decide what tactual sensations were to be expected. After a time, however, repeated experience made this use of the visual image much less strange; it began to be the common guide and means of anticipation."

Thus, the limbs began actually to feel in the place the new visual perception reported them to be.

"The vivid connection of tactual and visual perceptions began to take away the overpowering force of the localization lasting over from normal vision. The seen images thus became real things just as in normal sight. . . . Objects lying at the moment outside the visual field (things at the side of the observer, for example) were at the first mentally represented as they would have appeared in normal vision. But later I found myself bringing the representation of unseen objects into harmonious relation with the present perception. They began now to be represented not as they would appear if normal vision were restored, but as they would appear if the present field of vision were widened or moved so as to include them. In this way the room began to make a whole once more, floor and walls and the prominent objects in the room getting into a constant relation to one another, so that during a movement of the head I could more or less accurately anticipate the order in which things would enter the visual field."

By the third day, Stratton found that things had been interconnected into a whole by piecing together the parts of the ever-changing visual fields.

"As to the relation of the visual field to the observer, the feeling that the field was upside down remained in general throughout the experiment. At times, however, there were peculiar variations in this feeling according to the mental attitude of the observer toward the present scene. . . . On removing the glasses on the third day, there was no peculiar experience. Normal vision was restored instantaneously and without any disturbance in the natural appearance or position of objects."

Stratton summarized this first experiment on displaced vision in this way:

"I might almost say that the main problem — that of the importance of the inversion of the retinal image for upright vision — had received from the experiment a full solution. For if the inversion of the retinal image were absolutely necessary for upright vision, as both the projection theory and the eye-movement theory hold, it is certainly difficult to understand how the scene as a whole could even temporarily have appeared upright when the retinal image was not inverted."

Only the head and shoulders, which could not be seen at all under the circumstances, seemed to be in abnormal relation to the scene.

"That these parts of the body should have stubbornly refused to come into harmony with the new arrangement is easy to explain. The only visual experience I had had of them was the normal visual experience, and this remained firm in memory without the possibility of displacing it by repeated contradictory visual perception under the new conditions. . . . No doubt the merely tactual experience of the unseen parts of the body and of their relation to the seen parts must inevitably have produced in time a new indirect visual representation of these unseen parts which would displace the older representation brought over from actual vision. The gradual organization of the whole experience would certainly produce this result, although it would undoubtedly require more time in the case of the unseen parts of the body than in that of the parts plainly visible.

"In fact, the difficulty of seeing things upright by means of upright retinal images seems to consist solely in the resistance offered by the long-established previous experience. Any visual field in which the relations of the seen parts to one another would always correspond to the relations found by touch and muscular movement would give us 'upright' vision, whether the optic image lay upright, inverted, or at any intermediate angle whatever on the retina. Only after a set of relations and perceptions had become organized into a norm could something enter which was in unusual relation to this organized whole and be (for instance)

upside down. But a person whose vision had from the very beginning been under the conditions we have in the present experiment artificially produced, could never possibly feel that such visual perceptions were inverted."

It is clear from Stratton's conclusions that he believed in the empirical theory of perceptual development, and felt that an individual with experimentally-inverted vision would probably *in time* become completely adapted. It is also clear that Stratton's adaptation within three days was variable, incomplete, and dependent upon touch and kinesthesis. Hoping to achieve a more complete adaptation, he carried out a second experiment on visual inversion for a longer period of time.

Second Inversion Experiment

Stratton's second experiment[296] duplicated his first except that the fitting of the telescope to the face and eye was improved. This study went on for eight days and involved wearing the lenses for 87 hours. His eyes were blindfolded when the telescope was not worn. He spent much of his time in a secluded garden, but every evening took a long walk through the village, wearing the monocular telescope. On the first day:

"The entire scene appeared upside down. When I moved my head or body so that my sight swept over the scene, the movement was not felt to be solely in the observer, as in normal vision, but was referred both to the observer and to objects beyond. . . . Almost all movements performed under the direct guidance of sight were laborious and embarrassed. . . . The unusual strain of attention in these cases, and the difficulty of finally getting a movement to its goal, made all but the simplest movements extremely fatiguing. . . . Relief was sometimes sought by shutting out of consideration the actual visual data, and by depending solely on tactual or motor perception and on the older visual representations suggested by these. But for the most part this tendency was resisted, and movements were performed with full attention to what was visually before me. . . . In order to write my notes, the formation of the letters and words had to be left to automatic muscular sequence, using sight only as a guide to the general position and direction on my paper. When hesitation occurred in my writing, as it often did, there was no resort but to picture the next stroke or two in pre-experimental terms, and when the movement was once under way, control it visually as little as possible."

Stratton also stated that there were some signs of nervous disturbance, "of which perhaps the most marked was a feeling of depression in the upper abdominal region, akin to mild nausea." During the second day:

"Movements . . . had in many respects grown less laborious, and were performed more on the basis of the actual sight-experience, and less by excluding these as a means of guidance. . . . Unseen objects could, by force of will, be represented in harmony with things in view, more easily than on the preceding day. . . . As to the 'uprightness' or inversion of things, the general feeling was that the seen room was upside down; . . . When I looked out over a wide landscape, the position in which I felt my body to be and the position of the scene before me were surely discordant and unnatural."

Stratton took a long walk that evening and was unable to recognize the normally familiar surroundings. He concluded that, "Recognition evidently depended largely on external relations of position and direction, and, with a disturbance of these, the objects themselves seemed strange."

By the third day he noted he was:

". . . beginning to feel more at home in the new experience. . . . Walking through the narrow spaces between pieces of furniture required much less care than hitherto. I could watch my hands as I wrote, without hesitating or becoming embarrassed thereby. Yet I often stretched out the wrong hand to grasp a visible object lying to one side; right and left were felt to be by far the most persistently troublesome relations when it came to translating visual into tactual or motor localization. . . . Head-movements were still accompanied by a slight swinging of the scene, although in a markedly less degree than on the first day. . . .

"Other factors besides volition or even recency of visual perception were observed to have an effect on the direction in which unseen objects were represented. The position of the shadow of my body in the visual field, for

instance, involuntarily strengthened the new representation of my body. . . . In this way and from other influences, there was coming to be a more vital connection between my actual perceptions and the larger visual system of merely represented objects. . . . The rooms beyond the one I was in, together with the scene out of doors, could be represented in harmonious relation with what I was actually looking at. . . . That the new experience was getting a more stable place in my mind, was perhaps shown by the involuntary recurrence of scenes in their new visual relations, after actual perception had ceased — when I closed my eyes, for instance, or in the evening when my glasses were removed and my eyes were blindfolded."

On the fourth day, the "new experience had become even less trying. There was no sign of bodily discomfort. . . . During the day, actions appropriate to the new visual perceptions frequently occurred without any conflict or apparent tendency to react by a misinterpretation of visual positions." Stratton discovered a simple means of obtaining without calculation the use of the proper hand in picking up things on the floor. "If, with one of my feet near the object, I gave a tap or two on the floor before I stooped to pick it up, the proper hand immediately came into play." He also discovered that:

"The character of the representation of things not actually in sight was influenced by the recency of their visual perception and by the closeness of their relation to things in sight. . . . The feeling of the inversion or uprightness of things was found to vary considerably with the strength and character of the representation of my body. When I looked at my legs and arms, or even when I reinforced by effort of attention their new visual representation, then what I saw seemed rather upright than inverted."

On the fifth day mistakes were no longer made in selecting the correct hand to pick up objects, or in running into obstacles. The right direction was taken in walking, and the entire house could be traversed with visual guidance alone, although movements were still awkward and cautious. Objects and people were often seen without a feeling of incongruity, that they were reversed in position from their normal appearance.

"But in general the most harmonious experiences were obtained during active operations on the scene before me. In rapid, complicated, yet practiced movements, the harmony of the localization by sight and that by touch or motor perception . . . came out with much greater force than when I sat down and passively observed the scene."

The findings of the sixth and seventh days were very similar. On pacing up and down, "There was perfect reality in my visual surroundings, and I gave myself up to them without reserve and without being conscious of a single note of discord with what I saw."

On these days, one of the most striking facts was that the extent of movements was inappropriate. Yet few misdirected movements of the hands were made, and fewer still by the feet. Discordant feelings came from the shoulders when the hands were moved, but not from the hands. Conflict still occurred between the old and the new in localization of parts of the body. The palm of one hand in touching objects was mistaken in visual localization. On the evening walk, however, the beauty of the passing scene was enjoyed for the first time. On the eighth and last day:

"The illusion of contact on the opposite hand to the one actually touched arose as on the two preceding days. I often hesitated which hand was the appropriate one for grasping some object in view, began the movement with the wrong hand and then corrected the mistake. . . .

"Localization of sounds varied, being different when the source of sound was in sight from what it was when this was out of sight, and also in the latter case differing with different directions of attention, or with different suggestions as to the direction from which the sound came. . . . The tapping of my pencil on the arm of my chair seemed without question to issue from the visible pencil."

When the time came for removing the glasses at the close of the experiment, Stratton thought it best to preserve as nearly as possible the size of the visual field to which he had grown accustomed, so that the observed effects could be attributed to the visual reversion and not to a sudden widening of the visual field. He had his assistant remove the tube with the lens in it and replace it with an empty black-lined paper tube that gave about the same range of vision. He stated that upon opening his eyes:

". . . the scene had a strange familiarity. The visual arrangement was immediately recognized as the old one of pre-experimental days; yet the reversal of everything from the order to which I had grown accustomed during the past week, gave the scene a surprising, bewildering air which lasted for several hours. It was hardly the feeling, though, that things were upside down.

"When I turned my body or my head, objects seemed to sweep before me as if they themselves were suddenly in motion. The 'swinging of the scene,' observed so continuously during the first days of the experiment, had thus returned with great vividness. . . .

"Movements which would have been appropriate to the visual arrangement during the experiment, were now repeatedly performed after this arrangement had been reversed. . . . I found myself more than once at a loss which hand I ought to use to grasp the door-handle at my side. . . . And in writing my notes at this time, I continually made the wrong movement of my head in attempting to keep the centre of my visual field somewhere near the point where I was writing. I moved my head upward when it should have gone downward. . . . And this to such a degree as to be a serious disturbance."

Stratton also experienced nausea and the feeling that the floor and other visual objects were swaying, and objects in the room, at a distance of ten or twelve feet, seemed to have lost their old levels and to be much higher than they were either during the experiment or before the experiment.

"It is clear, from the foregoing narrative, that our total system of visual objects is a comparatively stable structure, not to be set aside or transformed by some few experiences which do not accord with its general plan of arrangement. . . . To say that the older visual directions persisted because the older tactual directions remained in force, is certainly no sufficient answer unless we can show that visual direction is dependent on tactual direction. But the preceding narrative furnishes strong evidence against such a view . . . the facts in the present case are more accurately described when we say that the discord was . . . between the visual directions suggested by touch and the visual directions given in the actual sight. The real question then is: Why did touch-perceptions so persistently suggest visual images whose positions and directions were in discord with the actual scene? The answer is found, I think, in the familiar doctrine of 'local signs' in touch and in sight, and in the farther assumption that a system of correspondence exists whereby a sign in one sense comes to be connected with and to suggest a particular sign in the other sense. . . . This correspondence of local signs is no doubt an important condition for our perceiving one and the same thing in different sensory fields. . . .

"It was repeatedly noticed in the course of the experiment that the total experience was much more harmonious during active moments of my body than when I inactively looked out upon the scene. This becomes intelligible when one sees how such movements gave additional vivacity to the new visual experience and to all that was in harmony with it, and tended to suppress those images of the body which did not accord with the new relations . . . the new localization of the body was the only one which was *practically important* when the visible environment had to be actively encountered. My actions could be guided, not by keeping in mind the pre-experimental localization of the body and noticing its relation to objects in sight, but only by accepting the new position of my body as *real* and constantly watching its relation to surrounding things. . . .

"The inverted position of the retinal image is, therefore, not essential to 'upright vision,' for it is not essential to a harmony between touch and sight, which, in the final analysis, is the real meaning of upright vision. For some visual objects may be inverted with respect to other visual objects, but the *whole system* of visual objects can never by itself be either inverted or upright. It could be inverted or upright only with respect to certain non-visual experiences with which I might compare my visual system — in other words, with respect to my tactual or motor perceptions . . . the restoration of harmony between the perceptions of sight and those of touch was in no wise a process of changing the absolute position of tactual objects so as to make it identical

with the place of the visual objects; no more than it was an alteration of the visual position into accord with the tactual . . . it was a process of making a new visual position seem the only natural place for the visual counterpart of a given tactual experience to appear in; and similarly in regard to new tactual positions for the tactual accompaniment of given visual experiences . . . new correspondences had to be brought about. But the tactual perceptions, as such, never changed their place. They simply got a new visual translation. . . .

"The experiment makes it clear that the harmony between sight and touch does not depend on the inversion of the retinal image. . . . The facts all go to show that the direction of movements of the head or eyes is not judged on purely muscular evidence, independently of the simultaneous changes in vision itself. On the contrary the movements are soon felt as having a direction opposite to that of the objects passing through the visual field. . . . It certainly makes the eye-movement doctrine of visual directions of little practical assistance for understanding the harmony between sight and touch."

Stratton concluded that the doctrine of a correspondence of local signs made provision for the special results of the experiment, "as well as for the normal course of our experience; which the current doctrines concerning the interplay of touch and sight seem hardly able to do."

Angular Distortion Experiment

According to Stratton,[297] his first two experiments showed how tactual localization is affected by disturbance of visual direction; they indicated that sensations of touch and movement may come to be referred to an entirely new direction in sight, but not necessarily to a new distance as well. Therefore, in a third experiment, he proposed to investigate the "harmonizing" of the senses of touch and sight when the discord between them involves both direction and distance. This third experiment of Stratton's is one of the first and one of the most important studies thus far carried out on size and distance constancy in visual perception.

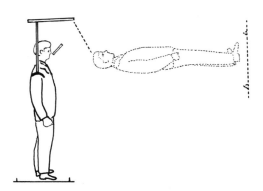

Figure 4-1. Stratton's[297] mirror method for obtaining a 90-degree angular displacement of the locus of vision that a person has of his own body.

Figure 4-1 shows the technique used by Stratton in this study. One mirror was mounted horizontally, face downward, above the head and extending forward. A second mirror was located in front of the eyes, face upward, at an angle of 45 degrees. Thus, Stratton viewed his own body as if it were disposed horizontally in front of him, as shown by the dotted figure. These mirrors were mounted in a fixed relation to one another in a frame, which was bound to the waist and shoulders so that free movements of body, head, and hands were possible. The head could be moved independently of the mirrors. A black cloth screened the immediate scene in front of the eyes from direct vision. The visual field obtained included the entire body and a restricted region around it, so that visual guidance of locomotion in relation to the immediate environment was possible. Stratton wore this contraption on three successive days for periods of 6, 10.5, and 7.5 hours respectively, or for about 24 hours altogether.

Some of Stratton's observations in this study were similar to those in the experiments on inverted vision, except that right and left were not confused in this mirror vision situation. Mistakes in controlling distance of movement were more evident than mistakes of direction. Objects other than the body were seen in their usual positions. With regard to his perception of his own body, Stratton observed:

"The visual projection remained for some time a mere reflexion or displaced image of the reality which was still thought of as lying in its normal position . . . even to the end I usually had only to shut my eyes to cause the older mental picture to surge back and drive from the field all but some faded remnant of the new perceptions. At times, however, even with closed eyes, I involuntarily thought of my body as in the position just seen. . . . This growing recognition of the projected image of my body as the real body was accompanied and doubtless aided by a waning opposition of the reports of touch and sight."

Impressions of touch occasionally suggested no other place than the one indicated by sight, but the most frequent and striking examples of such harmony were found during the more rapid and inclusive bodily movements, especially that of walking.

"In walking I felt as though I were moving along above the shoulders of the figure below me, although this too was part of myself, . . . I had the feeling that I was mentally outside my own body. It was, of course, but a passing impression, but it came several times and was vivid while it lasted. . . . But the moment critical interest arose, the simplicity of the state was gone, and my visible actions were accompaned by a kind of wraith of themselves in the older visual terms."

Stratton noted that correspondence of touch and sight in the case of his feet and lower legs was not easily disturbed, and that after these came the region of his hands. His head and shoulders, however, were far less tractable.

"It now seems evident that in addition to having the part perceptible by both touch and sight, it is important that the occurrence of a tactual sensation should be regularly signalised by some striking occurrence in the visual field, and *vice versa*. . . . The dermal and internal sensations arising from the head and chest are accompanied by visual changes which are less striking than those associated with the kinaesthetic variations in the feet and hands. What visible appearance there is of these former movements generally passes with less heed; and a longer time is consequently required to develop intimate connexions and instinctive cross-references between touch and sight than in the case of the legs and arms. . . . As to the feeling of the directions up, down, and level, there was at first an utter rejection of the directions suggested by the view, then an occasional confusion . . . finally cases where the apparent plane of the ground was accepted as the true level, and my body was felt as upright upon it. More frequently, . . . there was a compromise, in that the new visual directions were not accepted as final and yet I could not bring myself to feel that the true level was as different from the visible plane of the ground as I knew it must be."

Stratton interpreted his results as showing an achievement of harmony between touch and sight. He believed that this harmony depends on experience and on perception established by experience, and observed, "If we were always to see our bodies a hundred yards away, we would probably also feel them there." He rejected any view of interconnection between the senses that would assume that harmony between them requires identical location of their images.

Stratton also took up the question of childhood blindness, and its effect on later visual experience after sight has been gained through surgery. Unlike Helmholtz and von Kries, he was concerned about the report that some of these children are able to point to small objects as soon as they can see. He, in effect, denied that such reactions occur, and reaffirmed his belief that time and training are necessary for visual perception of direction after vision is regained.

Stratton summed up all of his work with an attitudinal interpretation of his findings. He said his experiments show that:

". . . the different sense-perceptions, whatever may be the ultimate source of their extension, are organized into one harmonious spatial system. The harmony is found to consist in having our experiences meet our expectations. . . . The essential conditions of the harmony are

merely those which are necessary to build up a reliable cross-reference between the two senses. This view, which was at first based on the results with the inverting lenses, is now given a wider interpretation, since it seems evident from the later experiment that a given tactual position may have its correlated visual place not only in any direction, but also at any distance, in the visual field."

WOOSTER'S EXPERIMENT

It was more than 20 years after Stratton's work before additional experiments were carried out on displaced vision. In 1923, Wooster[334] reported one of the first systematic studies on angularly displaced vision. Although this experiment is rarely cited in experimental literature, it is one of the best early psychological studies of visuomotor behavior. It was designed to extend Stratton's observations on the reorganization of touch and visual experience by analyzing how this reorganization is brought about and what factors are involved in it.

During a twelve-month period, Wooster carried out many observations on a total of 72 subjects, who wore a pair of

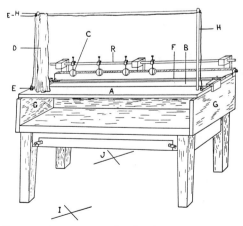

Figure 4-2. Wooster's localizing apparatus, showing shield over subject's hand (A), and movable buzzers (C), for localizing objects. (From Wooster.[334])

prisms which displaced the visual field about 21 degrees to the right. The experimental task was to localize visual objects with reaching movements. As shown in Figure 4-2, the objects, usually buzzers, were arranged in certain positions in front of the subject and within view. Subjects were asked to make a quick, automatic localization of the right arm to where the object appeared to be. Movement of the arm was hidden by a screen, and the subject's index finger came to rest against a board. Most subjects were tested on the first experimental day for localizing accuracy with normal vision, and thereafter worked with prism-displaced vision. Twenty localizations were made each day, five for each of the four positions. Subjects usually continued for ten days, or until the effects of distortion had been overcome, if less than ten days.

Localization of Displaced Visual Objects with No Knowledge of Results

In these first observations, subjects were required to reach toward the particular buzzer pointed to by the experimenter. Although no indication was given as to the accuracy of localizations, it was found that adaptation to prism-displaced vision took place gradually but slowly. After ten days of practice, accuracy had increased until the subjects' mean deviation from true localization was 40.5 per cent less than the deviation on the first day.

In a second experiment, special care was taken to eliminate all clues as to the nature of the visual distortion and to prevent all knowledge of results. The three subjects in this group were given no preliminary tests with normal vision, and later questioning disclosed that they had no knowledge of the nature or extent of the visual distortion. Yet, recovery of accuracy in these subjects was

equal to that of the first group. In still another experiment, the position of the localizing objects was shifted far to the left to determine whether the subjects' adaptation involved merely a shift toward the midline. The subjects in this group showed progressive increase in accuracy toward true localizations in spite of the fact that this involved movements made farther and farther to the left. Wooster concluded that the basis for improved accuracy, in the absence of any specific knowledge of results, was the discrepancy in eye-head orientation caused by wearing the prisms. Subjects had to move their eyes to the right to bring the displaced objects to the fovea, thus producing a discrepancy between "front" as defined by head position, and "front" as defined by eye position. It seems possible also that subjects may have adapted on the basis of discrepant auditory-visual cues of the experimenter. They saw her in one place but heard her voice in another.

Localization of Displaced Visual Objects with Auditory Clues

In this series, the role of sound in adaptation to distorted vision was tested. One buzzer was used, which was shifted in successive trials from one position to another, using the four positions shown in Figure 4-2. The subjects were first run blindfolded to test their accuracy of auditory localization in the four positions, and thereafter tested with prism-displaced vision, with the sound as an aid in localizing the buzzer. Results indicated that sound contributed little if at all toward improving accuracy over that found in the first series of experiments. Equivalent results were obtained when a bell with a visible vibrator was used as the localizing object, so that subjects would be sure to associate the sound with the object.

Localization of Displaced Visual Objects with Touch

In these experiments, one buzzer was used in the four positions, and it was lowered part way through a slit in the table so that the subject's finger would touch it when a correct localization was made. The first subjects were permitted no corrective movements, so that touch occurred only by chance as a result of an accurate localization. Their knowledge of error throughout the series did not speed up their adaptation over the first groups, who had had no knowledge. However, subjects who were permitted to make corrective movements after each false localization until they touched the buzzer improved very rapidly and to a higher level than any of the preceding groups.

Localization with Visual Perception of Error

An experiment was carried out with the apparatus arranged to give the subjects a view of their own finger at the end of each localizing movement. Although no corrective movements were allowed, adaptation to the displaced vision was just as effective — and perhaps slightly more so — than in the experiment just described involving active corrective movements but no view of the finger.

Localization of One Hand by the Other

In a final experiment, the experimenter placed the subject's left hand in position on the table as the localizing object. The left index finger extended down through the slit so that it could be touched when localized accurately by the right hand. Adaptation under this condition was much more rapid than for any other condition. In general, subjects performing with displaced vision learned to localize their own hand far more quickly than other objects.

Some of the spatial coordinations learned in these experiments were retained for long periods of time, and functioned with considerable effectiveness even after one or two years.

Summary of Studies

A first major conclusion of this study confirms an earlier judgment of Stratton. Wooster stated that her results clearly indicated that no major readjustment in localization could occur without specific localizing movements. In her words, "No readjustment to the changed visual situation occurred without definite reaching movements of the hand while the eye was fixed on the visual object." Her second major conclusion postulated that the subject had some sort of kinesthetic sensations (which she interpreted as coming from eye movements) which led to realignment of movement and vision in prism-displaced visual fields in which the subject had no absolute guide of true position.

Wooster concluded that the most rapid acquisition of localizing came when tactual-kinesthetic information from one part of the body (hand) served as clues for the localization. She concluded that the new coordinations were formed entirely on a sensorimotor basis, and that her study demonstrated that quantitative information concerning the development of space perception can be obtained with relatively simple and direct procedures.

BROWN'S EXPERIMENT

In another major study of displaced vision, Brown[32] investigated still another dimension of displacement — that of rotation of the visual field. His experiment analyzed some of the effects of rotation on depth perception and upon relative movement of head and eyes, and also demonstrated some of the limitations of adaptation to displaced vision.

Brown had observed that when stereoscopic pictures are rotated, their depth effect is reduced with rotation beyond about 40 or 50 degrees, and reversed with rotation near 180 degrees. He reasoned that if depth vision depends upon learning, as assumed by empirical theory, then practice under unusual conditions that at the outset afford little or no immediate depth would eventually lead to more definite depth perception. Consequently, he proposed to set up limited depth conditions by rotating the visual field, and then to determine how well subjects could learn to perceive depth under the circumstances.

The prismatic goggles used by Brown to rotate the visual field are diagrammed in Figure 4-3. The eye pieces of these goggles were brass tubes 1.7 inches in

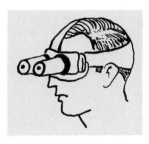

Figure 4-3. Brown's[32] experimental spectacles in which prisms were used to rotate the visual field.

diameter and 2.5 inches long. Each tube was equipped with two right-angle prisms, one in front of the other, each of which could be rotated independently. An effect called "leaning of the image" could be produced by rotating one of the prisms. The visual field presented to each eye could be displaced any desired amount to 360 degrees.

Special training procedures in distance discrimination and tests of depth perception and performance were employed in the study. The depth training involved positioning three brass discs, about 1 inch in diameter, located about four feet from the subject's eyes. The movement of these discs back and forth in the field was controlled by cables, in order to provide visual training in depth discrimination without kinesthetic cues of reaching. The test of depth vision employed two moveable cardboard plaques arranged against a neutral screen, located about 3.4 feet from the subject's eyes. The subject's threshold of depth perception or stereoscopic visual acuity was determined by moving one plaque relative to the depth of the other, using appropriate psychophysical procedures. Performance tests involving depth vision included a steadiness device, a star-tracing test much like that used in the standard mirror-tracing experiment, and a pendulum pursuit test, in which the pendulum moved in different directions. In the last, the subject followed a pendulum leaking water from a nozzle at its tip, attempting to collect the dribbling water in a container. The score depended upon the amount of water collected.

Acting as his first subject, Brown wore the prisms, which were set to rotate the visual field 75 degrees, continuously during waking hours for seven days. Four additional subjects wore them at 75-degree rotation for one half hour each day for 16 days and performed four of the tests and training exercises. A control subject trained in four tests with normal vision. The initial quantitative effect of a 75-degree rotation of the visual field was nearly to double the separation threshold of depth percep- tion as determined by the two-plaque test. Concerning his own experiences during seven days, Brown reported:

"The major initial difficulties for the subject were awareness of the tilted position of the objective world with consequent embarrassment in dealing with objects such as furniture, etc., and the fact that when the head was turned the entire field of objects seemed to move (in the opposite direction to the head rotation). . . . The tilting of the objective world was less noticed as time went on. . . . Parallel with this adaptation it became easier for the subject to move about in his rooms. . . . Judgment of near distance (within range of the hands) seemed to improve rapidly. . . . Another initial difficulty, the apparent movement of the field when the head was moved, progressively de- creased and disappeared. . . . Visual imagery was operative, but . . . slow in taking prece- dence over that of previous visual experience."

The results of the training and testing procedures with the other subjects indi- cated variable effects according to the test used. Only slight learning occurred in the steadiness test, but the star-tracing test showed improvement both in time and in reduction of errors. The pendu- lum test also showed marked learning effects, but striking deterioration of per- formance in this test would sometimes occur after peak efficiency had been reached.

Brown's general conclusions were that depth vision was reduced by rotating the visual field in proportion to the mag- nitude of the disorientation; that there was no conclusive evidence that practice markedly improved depth discrimina- tion with disoriented vision, although some improvement resulted from prac- tice; that there were marked individual differences in the effects of the disorien- tation; and that general adaptation to the experience of disoriented vision progressed with practice.

COX'S STUDY OF SPACE-REGULATED BEHAVIOR

Cox[55] conducted a very interesting study on spatially organized behavior with displaced vision and motion, using the Miles two-story duplicate maze illus- trated in Figure 4-4. Two stylus mazes are mounted in a wooden box, as shown, with the front of the box open to permit tracing the lower maze with a stylus while viewing the identical pattern of the upper maze. The lower maze is mounted on an inlaid circular turntable, so that its orientation with respect to the upper maze can be varied 360 de- grees. The lower maze pattern can also be turned over to reverse it in relation to the upper maze. The subject is re- quired to trace the two mazes simul- taneously, the upper with one hand and

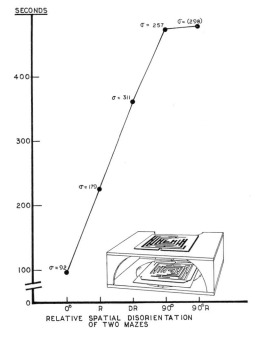

Figure 4-4. The Miles two-story duplicate maze and Cox's[55] quantitative results showing speed of maze tracing when the lower unseen maze is rotated relative to the upper visible maze. (Maze from Miles.[187])

the lower with the other. The fact that the subject must trace the lower maze while it is spatially disoriented with respect to the visible upper maze makes this experiment of Cox important in the study of disoriented vision.

Sixty-seven subjects were tested with five positions of the lower maze: zero-degree orientation with respect to the upper maze, 180 degree rotation or double reversal, 90 degree rotation, reversal in one direction (achieved by flipping the lower pattern over), and 90 degree reversal (achieved by flipping the lower maze over and rotating it 90 degrees). Unfortunately the conditions were not varied by subject, but were run for all subjects in the order named.

The mean time scores for the different conditions of disorientation are plotted in Figure 4-4, with conditions indicated on the abscissa (the letters R and DR represent reversed and double-reversed conditions, respectively). This curve was prepared from Cox's tabulated data.

Cox offered no theory or explanation of these results of her experiment, but became overly involved in analyzing some of the individual differences. She concluded her discussion by saying that the five motor-space problems presented in sequence on Miles' double maze were found to vary in difficulty in spite of the fact that they presented the same visual maze patterns.

"The problem was not one in learning; but it appeared that slow workers, those who had difficulty in solving the problems, did begin to learn the maze pattern. . . . The problems for the double maze were not 'trial-and-error' or 'trial-and-trial,' as would be the case with the ordinary blindfold maze; for here indirect visual guidance was provided by the upper maze. The types of cue and imagery used for guidance were found to show considerable individual difference. But a combination predominantly visual and secondarily kinaesthetic . . . proved effective for most subjects in solving the series of problems taken as a whole."

Cox's quantitative results, as summarized in Figure 4-4, can be interpreted in terms of our own systematic theory of motion, which we shall describe in detail in later chapters. The order of difficulty of the different displacements between vision and motion that were investigated by Cox is the order we would have predicted theoretically, and coincides with the order of difficulty as determined in our own many experimental observations on displaced visual feedback. Cox demonstrated experimentally for the first time that there is a quantitative variation in the effects of different conditions of visual displacement.

EWERT'S EXPERIMENTS

Ewert[74] was primarily concerned with repeating Stratton's first experiments, but used a binocular optical system instead of the monocular one employed by Stratton. Hence, the two studies are not really comparable, for, as Stratton showed originally, binocular telescopes, with their limited focus and fixed fields, modify the convergence-divergence factors in depth perception and impose a marked strain on convergence.

Ewert's study was a relatively long-term investigation of continuous exposure to inverted-reversed vision. Two subjects wore the experimental spectacles during their waking hours for fourteen days: the first subject for a total exposure period of 175 hours, 50 minutes; the second for 193 hours, 35 minutes. A third subject wore the spectacles for sixteen days for a total of 195 hours, 56 minutes. The telescope device used by Ewert, which is shown in Figure 4-5, consisted of an aluminum framework containing a double convex lens system, much like that used by Stratton. This telescope system was mounted in a headgear and gave an inverted and reversed field of vision 34.6 degrees in extent.

Figure 4-5. Headgear and experimental spectacles used by Ewert.[74]

Ewert's experiment, like Brown's and Wooster's, stressed objective testing of the relation between localization and perception. In systematic daily procedures, tests were made of touch localization, sound localization without vision, sound localization with vision, visual localization, pedal and manual localization, card sorting, finger identification, distance discrimination, and orientation. The subjects were asked also to give daily reports on their general perceptual orientation. Special arrangements were made at the end of the experiment to test for after-effects of wearing the lenses.

Touch Localization

A small square, about 2.5 inches on a side, was marked off on the dorsal side of the subject's left hand and 20 points marked on it. As an observer touched these points in random order, the subject, with his eyes open, attempted to localize each point as it was touched, using a pencil held in his right hand. In another series of tests, the right hand was marked in squares and localization was made with the left hand. The sub-ject closed his eyes when a point was touched and opened them to try to indicate the proper square. In general, it was found that inverted vision greatly inhibited tactual localization and decreased its accuracy. Points near the fingers and over bones were localized more accurately than other points. The normal tendency to err in the direction of the end of the hand was reversed by the lenses, causing more errors to be made in the direction of the shoulder. Learning took place in this test without the necessity of gross localizing movements, and seemed to be facilitated by knowledge of the nature of the disorientation. After removal of the spectacles, two subjects showed some interference in touch localization.

Sound Localization without Vision

A standard sound cage was employed in this test, which permitted moving and measuring the position of a buzzer sound source in several arcs near and around the subject's head. No vision was allowed during these tests. Two localizations were made at each of 25 randomly distributed points in the auditory field. In one series of tests, the subject responded verbally to indicate the position of the sound; in another, the subject localized by pointing with his finger.

There were no material alterations in sound localization, as made verbally or manually, due to wearing of the experimental spectacles. Nor were there any after-effects of the optical disorientation in the special tests at the end of the experiment.

Sound Localization with Vision Present

The sound localization cage was modified by fitting to its framework a screen which was marked off into squares. The buzzer could then be located with reference to a particular square, but the disorienting glasses would make its visual position appear different from its actual position. The results in these observations showed that sound localization was at first disturbed by the disoriented vision, but later aided when the subject understood and made correction for the visual disorientation. There were no after-effects of the inversion in this task, and there were no differences due to verbal and manual modes of localization.

When this series of observations was repeated with the buzzer hidden behind a cloth screen, it was found that the sound localizations were less reliable, and that there were marked individual variations in the degree of interference due to inverted vision.

Another series of tests was conducted with two buzzers visible in order to determine whether the interference effect of the visual disorientation would transfer to situations in which the inverted vision was not a distraction. In one case, the buzzers were arranged symmetrically so that, despite the effects of inverted vision, a buzzer would always be visible in the square from which the sound originated. In other tests the buzzers were arranged asymmetrically. When the buzzers were arranged symmetrically, sound localizations were accurate and there was no interference from the visual disorientation. In all tests of this series, the visual stimulus nearest a sound source was selected in a significant number of cases as the spatial source of sound.

Visual Localization

A screen was marked with squares and a visual object presented on it at randomly selected points. The subject pointed to the object, but made no corrective movements after the pointing member entered the visual field. Localizing reactions with both hand and foot were tested.

With manual localization in this task, there were no errors with normal vision.

Effects of the optical disorientation were overcome by the twelfth day of the adaptation, but there were marked after-effects in the localizing behavior after the lenses were removed. The same results were found for pedal localization, except that not all errors had been eliminated by the fourteenth day of adaptation. Also, there was some error bias toward the right with manual localization, but no such bias occurred with pedal localization.

Card Sorting

A Jastrow card-sorting device was used, which contained nine compartments as receptacles for sorted Flinch cards. Card-sorting scores were obtained prior to, during, and after the period of visual disorientation. The effects of the disorientation on this test were especially clear. The visual inversion and reversal had a very marked interference effect, but this was almost completely overcome during the fourteen days of practice, and steady learning progress was noted. The interference effects under inversion did not transfer, after removal of the lenses, to performance of the task with normal vision.

Finger Identification

The subject extended both hands in front of him on a table surface with palms down. The fingers were numbered from 1 to 10. On a call of a finger number, the subject was required to raise the corresponding finger. In one series, the subject saw his fingers, and in another series he did not. When the fingers were in view, localization was greatly hindered, and this interference was not overcome during fourteen days of practice at the task. The fingers giving the most errors were fingers 4, 5, 6, and 7, i.e., the index fingers and thumbs of the two hands. When the fingers were not seen, however, there was little or no effect of the visual disorientation on this task. There were no after-effects of the disorientation on this task, carried out with or without vision.

Distance Discrimination

Only one subject was used in this depth test, which involved judgment of the relative distance of two black threads disposed vertically against a neutral gray background. The visual disorientation produced a marked tendency to reverse relative position in this task, and practice did not reduce this tendency. There were few correct responses made in this test throughout the 14 days of disorientation. This finding was in sharp contrast to the perfect record of judgments prior to wearing the lenses. There were no after-effects of the disorientation on performance after the lenses were removed.

Perceptual Orientation Tests

This series of tests consisted of daily reports on the orientation of the visual field. Different types of simple localizations were used, involving combined use of vision and other senses without overt movement. The main observations here were simply that the binocular telescopes not only inverted and reversed the frontal plane of vision but also reversed near and far. Within this completely inverted field of vision, the subjects' reported localizations were accurate relative to the field, but reversed in the up-down, right-left, and near-far axes with respect to actual position. Thus judgments of position of hands or objects were always incorrect.

These inverted and reversed perceptions of position remained throughout the experiment, and were not altered by practice in the other tests. The modified behavior in these tests did not persist

as an after-effect in any measurable form after the lenses were removed.

General Observations

Ewert recorded a number of general observations concerning some of the effects of the displaced vision on motion. He reported, "Eye movements necessary for foveal fixation of objects in space during disorientation are antagonistic to movements during normal vision. This antagonism is, perhaps, chiefly responsible for the interference which appears in the gross bodily activity." Some further observations were:

"1) Movement, in general, seems to be accelerated immediately upon assuming disorientation and immediately after disorientation.
"2) Eye-head movements resulted in giddiness as well as in inhibition of motor eye-head coordination.
"3) Individuals vary as to the length of time that dizziness persists in disorientation.
"4) No giddiness was experienced under the following conditions: a) Eyes open and head and objects stationary. b) Eyes closed during head movement. c) Eyes open and objects moving. d) During very rapid head movements.
"5) Directions are seen reversed in movement during disorientation. This illusion is so strong that it cannot be inhibited."

Conclusions

Ewert's conclusions are best related in his own words:

"1) Inverted vision is found to serve as a forceful distraction to normal touch, sound, and kinaesthetic localization, when this behavior is carried on in the field of view. . . .
"2) In all forms of activity where overt localizing responses are present there is rapid adjustment to the distracting visual interference. . . . In most of the experiments, learning consists in a gradual dropping out of the number of errors made, instead of in decreasing the average extent of the errors. . . .
"3) In most of the experiments the newly acquired behavior during visual inversion did not persist in a measurable form upon the removal of the lenses. . . .
"4) In general, the displacements or errors of localizations are of a nature which indicates

that they are directly due to an inverted visual distraction. . . .

"5) Continuous inverted vision apparently has a neutral effect upon sound localization when the source of the sound is in the non-visual field. . . .

"6) In cases where more than one receptor is stimulated simultaneously, the forthcoming behavior is a resultant response initiated reciprocally by the various receptors involved. . . .

"7) The dominancy of receptors in a given environmental situation is greatly influenced by the instruction stimulus. The human being is able to develop a consistent response to either a visual, tactile, kinaesthetic, or an auditory stimulus . . . inhibiting the sense data from those receptors which may serve as distractors.

"8) Interference in sound localization due to the effect of inverted vision does not transfer to or persist in situations where inverted vision is not a distraction. . . .

"9) Constant interference during visual disorientation does not prevent the steady growth of a habit.

"10) Disorienting the visual field 180° results in a marked tendency to invert distances.

"11) The illusory visual disorientation effect did not change noticeably during a 14-day period of continuous inversion.

"12) Immediately upon assuming disorientation and immediately after disorientation, the subjects behaved as though the movement of visual stimuli were abnormally rapid.

"13) The eyes are readily educable to new compensatory reflexes.

"14) Directions in movement during disorientation are responded to as though reversed. This behavior cannot be inhibited."

SIIPOLA'S EXPERIMENTS

Siipola[239] conducted one of the first experimental efforts to compare different dimensions of displaced vision and their relative effects upon performance. Her work included two experiments that made use of mirror-drawing techniques. The first study compared the effects of front-back, right-left, and combined front-back and right-left reversal of vision on mirror-tracing performance. The second, one of the first controlled experiments on the effects of sensory or perceptual pretraining on learning,

attempted to determine whether observation of performance with disoriented vision would aid adaptation to such disorientation.

Comparison between Dimensions of Displacement

In introducing her study, Siipola noted that, although mirror drawing had been introduced into experimental psychology about 1910, the available information about the technique and the problems associated with it was quite limited (as it still is). The purpose of her experiment was to discover whether "mirror-drawing under conditions in which movements in both the left-right direction and the up-down (sagittal) direction appear reversed from normal would be more difficult than under conditions in which movements in only one of these directions appear reversed. Three groups of subjects (A, B, and C) performed the task of tracing a pattern under similar conditions except for the position of the mirror." For those in Group A, the mirror was placed in front of the subject so that movements in the sagittal direction appeared reversed in the mirror; for those in Group B, the mirror was placed at the left of the subject to produce an apparent left-right reversal of movements; and for Group C a double mirror was used to produce an apparent reversal of both left-right and up-down movements. One hundred sixty-two subjects were used; 89 in Group A, 39 in Group B, and 34 in Group C. The mirror was placed 6 inches from the edge of the pattern to be traced, and the pattern, which is shown in Figure 4-6, was placed at a uniform distance from the subjects. The subjects worked for both speed and accuracy in their tracings.

The results of this experiment:

". . . indicate that learning to adjust to a situation in which both left-right and up-down

Figure 4-6. The tracing pattern used in Siipola's mirror study. (From Siipola.[239])

movements appeared reversed (Group C) is not any more difficult than learning to adjust to a situation in which movements in only one direction appeared reversed. . . . These results carry the strong implication that one may not think of the learning process in mirror-drawing simply as one in which just so many previously learned eye-hand coordinations are broken down and relearned. If the process were of such a nature, the double-reversal would have been necessarily most difficult, since in this situation the visual cues for each of the movements were contradictory to the usually appropriate kinesthetic data. To explain why the difficulty of the double-reversal is equal to that of the single-reversals, one would need to know much more about the organization of visual and kinesthetic space under normal conditions as well as under the unusual conditions of the mirror-drawing task."

In discussing the reliability of her results, Siipola noted that there were marked individual differences within each group (usually true of results in mirror-drawing experiments), and "it is obvious that our summary results based upon group averages give only a crude and tentative answer to the problem."

Siipola had each subject answer a short questionnaire on whether they had consciously figured out the nature of the reversal involved, and which moves they had found the most difficult. The answers indicated that:

"Only 23 per cent of the 162 subjects reported that they consciously determined the nature of the reversal and calculated their moves on that basis . . . only about 60 per cent of the sub-

jects in each group were able to guess the true nature of the reversal. . . .

"It seems difficult to explain why so many of the subjects had misconceptions of the nature of the reversal caused by the mirrors. However, this fact is not so surprising when one considers the peculiarly complicated conditions under which the subjects were required to adjust to a new world of space. For although during the mirror-drawing trials the subjects were functioning in a mirror world to a certain extent (the peripheral part of the field was normal), during the intervals between trials the subjects were behaving in a normal room where all the rules of normal space held. . . .

"In view of these conflictful conditions, it is not surprising to learn from the introspective data that during the mirror-drawing itself some of the subjects adopted reference points in the mirror reflection."

Some used themselves as reference points, others used objects, either in the mirror reflection or outside, as reference points for their movements, and, "These reports show that the different types of adjustment made to the complicated conditions of this experiment demanded different conceptions of the exact nature of the reversal."

In regard to the question, "What moves did you find most difficult?", the answers showed:

". . . that the most difficult movements for groups A and B were not the expected ones. Instead most of the subjects in Group A (up-down reversal) found left-right movements most difficult, and most of the subjects in Group B (left-right reversal) found up-down movements most difficult. The actual drawings of the subjects supported these data. Since the direction of the movements giving the greatest difficulty was not the same as the direction of the movements reversed by the mirror, it is no wonder that many of the subjects failed to guess the true nature of the reversal. . . .

"That the normal visual-kinesthetic system was definitely disrupted in the case of some of the students was dramatically illustrated by their inability to perform every day motor acts after the experiment. In a few cases this disruption affected even the highly mechanized habit of walking.

"It is clear from this account of the introspective data that the tremendous variability of the results and the seeming misconceptions of the nature of the reversals were related to three factors: the variety of adjustments made to the unstable spatial framework caused by the simultaneous (or alternate) presence of two conflictful visual-kinesthetic systems, the changes in the stability of this framework during the ten trials, and the unexpected loci of the major difficulties in tracing the pattern."

In conclusion, Siipola stated that, "We need particularly to know more about the organization of visual and kinesthetic space under normal as well as under unusual conditions such as those of mirror-drawing."

Perceptual Pretraining Study

In a second experiment, Siipola tested whether subjects who merely observed mirror-reversed tracing performance of others would thereby be aided in their own initial performance of the task. Three groups of subjects were used — a control group that did not observe or practice the mirror-drawing task, an observation group that observed the learning of other subjects, and a bilateral-transfer group that was trained in the mirror-tracing task with one hand and then transferred to the other in the test series.

The results of this experiment — the first successful investigation of perceptual pretraining with displaced vision — showed that the control group was poorest in the test series of mirror tracing, the perceptual observation group was clearly superior to the nontrained control group, and the bilateral-transfer group was superior to both of the other groups.

Siipola concluded that considerable benefit derives from observation as a method of training, although, "A comparison of the results for the bilateral-transfer groups with those of the observation groups shows that in both experiments the gain was greater for the former. . . . Apparently in mirror-drawing, practice with the bilaterally symmetrical part of the body is superior to

observation without any actual motor practice, even though the movements and kinesthetic experiences of one hand are not identical to those of the other hand." However, the fact that observation alone had some effectiveness in improving later performance "is an important finding for mirror drawing, since it is so often thought of as a strictly trial-and-error type of task."

SUMMARY

1. The geometric problems of behavior — how motion conforms with stimulus patterns — found early expression in the question of the significance of the inverted retinal image. Helmholtz met this problem by formulating his empirical theory of space perception, which proposed that perception of spatial properties is learned, and, therefore, the orientation of the retinal image is of no basic significance. Observations on visual training of children born blind who gain their sight through surgery, and on certain phenomena of strabismic vision seemed to support this view.

2. The first systematic experiments on displaced vision were carried out by Stratton, who wore a monocular inverting-reversing telescope first for three days and later for eight days. Although he did not achieve complete adaptation, he felt that his results confirmed the empirical theory. An important finding was that active movements facilitated adaptation to the visual movements. Stratton concluded that the real meaning of upright vision is a harmony between touch and sight, which he believed was learned.

3. In a third experiment, Stratton wore on three successive days a system of mirrors which made his body appear to be stretched out horizontally before him. He found that he could harmonize touch and sight most readily for those

parts of the body for which he had easily identifiable visual and tactual experience. Thus, this harmony was achieved first for feet and legs and hands, but was difficult with respect to head and shoulders. Stratton thought that this mirror experiment showed that a new system of distance perception could be learned as well as new directions that were demonstrated by the first two experiments.

4. Wooster tested a number of subjects in manual localizing behavior while their vision was angularly displaced by means of prisms. After ten days of practice, with 20 localizations per day, mean accuracy had improved only moderately. When auditory cues were added to visual, accuracy was improved very little. However, active touch of the localizing object, to correct an inaccurate localization, made adaptation more rapid and the final accuracy higher. These results confirmed the importance of specific movements in adaptation to displaced vision.

5. Brown tested depth perception with rotation of the visual field 75 degrees, a condition which initially gives little perception of depth. There was no conclusive evidence that depth discrimination improved much with practice under this disorienting condition.

6. Cox used a two-story maze to study learning of the pathway when the unseen pattern was disoriented with respect to the seen pattern. Subjects learned most rapidly with 0 degrees orientation and then with reversed, inverted-reversed, and 90-degree rotation orientations, in that order. These differential results would be predicted by our theory of the feedback control of motion.

7. Ewert repeated Stratton's conditions of inversion-reversal with binocular vision, using daily objective tests of adaptation. He found that the displaced vision interfered markedly with normal tactual, auditory, and kinesthetic localizations carried out in the field of view, although subjects adjusted rapidly to the displacement. After removing the lenses, there were but minor aftereffects. He found a marked tendency in his subjects to invert distances as well as the up-down and right-left axes, so that localizations were apt to be intrinsically correct in a completely inverted perceptual field.

8. Siipola compared mirror drawing when right-left movements appeared reversed, when up-down movements appeared reversed, and when both axes were reversed, but found no significant differences in performance. In a second study investigating perceptual pretraining, she found that subjects who observed the mirror performance of others learned it better than subjects with no pretraining, but not as well as subjects who learned first with one hand and then transferred to the other hand for the test trials.

CHAPTER 5

RECENT STUDIES OF DISPLACED VISION

Prior to 1940, experiments on the effects of visual displacement constituted a very respectable body of research on the spatial problems of perception. Methods of observation were developed to deal with almost every major aspect of spatially disoriented vision. The principal weakness in this earlier work, as, indeed, in later studies, was the inadequate theoretical formulation of the phenomena studied. The designs of experiments and their results held a significance for behavior science that was never fully recognized. From Strat-ton[295-297] on, the guiding interest of investigators was in the process of development of perception in the individual. They hoped to prove or disprove that subjects performing in displaced visual fields would learn perceptually stable vision, much as the child develops a consistent perceptual orientation to his environment during the first few years of life. The question was whether the learning process would lead to reorientation and stabilization of the displaced visual world.

Although Stratton's studies were contradictory and ambiguous, many accepted them as strong evidence in favor of Helmholtz's[116] empirical theory of perception. However, this uncritical acceptance was not to last. The experiments of Wooster,[334] Brown,[32] and Cox[55] offered no conclusive proof of the empirical theory, and with Ewert,[74-76] research and theory in this field reached a kind of stalemate. The role of learning in perceptual development had not been defined conclusively.

Because these early studies of displaced vision formulated the problems, conditions, and results in general psychological terms, rather than analyzing the critical variables in spatial and strictly behavioral terms, they tended to treat all kinds and dimensions of displacement as psychologically equivalent. Only Cox and Siipola,[239] among these early workers, made the point that the problem of perceptual disorientation, including the much-studied events of mirror drawing, goes beyond general learning phenomena, and entails consideration of different dimensions of disorientation, and of differential perceptual adaptation to these dimensions. Notwithstanding these observations, neither Cox nor Siipola interpreted their interesting findings in terms other than those associated with learning or intelligence.

A Re-evaluation of Stratton and Ewert

Late in the 1930's, a study carried out by Peterson and Peterson[208] attempted to re-evaluate the perceptual and introspective aspects of Stratton's and Ewert's work. Peterson and Peterson followed Ewert's interpretation of his results as being in direct conflict with those of Stratton, although from our point of view this interpretation was not warranted. In Stratton's first two experiments, he certainly did not achieve conclusive perceptual and motor adaptation; it was only in his third study, with angularly displaced vision, that a relatively complete adaptation occurred. Nevertheless, it was in the hope of resolving the supposed conflict between Stratton and Ewert that Peterson and Peterson carried out their study.

Peterson and Peterson designed a binocular lens system like that used by Ewert. The system inverted the up-down axis of vision, as well as reversing the right-left and depth relationships. One of the experimenters wore the head piece and glasses for 14 days, and then some 8 months later wore them again

for a short period of testing. The experiment was conducted as a general adaptation study, and did not involve detailed testing of motor performance. Within the 14-day period, normal vision — in the sense of perceiving visual direction and location as correlated with motor activity, and as a stable experience with established reference orientation — was never achieved.

Peterson and Peterson's important contribution to the method of studying displaced vision was to retest the subject's visuomotor coordinations after 8 months. During the first 14-day period, they had observed that certain of the subject's ordinary activities — including locomotion, object manipulation, body care, and so forth — had become modified through adaptation to the disorienting conditions. Eight months later, when the lenses were worn again, the subject demonstrated a retention of these learned modifications with very little loss. These results suggest rather conclusively that adaptation to displaced vision involves the learning of highly specific responses, and that the general perceptual adaptation which most investigators have sought cannot be achieved independently. Unfortunately, Peterson and Peterson did not provide any fresh insight into the nature of the problem they studied, or into the significance of their results. Instead, they noted that Stratton too, in his first studies, had failed to achieve complete perceptual reorientation, although he had assumed that eventually the visual world would appear upright. They concluded with the observation that prior experiments had been in almost complete agreement on angular displacement of the locus of vision, except for the results of Stratton's third study. The only sense in which the studies of displaced vision had been inconclusive was in providing final proof of the learning theory of perceptual development.

STUDIES OF DISPLACED VISION IN ANIMALS

The unsatisfactory nature of the studies on displaced vision up to the 1930's led Foley[91] to attack the problem in a novel way. Foley was not convinced by Stratton's and Ewert's results. He felt that perceptual-motor activity entails factors other than learning, and that to establish the basic facts of spatial disorientation it is necessary to study subjects other than man. Therefore, he conducted an investigation of inverted and reversed vision in the rhesus monkey.

Displaced Vision in a Rhesus Monkey

Foley constructed a binocular lens system like that used by Ewert, adjusted in size to fit the head of an adult female rhesus monkey. These lenses produced up-down inversion, right-left reversal, and reversal of depth. When this device was secured to the monkey, the effect was dramatic. The animal made a few exploratory maneuvers (misdirected, of course) and thereafter went into a comatose state of immobility from which it scarcely emerged for five or six days. It was not obviously nauseated, as had been reported frequently by human subjects, but simply would not move. Its only successful attempts at locomotion on the first day were in a backward direction — an effect that is interesting in view of the depth reversal produced by the glasses.

On each successive day of the experiment the monkey tried further activities of some sort, usually without success, but remained immobile most of the time through the fifth day. By this time the general activity level was a little higher, and the nature of coordination improved. On the sixth day it showed increasing ability to locate food and other objects, but still lapsed into prolonged periods of immobility. Foley stated that by the seventh day the animal had achieved virtually a complete adaptation of the disoriented vision, as determined by the accuracy of overt localizing reactions. The lenses were removed on the eighth day, and an almost immediate adaptation to normal conditions of vision occurred. Only the activities of climbing and jumping seemed to be disturbed by the carry-over from the experimental period. These traces of interference with normal behavior due to the adaptation to displaced vision persisted until about the third day of normal vision.

Foley's interpretation of this experiment generally followed the doctrine that learning is the basis of perception, as proposed by Helmholtz and Stratton, but he by no means offered his results as full confirmation of the view. It could not be said that the monkey had achieved an efficient normal level of visuomotor behavior, or that it had followed a modified course of developmental learning which resulted in a successful reorientation of the visual field. In effect, these results on the monkey were very similar to previous observations on human subjects. The effects of displaced vision were severe, but some degree of adaptation in visuomotor coordination occurred. These modified responses were specific to the conditions in which they occurred and interacted with subsequent normal visual activity only in the most limited way, but there was no basis for assuming an independent perceptual reorientation as distinct from the observable changes in overt movements. Perhaps the most significant of Foley's findings was the severity of the effects of displaced vision on the monkey's behavior. It is doubtful that a monkey so hampered could have survived in the wild state, either initially or after some days of adaptation.

Figure 5-1. Pfister's[209] rooster, wearing reversing prisms. (Based on photograph, courtesy of Ivo Kohler.)

Displaced Pecking in Chickens

Pfister[209] mounted right-left reversing prisms over the eyes of adult chickens (as shown in Figure 5-1) and observed the effects on their ability to locate grain in pecking. He noted a severe disturbance in their pecking behavior. Two hens which wore the prisms for three months showed no material improvement in their pecking coordinations.

A more extensive study of newly hatched chicks was carried out by Hess.[119] The chicks were hatched in darkness and fitted with thin rubber hoods containing plastic goggles. For ten chicks, the goggles consisted of thin plastic plates that produced no visual distortion. Twelve chicks wore prisms that displaced the line of sight seven degrees to the right, while six chicks wore prisms that displaced the line of sight seven degrees to the left. All of the chicks were tested for pecking accuracy, and the spatial distributions of their pecks around food particles were recorded.

On the first day the pecks of the control group had a relatively small range and were centered about the food target. Both of the experimental groups showed a mean displacement of their pecks that conformed to the visual displacement imposed by the prisms. That is, the chicks with a line of sight displaced seven degrees to the right pecked on the average seven degrees to the right of the food target, while the chicks with left visual displacement pecked to the left. During four days of practice there was no change in the means of the distributions. While accuracy improved both in the control group and in the experimental groups in that the distributions of their pecks covered a smaller area, the midpoints of the distributions did not change. Not a single chick with displacing prisms learned to correct for the displacement. The experimental chicks probably would have starved to death if the experiment had not been discontinued.

Hess makes the following observations about his results: "We must conclude that the chick's visual apparatus for locating objects in space is innate and not learned. . . . Furthermore, the chick whose visual field was displaced appeared unable to learn through experience to correct its aim. . . . Apparently the innate picture which the chick has of the location of objects in its visual world cannot be modified through learning if what is required is that the chick learn to perform a response which is antagonistic to its instinctive one."

The studies thus far carried out on the effects of displaced vision on animals can only cast doubt on the importance of learning in the development of perceptual-motor integration. The adaptation of the monkey to visual disorientation was limited, and the adaptation of the chick, in the behavior studied, was apparently nonexistent. We can only conclude that, although learning is the mediating circumstance for whatever adaptation does occur to visual displacement, it cannot be considered the primary organizing process of perception and motion.

KOHLER'S STUDIES

Kohler's[149-152] extensive studies in the field of displaced vision (dating from about 1939) were extensions of the work begun by Erismann at the University of Innsbruck in 1928. Erismann was the director of the psychological laboratory at Innsbruck throughout Kohler's work, and helped construct the optical devices used for inversion, reversal, and angular displacement of the field of vision. Using mainly students, assistants, or research associates as subjects, Kohler and Erismann conducted their observations in this relatively modest student laboratory and in the streets and fields near the university. Kohler contributed some experimental innovations to the study of distorted vision, as well as a revised statement of the role of learning in perceptual orientation.

Kohler's work has attracted much interest in this country. Most of his papers have been translated into English and have been widely distributed. In some quarters this work has been interpreted, not too critically, as resolving the basic question of learning versus maturation in the development of space perception,[324] or in justifying the psychic interpretation of the perceptual process.[103] A motion picture summation of how people see in inverted visual fields, prepared by Erismann and Kohler[73] themselves, is, unfortunately, a not too accurate report of the nature of their experimental results. In this section, we have attempted to summarize Kohler's studies and his theoretical conclusions, working in part with his original papers, but using also translations prepared by others.

Theoretical Orientation

Kohler's studies covered several aspects of displaced vision, including the effects and the after-effects of up-down inversion, right-left reversal, and sus-

tained exposure to prism-produced displacements of the line of sight. In addition, he and Erismann made observations of the effects of wearing strong lenses, such as those used to correct near- and farsightedness, and of wearing colored filters over the eyes. We shall review here only those studies involving spatial displacement of the visual field.

Because Kohler conceived of his work as studies in "rehabituation" — replacing old habits with new — he conducted his experiments in the tradition of Stratton, i.e., his subjects wore the experimental optical devices continuously during the day, and were allowed no exposure to ordinary or normal conditions of vision. He felt that earlier studies had not allowed long enough periods of exposure to the conditions of disorientation, and, consequently, carried on his own experiments for more prolonged periods, sometimes for more than a month. Because he was primarily interested in the "inner" habits of perception, as he himself defined the term, he intentionally stressed the introspective or interpretative approach and made few controlled tests of motor performance. Considering the limited number of critical observations made under some of his experimental conditions, one is never sure to what extent this introspective method influenced his conclusions. As he himself observed, attitude is a decisive influence in determining what the subject reports in regard to judged orientation.

In brief, Kohler looked upon experimentally imposed visual displacement as a procedure for altering a fully developed state of perception. By requiring the subject to return artificially to an earlier state of incomplete development, the process of perceptual development itself could be observed. The assumption was that the processes that lead to adaptation to the disoriented conditions are identical to those that define normal perceptual development in undistorted environmental fields. No new forces or laws were postulated.

In order to assess the significance of Kohler's work and to evaluate his interpretations of his experimental results, we must try to understand the theoretical position from which he operated. In the European tradition, he thought of perception as a form of inner experience, available only to introspection. Although he observed the overt motor adjustments to his experimental conditions, he always stressed the inner perceptual experiences of the subject. He described perception as a form of "inner" habit, as opposed to "outer" observable habits. Habits are advantageous as economizers of body energy except when they interfere with some new adaptation. Thus, in any process of rehabituation, such as in the displaced vision studies, the interference of old habits with new adjustments is distasteful and enervating. For example, subjects wearing inverting optical devices could become frightened of their own feet. Although unpleasant, the rehabituation experiment is a kind of probe with which to analyze the interweaving of habits, and can be considered as complete only when the disturbed aspect of perception is completely conquered. Kohler considered studies with a behavioral bias, such as those of Ewert and Snyder and Pronko[275] (to be described later), as faulty because they never achieved complete rehabituation.

In criticizing the work of other experimenters, Kohler defined his major interests and also indicated his own limitations. He objected to studies which had been concerned only with outer, observable behavior and not with the inner habits of perception. As we have said, he stressed the importance of complete rehabituation, although one might question whether his own subjects ever achieved this desired state. Finally, with respect to methodology, he betrayed perhaps his greatest weakness — his incomplete analysis of the spatial variables

involved in various types of visual displacement. He objected to the optical systems used by Ewert and Snyder and Pronko because they produced both inversion and reversal; he insisted that such a combination offers increased difficulty to the subject and is a barrier to observation of details. Actually this assumption of Kohler's was wrong, for we have ample evidence that combined inversion-reversal is almost always easier than inversion alone. What Kohler failed to observe was that his own optical methods of inverting and reversing the visual field introduced additional distortions of visuomotor integration which certainly must have affected the nature of his results.

Right-Left Reversal

The goggles and prism mount used to reverse the visual field right to left are shown in Figure 5-2. The prisms were adjusted to produce corresponding images of a fairly restricted visual field: 33 degrees high and 25 degrees wide. The prisms also reversed depth cues, and apparently subjects never corrected their disorientation of depth. Kohler himself wore these prisms for 24 days, and another subject wore them for 37 days.

REVERSING PRISMS

Figure 5-2. The prisms used by Kohler[149] to produce right-left reversal of vision.

Kohler's introspective account of the initial effects of wearing these reversing prisms described the reversed world as containing both reversed places and reversed objects. Symmetrical objects did not appear reversed, but objects and situations with an established right-left relationship appeared reversed.

EFFECTS ON MOTION. In describing the effects on movement, Kohler distinguished three categories. First were movements that were not affected, such as eye movements made with the head held stationary. Second were movements that could be made without difficulty, although perceived as reversed, such as bringing a spoon to the mouth. Writing was included in this category, as long as it did not involve detailed visual control. (Kohler said writing produced the impression that the ego was separated from the body.) Finally, movements guided entirely by vision were disturbed by the reversal; this is exemplified by following a prescribed path or steering a vehicle. Figure 5-3 shows a diagram of the path followed by a subject while wearing the reversing prisms, and an illustration of a subject signaling a turn in the wrong direction while riding on a motorcycle.

Days and even weeks were spent in correcting movements disturbed by the reversal, some of which were repeated incorrectly hundreds of times. The subject tried to correct such movements, not because of false conscious perception, but because he couldn't endure false movements. One method was just to think about what he was doing, but that technique had limitations. Blocks occurred, especially if the situation appeared dangerous. Another method was to move in the direction opposite to what appeared to be correct. This slowed down movements considerably, but was the simplest solution and helped in such general movement patterns as walking and finding doors. Quick localizing movements were the most difficult to correct.

Overcoming the effects of the prisms actually began with cutaneous probing, not with vision. The subject learned to cancel out visual cues, although still using his eyes. After two or three weeks, movements such as walking, turning, avoiding obstacles, and reaching could be made almost without error, although conscious visual experience still remained reversed. Motor corrections were made through the use of touch before conscious vision was rehabilitated to any noticeable degree. During this process of adjustment, there was a reduction in

GAIT

B

ORIENTATION

Figure 5-3. Some of Kohler's[119] tests of behavior during right-left reversal of vision. A. Path followed by a subject. B. Signaling the wrong turn while riding on a motorcycle. (Based on photographs, courtesy of Ivo Kohler.)

strength of the right-left orientation of the body, so that when one attempted to turn one way with his eyes closed, he might turn the opposite way.

According to Kohler, no specific daily tests were made of motor coordinations because a subject could perform these tests without error when he developed a direct relation to the world around him. By this he apparently meant that when a subject achieved a general perceptual adaptation to some situation, he could perform all kinds of activities in it.

PERCEPTUAL OBSERVATIONS. Although it was not clearly stated, the suggestion was that after two or three weeks some things were perceived as reversed in direction from other things. Inscriptions on buildings, for example, were seen as mirror writing, but objects in them were seen correctly. Pedestrians on the streets were located on the correct side, but the right-left relations of their shoulders were seen as reversed. It was said that perceptual relationships were seen correctly when touch and kinesthesis dominated, but when vision dominated, the relations were reversed. Different parts of the same scene could be seen in both the old and new ways. Although general observation of a scene was likely to produce the old-type perceptions, objects which could be touched were perceived in the new way and gradually influenced more and more of the visual field. A critical attitude, however, reawakened all the old habits of perceiving.

DEGREE OF ADAPTATION ACHIEVED. Kohler made no direct statement about how complete his own judgment was after 24 days of prism-produced reversal. However, he said that the other subject, after 37 days, had progressed considerably beyond his own stage of adaptation. This second subject was said to have achieved almost completely correct impressions, even in the perception of letters. Words were seen first in the new way, but were seen as reversed if looked at attentively. However, apparently

neither subject corrected perceptually for the reversal in depth cues.

AFTER-EFFECTS. In Kohler's case, the immediate after-effects were said to have lasted several hours after the prisms were removed. There were some discrepancies in perceiving the right-left relationships of different objects. Some movement effects were observed much longer, perhaps as long as two weeks. This was especially true of apparent movements of the visual field produced by changing position of the head and body.

The other subject reported that when the prisms were removed he saw the whole room in which he was standing as reversed. Letters such as *p, q, b,* and *d* were seen as mirrored.

KOHLER'S CONCLUSIONS. Kohler felt that he had clarified some of the phenomena reported by Stratton, in particular the influence of overt motion in harmonizing vision and bodily experience. He concluded that, basically, right-left relations are not of a visual nature, but are grounded in behavioral relationships. Only by overt manipulation of objects do perceived relations achieve direction. When the visual field is reversed, new right-left directions can be set up by establishing certain manipulative spheres of activity. To see in the right direction, one must manipulate in the right direction.

The old established relations of right and left can persist after the visual field has been reversed and can interfere with adaptation. It is this effect which leads to discrepancies in perception of right-left relations of different objects or parts of objects.

Kohler commented that the experiments on rehabituation stand in a distinctive intimate relation to depth psychology, wherein hidden causes are discovered by indirect methods. He felt that parallels could be drawn between his work and the depth field because of the results obtained by applying critical

introspection to the process of rehabituation.

Mirror-Produced Inversion

Kohler credited Erismann with the
idea of using a mirror mounted horizontally in front of the face as a method of
inverting the visual field. In an improvement of this technique, as shown in
Figure 5-4,A, a mirror about six inches
square was mounted so that it extended
outward horizontally from the forehead above the eyes. With this device,
the subject looked through a slit to get
a limited inverted field of vision, which
shifted with every movement of the
head. A view of the feet could be
obtained by tipping the head forward.
Figure 5-4,B, shows a subject performing a pointing test.

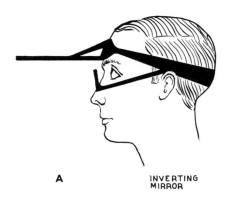

A   INVERTING
                     MIRROR

B

                     POINTING

Figure 5-4. A. The mirror headgear used by
Kohler[149] to produce up-down inversion of
vision. B. A pointing test during inverted vision.

Mirror-produced inversion has quite
different effects from inversion produced
by telescopic lenses, quite aside from
the difference between simple up-down
inversion and the combined inversion-
reversal produced by the lenses. The
mirror shifts the direction of gaze, as
the lenses do not. Also, using the mirror,
the environment moves with every
movement of the head, but when the
head is held stationary, eye movements
do not move the environment. There
are no disturbances of accommodation
and convergence with the mirror as there
are with the binocular lens system, except those associated with the redirection of gaze.

The combined effects of the mirror
inversion with redirection of gaze —
plus the fact that every head movement
moved the environment — made some of
Kohler's subjects sick, so that they could
not go on with the experiment. The
effects reported were nausea, dizziness,
depression, and pain from the mirror
mount. Subjects who continued with the
experiment had to be cared for by an
assistant during the initial periods of
wearing the mirror, not only to protect
them from dangerous movements, but
also to see that their basic needs and
activities were taken care of. Observations were reported from three subjects
who wore the mirror respectively for 6,
9, and 10 days.

EFFECTS OF MIRROR INVERSION. The
effects noted for the different subjects
were in general agreement. There was
a fairly rapid motor adaptation during
the first few days. Perceptual adaptation
— in which the inverted field appeared
upright — proceeded more slowly, and
was aided by touch and manipulation of
objects in the field. One subject reported
that logically related events, such as
lighting a candle, promoted correct seeing. The 6-day subject had limited upright vision at the end of 6 days; the
9-day subject reported that upright
vision was fully developed in 9 days.

He also reported a transition period in which all objects were seen as upright, no matter how they actually were oriented.

AFTER-EFFECTS. The first subject reported after-effects of the mirror inversion for only a few minutes after the mirror was removed, and then only when indicators of vertical direction were not present in the visual field. The second (9-day) subject reportedly perceived the normal visual field as inverted for several hours after the mirror was removed. For several days traces of disorientation were observed after waking in the morning. Inverted reflections seen in water seemed more real to him than the objects themselves.

INTERPRETATIONS. In none of his writing did Kohler make many comments about the results of these inversion studies. He noted that subjects adapted faster to mirror inversion than to prism-produced reversal, and also noted the similarity of reports of partial reorientation in both studies. With both mirror inversion and prism reversal, subjects reported that some objects in the visual field would appear disoriented while others appeared properly oriented. He wrote as if the subjects in this inversion experiment achieved a true general perceptual reorientation of a pictorial quality.

Angular Displacement of the Line of Sight

Kohler used prisms of limited optical power to bend the rays of light entering the eye. In viewing an object through a prism of this sort, the eye must move laterally from its normal position to bring the image of the object to the fovea. Figure 5-5 illustrates the optical relationships when binocular prisms are worn. Kohler also used monocular prisms while covering the other eye.

Figure 5-6 illustrates a second experimental condition with partial prisms.

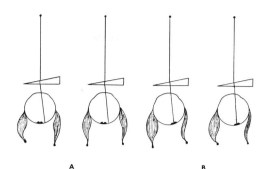

A   B

Figure 5-5. The optical effects of wearing laterally-displacing prisms. A. Eyes in the "phoria" position. B. Eyes deviated so that the prism-displaced image falls on the fovea.

In this case, plain glass or no glass was used over the top half of the eye, and a prism over the bottom half. With the eyes in the normal or in the "phoria" position, rays from the top half of the

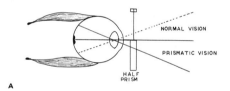

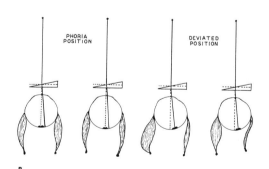

Figure 5-6. The optical arrangement of the "half-prisms" used by Kohler.[149] A. Lateral view of top and bottom section of half-prism. B. When upper part of object image falls on the fovea, lower part is displaced; when lower part of object image falls on the fovea, upper part is displaced.

visual field would fall normally on the retina, while rays passing through the prism in the bottom half would be displaced laterally, thus splitting the visual field.

GENERAL EFFECTS AND AFTER-EFFECTS. The general effects of wearing either binocular or monocular prisms which displaced the line of sight included the apparent bending of lines, distortion of angles, slanting of the floor, and convergence and divergence of parallel lines in the visual field. Stimuli might appear brighter in some regions of the retina than in others. With continued viewing, bent lines and distorted geometrical figures lost some of their distortion. When the head or body moved, phantom movements of the environment occurred.

As adaptation continued, some subjects observed alternation between past conditions of perception and modes induced by the prisms — an effect that was enhanced by the wearing of half prisms. In general, subjects wearing binocular or monocular prisms of less than 20 degrees displacement adapted in their movements and perception, sometimes by means of deviated head positions. Subjects did not adapt consistently to prisms of 20 to 30 degrees displacement, or to half prisms. In both of these conditions, disoriented perception persisted, along with movement limitations in reaching and localizing.

After the prisms were removed, the subjects perceived bending of lines and distortion of angles and figures in directions opposite to those which had been induced by the prisms initially. After-effects were sometimes quite variable, with periods of normal perception alternating with periods of perceptual distortion. The most persistent after-effects occurred with relationships which had required the longest adaptation periods; the most long-lasting of the specific after-effects — sometimes lasting for weeks — was the perceived bending of straight lines.

BINOCULAR ANGULAR DISPLACEMENT. Three subjects wore binocular prisms that displaced their line of sight 15 degrees for periods of 5, 10, and 18 days respectively. The usual effects and after-effects as described above were observed. The 10-day subject reported some degree of adaptation after one day, elimination of phantom movements on the second day and of slanting and bending on the sixth day. He skied successfully on the sixth day. The 18-day subject adapted more slowly to the prisms and experienced the usual after-effects for weeks afterwards. Line bending ceased after 23 days.

MONOCULAR ANGULAR DISPLACEMENT. Seven subjects wore monocular prisms that displaced the line of sight from 5 to 30 degrees, for periods of from 5 to 36 days. In addition, one subject wore a 15-degree prism for about 84 days, then a compensating prism (shifting the field in the opposite direction) for 10 days, and finally a 20-degree prism for a month, making an experimental period of 124 days.

One subject wore for five days a prism which displaced his line of sight vertically 5 degrees. Besides the usual effects and after-effects, he reported behavioral adaptation in one day, and persistence of behavioral after-effects for days.

A subject who wore a 10-degree lateral displacing prism for 22 days reported that the after-effects persisted for weeks, and that they were also observed with the eye which had been covered during the experimental period.

Three subjects wore 20-degree prisms for 6, 8, and 36 days respectively, and one wore a 20-degree prism for 8 days, followed by a 30-degree prism for one more day. The first subject reported usual effects, with after-effects which lasted for 3 to 4 days. No statement was made as to the degree of adaptation. The second subject reported incomplete behavioral and perceptual adaptation. He used a head deviation to correct for his displacement, thus reducing errors in perceived direction. He quickly achieved normal vision after the prisms were removed. The 36-day subject achieved behavioral and perceptual adaptation only when his eyes and head were straight forward. He observed slight after-effects for months with both the prism-covered eye and the blinded eye. The subject who was shifted from 20 to 30 degrees was reported to have achieved incomplete behavioral and perceptual adaptation with the 20-degree prism, showing no progress in reaching or localizing. He observed intermittent after-effects. No specific comments were made on the effects of the 30-degree prism.

The description of results on the subject who wore three different prisms for a total of 124 days is too general to define the effects of the different displacements. Observations were made on the color effects of prism displacement.

DISPLACEMENT OF HALF THE VISUAL FIELD. Two subjects wore monocular half-prisms, one of 10 degrees displacement in the lower half of the visual field (12 days) and one of 10 degrees in the upper half of the field (50 days). The first subject reported that a unified visual field occurred sporadically by the end of 12 days. After removing the prism, the after-effects included intermittent double vision. The second subject reported the usual effect of conflicting vision between upper and lower halves of the visual field, with increasing adaptation after 10 days. His eye movements were disturbed due to the discrepant fields. There was no clear statement of the degree of adaptation at the end of the 50 days.

Theoretical Summary

Kohler looked upon his studies of rehabituation to distorted visual fields as probing the fundamental nature of perception and its development. He felt that classical psychophysics could not describe perception as it occurs in everyday life, and that to insert an organizational process between stimulation and perception — as the gestaltists did — was unnecessary. Rather, the development of perception must be reconstructed by studies on rehabituation to understand how external events define perceptual processes. Two tendencies operate to give stability to perception during development and to determine perceptual differentiation. One is the mechanism of adaptation and the other is using the adaptational process to meet the requirements of any given perceptual situation.

Kohler resorted to terms drawn from learning and conditioning doctrine to explain the development (and redevelopment, in distorted visual fields) of perceptual phenomena. He postulated that simultaneous stimulation of more than one sense modality follows set patterns on particular occasions, with some stimuli being of a higher degree. The organism adapts by forming associations based on these patterns. Such associations account for some of the effects and after-effects of the visual displacement studies; for example, associations are formed between direction of movements and what is seen. This associative process was also described as involving conditioned sensations, acquired by conditioning sensations to movement. Further, some effects involve codetermined adaptation, a step beyond simple conditioning of sensations. The generalization of adaptive effects from one eye to another in the monocular prism studies is an example of such codetermination. Drawing again on pavlovian terms, Kohler spoke of higher-order stimulus effects in rehabituation; the head-eye relationship makes possible different perceptual effects depending on which specific movements or pattern of movements occurs.

Kohler derived two main principles from his experiments, and the theory on which they were based. The first is that organisms can find and adjust to invariants of stimulation. This process is a preliminary step in learning. The second is that previous adjustments and experiences influence present stimulus patterns. Thus, stimulus patterns of a higher order are able to regulate sensibility in a multiple way. In general, the adaptation process in visual displacement studies shows that insurmountable barriers do not exist between the different sense modalities or between motor activities and sense modalities.

Critical Evaluation

In view of the significance attached to Kohler's work by many psychologists, the experiments warrant some additional discussion in terms of the following points: Do the experimental results show what they are purported to show? What is the meaning of the findings relative to the results of earlier studies? How well do the studies confirm the specific hypotheses upon which they were based?

The main factual question is to what extent Kohler's subjects established relatively normal and efficient visuomotor coordination and perception under conditions of inverted or reversed vision. Both he and others who have discussed his work have seemed to assume that such complete adaptation came as a matter of course. However, complete adaptation was not demonstrated clearly in any of the experiments on inversion and reversal. One of the two subjects in the right-left reversal study and one of three in the mirror inversion study are described at times as having achieved complete adaptation, but if the experimental observations are read in detail, discrepancies are found. For example, it was implied that the depth distortion produced by the reversing prisms was never corrected, and one observation on the subject who wore these prisms for 37 days was that "nearly" complete adaptation was found. In the mirror inversion studies there are

discrepancies and limitations of reporting. Although the second subject was said to have achieved upright vision with the mirror, the implication for the other two was that perceptual reorientation was incomplete, and was dependent on specific manipulations.

Over all, the evidence is that Kohler's findings on inversion and right-left reversal of vision are very similar to the results of Stratton and Ewert, although Kohler's experiments were conducted less systematically and reported less completely than the earlier studies. His described levels of adaptation with mirror inversion are probably equivalent to Stratton's[297] results with the 90-degree mirror displacement. Kohler studied inversion and reversal of vision as separate dimensions of disorientation, whereas Stratton[295, 296] and Ewert[74] inverted and reversed the visual field simultaneously. Nevertheless, Kohler's subjects experienced just as much, if not more, nausea and difficulty as the earlier subjects, and apparently adapted no more successfully.

Kohler's work on angularly displaced vision is presented to give the impression that complete motor and perceptual adaptation can be achieved with such angular displacement, but the specific experimental observations suggest a somewhat different interpretation. None of the subjects who wore prisms that displaced the line of sight more than 15 degrees could be said without reservation to have adapted to the displacement. The human visual system has a range of tolerance for angular displacement within which it can compensate, and Kohler's subjects gave no evidence of unusual achievements beyond that moderate range.

Another major question is whether Kohler's hypotheses concerning general perceptual rehabilitation were confirmed by his results. All of his descriptions of actual results — especially those dealing with the necessity for specific manipulative and motor adaptation as a pre-requisite for establishing new situational visual orientation — suggest that the perceptual reorientation achieved was not general but highly specific. The observations on intermittency of orientations also suggest this same conclusion. We are left with the notion that the actual descriptive observations do not always conform to Kohler's interpretations of his results.

Kohler's whole concept of the meaning of the rehabituation experiment rests on the assumption that the conditions and results of experimentally displaced vision duplicate the critical features of normal perceptual development. We cannot agree with this assumption. Whereas all experimental observations have indicated that learning in displaced visual fields is highly specific, all of our knowledge of infant development suggests that general modes of adaptation develop first, to be followed by more and more specific differentiations. Infants develop first the larger responses, the grosser orientations, and only gradually develop the ability to perform movements which are precisely organized according to the spatial characteristics of the environment. In contrast, subjects performing under conditions of visual displacement learn the small, specific manipulations first and only gradually — if ever — can modify their more general visuomotor coordinations.

Throughout Kohler's work there is definite playing down of the efforts of earlier objective investigators to quantify, to test, and to specify particular conditions of behavior and perception. Instead the emphasis is placed on the introspective and interpretative approach — an emphasis that is not only stated but shows up in the nature of the available reports. Kohler's many original ideas and techniques, including the use of half-prisms, are deserving of a more objective experimental treatment.

RECENT STUDIES WITH EXPERIMENTAL SPECTACLES

The most recent experiments using experimental spectacles to study displaced vision will be summarized here before going on to a number of physiological studies bearing on the general problem.

Personality Correlates of Perception in Reversed Visual Fields

Kottenhoff,[154, 155] who served as one of Kohler's subjects, carried out a study of his own attempting to correlate perceptual variables in reversed visual fields with personality characteristics. Twelve subjects wore right-left reversing prisms while being rotated in a swivel chair. After being rotated, they were asked to compare the speed of movement of the visual surround which they had experienced in the chair with that of a moving band of paper presented to them. The results of these judgments were then compared with scores on two personality tests: a self-rating scale of introversion and extroversion and the Rhathymia scale of the Guilford-Martin inventory, which also provides an introversion-extroversion score.

Kottenhoff reported that he found a linear correlation between the speed of movement experienced by subjects during reversal of the visual field and scores made on the introversion-extroversion scales. Extreme introverts were said to report faster rates of movement (as compared with the moving band), less extreme introverts showed an adjustment in either direction, while the extroverts all reported slower rates of movement during the test.

Notwithstanding the promise that this particular study may have for research on personality and clinical psychology, the results should be appraised critically in relation to our general knowledge of behavior. First of all, the results of this experiment are almost embarrassingly precise, in view of the fact that self-rating scales of personality, which rarely have a reliability coefficient of over 0.50, were used as a source of data to be correlated with vision and motion variables. Moreover, the number of experimental variables adjusted simultaneously compares strangely with the directness and simplicity of the conclusions, i.e., that the introversion-extroversion dimension correlates directly and precisely with the perceived speed of movement in reversed fields.

Experiments of Snyder and Pronko

The experiments of Snyder and Pronko[275] and of Snyder and Snyder[276] are distinctive in two ways. They obtained some clear-cut performance curves which indicated the rate of

adaptation to inverted and reversed vision over a period of 30 days, and they repeated Peterson and Peterson's[208] effort to determine many months later the retention of the adaptive level achieved. Their procedures were much like Ewert's, except that they did not require continuous reports of perceptual orientation. They used a binocular lens system, similar to Ewert's, that produced up-down inversion, right-left reversal, and reversal of depth cues of a visual field 20 degrees in extent (Fig. 5-7, A). With a theoretical orientation similar to that of Stratton and Kohler, they proceeded from the assumption that the visual distortion experiment would enable them to study normal development of perception as it occurs in infants.

With one subject (Snyder) wearing their experimental spectacles for 30 days, Snyder and Pronko depended on

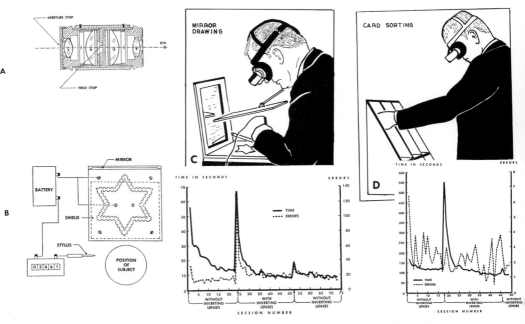

Figure 5-7. Methods and results of Snyder and Pronko's study. A. The binocular telescope system. B. Plan of the mirror-drawing test. C. Subject performing mirror drawing, and curves of adaptation on this test. D. Subject performing card sorting, and curves of adaptation on this test. (Telescope, maze, and graphs from Snyder and Pronko;[275] other drawings based on photographs from same source.)

specific tests to chart the course of adaptation. General orientation tests included walking on a curved line, and reaching. Before, during, and after the experimental period, the subject was tested on the Minnesota Rate of Manipulation Test, the Purdue pegboard, a mirror-tracing test (Fig. 5-7, B, C), and a card-sorting test (Fig. 5-7, D).

QUANTITATIVE DATA ON ADAPTATION. Two pairs of performance curves, on mirror tracing and card sorting, are shown in Figure 5-7. Both time and error curves are given. Performance in card sorting, a task requiring relatively little visual control, was affected very little in terms of accuracy by the combined inversion-reversal of the visual field, although performance time increased markedly when the spectacles were first worn. In contrast, both time and errors in mirror tracing increased when the visual field was displaced. The mean errors in mirror tracing for the last five trials of the 30-day experimental period were about a third more frequent than errors made in the five trials just before the period of visual distortion. A task which required constant visual guidance suffered from the visual distortion, and did not recover in 30 days. Comparable effects were found with the other two tasks. The Minnesota Rate of Manipulation Test, a cylinder turning task requiring little visual control, actually was performed faster at the end of the distortion period than it had been just before distortion. However, performance on the Purdue pegboard, which requires considerable visual guidance, showed a mean time for the last five predistortion trials of 56.2 seconds, and a mean of 60.1 seconds for the last five trials of the distortion period, an increase of 7 per cent.

The after-effects of the displacement period also were different for the various tasks, depending on the relative degree of visual guidance needed. Mirror tracing, the task which had been disturbed most severely by the distortion, showed after-effects over a period of roughly two weeks, while the other tasks recovered to their predistortion level after one day.

PERCEPTUAL ORIENTATION. The relative perceptual orientation of the subject in this study was shown to be a matter of critical attitude. He reported that he did not think of his orientation as unusual, unless he was asked specifically about it. When he was required to note the nature of his orientation at the end of the 30-day period, a feeling of comparative disorientation of the visual field then, and only then, became evident.

SNYDER AND PRONKO'S CONCLUSIONS. In summarizing their results, Snyder and Pronko were inclined to overlook the significant differences which they found with different types of tasks, and to stress the fact that learning did occur with all tasks after the initial disruptive influence of the visual distortion. They drew the following specific conclusions:

a. Past experience of the individual affected the initial and final performance in the tasks.

b. Restriction of the visual field did not affect performance on these tests.

c. Visual disorientation at first severely impaired performance in these tests.

d. "During the 30-day period that the inverting lenses were worn, the visuomotor coordinations were refashioned so that the subject performed even better than before the lenses were put on."

e. When the lenses were removed, performance again was disturbed, but only slightly.

f. The course of learning under visual disorientation was fast at first, slower later.

g. The course of learning in the tasks was disrupted by introduction and removal of the lenses, but proceeded progressively despite these disrupting factors.

Several discrepancies are immediately obvious between Snyder and Pronko's recorded observations and these conclusions. For example, their data on mirror drawing and the Purdue pegboard do not confirm conclusions d, e, and g. Mirror drawing, especially, was severely impaired by the distortion so that it did not recover in 30 days, showed severe and long-lasting aftereffects, and scarcely showed "progressive" learning effects. Our own view is that the differences between tests constitute some of the most significant findings of this carefully controlled study, and should be emphasized rather than minimized.

Snyder and Pronko attempted to equate their study of the behavior of an adult psychologist wearing a pair of inverting-reversing lenses with an analysis of perceptual development in the infant. They speculated that perception does not exist at birth, but comes into being only as a result of a series of "contacts" between the organism and features of its environment — as when the infant comes into continued contact with objects and reaches for them.

RETENTION TESTS. Two years after the initial experiment, the subject, Snyder, resumed wearing the inverting-reversing lenses for one hour per day throughout a 30-day period, and was retested in the specific performance tests.[276] There was near perfect retention of the levels of performance which had been achieved at the end of the original period of displaced vision, indicating that learning in the later period was continuous with that of the initial period. These observations confirm the findings of Peterson and Peterson in showing that practice and learning under conditions of visual displacement are relatively specific to the task situation, and that learning achieved with disoriented vision is not obliterated or even seriously interfered with by inter-

vening conditions of normal visual perception.

ANATOMICALLY DISPLACED FEEDBACK

There have been two series of experiments dealing with anatomical displacement of sensory feedback, and its effects on patterns of motion. Both of these approaches have yielded results of great significance to a general theory of motion organization.

Von Holst and Mittlestädt

In a summary of his experiments on disoriented perception (written in English), von Holst[128] described his work as an investigation of the relations between the central nervous system and the peripheral organs. This central problem of behavior physiology, according to von Holst, is inadequately dealt with by the methods and concepts of reflex action; and the concept of chain-reflex coordination, as derived from the study of isolated mechanisms, is recognized virtually everywhere as wrong in principle. The central nervous system cannot be considered a static transmission system, called into action by afferent impulses only to lapse into inactivity as soon as the impulses are communicated to the motor system. Rather, the brain centers themselves are dynamic action centers which impose their organizing effects not only on the motor impulses but on the afferent systems as well. Accordingly, von Holst approached the problems of behavior analysis from the center out, instead of from the outside in.

In defining his theory, von Holst proposed several basic terms. The total of all afferent impulses he called *afference*, and the total of all efferent impulses, *efference*. There are two types of afference, according to von Holst: *exafference*

refers to those afferent impulses resulting
from external stimuli, and *reafference*
means those impulses which arise because of movement of the organism.
Reafference should not be confused with
proprioceptive stimuli, however, for it
can come from any type of receptor. For
example, if the organism is still and the
environment moves, the visual stimuli
of movement are exafference; but if the
environment is still and the eyes or head
or body moves, the visual stimuli of
movement are reafference. The distinction between the two is made in the
central nervous system; von Holst did
not explain how, but simply remarked
that an organism must be able to distinguish between its own movements
and movements of the environment.

Von Holst used the concept of reafference in his account of how movements are regulated. In brief, his theory
states that an efferent impulse which
initiates a movement leaves an image of
itself in the central nervous system — an
efferent copy. The movement itself produces reafference; if the reafference is
of the same degree as the efferent copy,
it negates the copy, and nothing else
occurs. If it is less than the efferent
image, a plus difference remains; if the
reafference is too great, a minus difference remains. These differences have
definite effects, according to the nature
of the system.

Von Holst's experimental work, some
of it carried out with Mittlestädt,[129]
was concerned mainly with tropistic
movements in invertebrates and fish.
Our main interest here is in their
experimental displacements of sensory
feedback carried out by anatomical
procedures. For example, Mittlestädt
studied the forced orientation movements of the fly, *Eristalis*, in a rotating
striped visual field. As diagrammed in
Figure 5-8, a normal fly (top drawing)
turns in the same direction as the rotating black and white stripes. Now
Mittlestädt rotated the heads of some

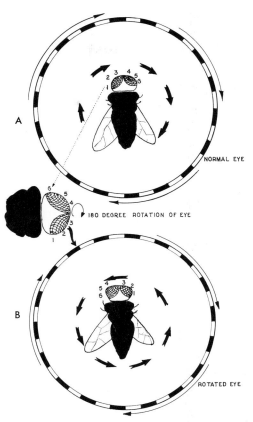

Figure 5-8. The effect of rotating the head of
the fly *(Eristalis)* on the optomotor (optokinetic) reflex. A. Normal fly moves in the direction
of the rotating visual field. B. Fly with head
rotated 180 degrees moves in the direction
opposite that of the moving visual field. (Based
on von Holst.[128])

flies 180 degrees in relation to the body,
and secured them in that position. In
this position, the fly's left eye was on the
right, and its right eye, on the left. When
such a fly was placed in the rotating
visual field, as shown in the bottom
drawing, the visual signals were reversed
and the fly turned opposite to the direction of rotation.

A normal fly in a striped visual field
does not show this oculomotor reflex if
the field is stationary and the fly moves
(in response to some other stimulus, such

as smell), even though visual stimuli from the stripes move across the retina. In von Holst's terms, this is because the stimuli in this case are reafference, and cancel out the efferent image of the movement in the brain. Flies with rotated heads acted very differently, continuing to turn in the same direction as the initial movement. Von Holst explained this by saying that if such a fly moves — say to the left — in a striped field, it has in its central nervous system an efferent copy of left-movement, but because of the abnormal position of its eyes, the reafference from the visual stimulation is reversed in sign. That is, the visual reafference indicates right-movement, and instead of canceling out the efferent image of left-movement it leaves a plus difference and the fly continues to move to the left. Continued movement produces continued reafference of reversed sign, and the fly spins until exhausted. Similar results were found in fish in which the eyes had been rotated 180 degrees.

Another demonstration of the role of reafference in regulating movement was to make the statoliths of a fish heavier by imposing a centrifugal force. The increased weight served to increase the magnitude of reafference from the labyrinthine system. Now when the fish moved, the released reafference from this gravity system was greater than normal, more than cancelled out the efferent copy of movement, and decreased the animal's ordinary reactions to gravitational stimuli.

Von Holst's[128] major theoretical concepts can be summarized in his own words:

"We shall propose that the efference leaves an 'image' of itself somewhere in the CNS, to which the reafference of this movement compares as the negative of a photograph compares to its print; so that, when superimposed, the image disappears. . . . A motor impulse, a 'command' . . . from a higher centre . . . causes a specific activation in a lower centre, . . . which is the stimulus-situation giving rise to a specific efference . . . to the effector . . . (i.e., a muscle, a joint, or the whole organism). This central stimulus situation, the 'image' of the efference, may be called 'efference copy'. . . . The effector, activated by the efference, produces a reafference . . . which returns to the lower centre, nullifying the efference copy by superposition. . . . When the efference copy and the reafference exactly compensate one another, nothing further happens. When, however, the afference is too small or lacking, then a + difference will remain or when the reafference is too great, a — difference will remain. This difference will have definite effects, according to the particular organization of the system. This difference can either influence the movement itself, or for instance, ascend to a higher centre and produce a perception."

As an example of a perception from left-over reafference, von Holst cited a situation in which a false visual perception of movement occurs. If, while the eyes are fixated and the eye muscles are anesthetized, the individual has an "intent" to move his eyes, he has an efferent copy of the motor impulse even though no movement actually occurs. With no visual reafference to negate this efferent image, it ascends to higher centers and produces the false perception that the visual environment has moved.

Within this theoretical framework, some very interesting research has been reported and is still in progress, some of which, like the experiments just described on Eristalis, involves anatomical displacement of sensory feedback. We find such studies very significant in their implications for any theory of perceptual-motor integration, even though we cannot subscribe whole-heartedly to von Holst's interpretations. Anticipating such criticism, however, especially from people who might be overly interested in the finer points of neurophysiology, he insists that each level of investigation should be allowed its own language, so that it can develop along its own lines, unhindered by possibilities of misinterpretation.

Sperry and Stone

In a series of studies bearing on general theory of growth, development, and functioning of nerve pathways, Sperry[281-288] has used anatomical techniques of displacing sensory feedback which have yielded important new knowledge. These experiments and others have invalidated a long-accepted view in psychology and physiology that animals with interchanged afferent or efferent inputs in time would learn to correct for these anatomical displacements.

Systematic anatomical displacements of visual feedback in amphibians can be carried out in four dimensions, three of which are diagrammed in Figure 5-9 for the frog. By rotating the eyes 180 degrees, a combined up-down (dorsoventral) inversion and front-back (nasotemporal) reversal can be achieved. The eyes can also be removed, interchanged, and grafted into position on the opposite side of the head. By this method, an up-down inversion can be achieved without disturbing the front-back axis, or a front-back reversal can be effected without disturbing the up-down orientation. In addition, the optic nerves can be cut and grafted to the opposite stumps to effect a reversal of impulses from the right and left visual fields.

After anatomical displacements of this sort, the frog (after growth or regeneration of the nerve fibers) shows reactions which are displaced in the same dimension as the anatomical displacement. The arrows in Figure 5-9 represent the direction of striking at food which appears in the frog's field of vision. With rotation of the eye, the frog strikes at a point 180 degrees opposite the food, showing displacement in both the up-down and front-back dimensions. When the eye is grafted with an up-down inversion, the frog strikes correctly in the front-back dimension, but inverts the dorsoventral dimension. And with front-back reversal,

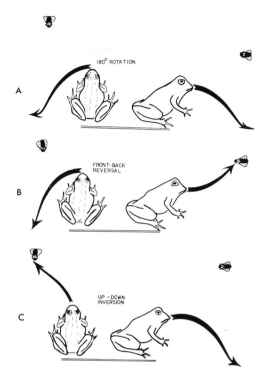

Figure 5-9. Effects on frog's striking reflex as a result of anatomical displacement of the frog's visual system. A. With 180-degree rotation of eyes, motion is displaced 180 degrees. B. With front-back reversal, striking is displaced horizontally. C. With up-down inversion, striking is displaced vertically. (Based on Sperry.[286])

the frog reverses its striking front to back but not dorsoventrally. When the optic nerves are cut and interchanged, the frog shows reversed optokinetic reflexes and right-left reversal of localizing reactions. None of these false localizing reactions is corrected by experience.

Stone[294] also showed that rotated or grafted eyes in amphibian embryos, prior to the onset of vision, led to disorientation of vision which persisted throughout the animal's life.

Among the nonvisual afferent nerve displacements studied by Sperry were crossing of the sensory nerves to the

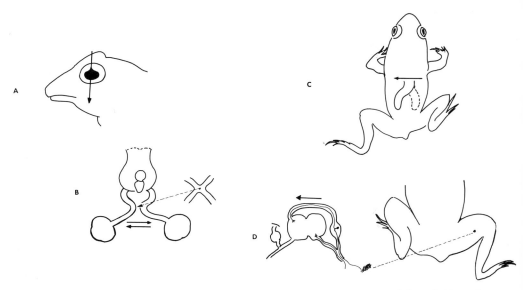

Figure 5-10. Methods of anatomical displacement of sensory input in amphibia. A. Inverting eyes leads to inversion of visually-guided movement. B. Reversing optic pathways at chiasm leads to reversal of visually-guided movement. C. Right-left reversal of skin flap leads to reversal of wiping and scratch reflexes. D. Right-left reversal of sensory nerve input from hind leg leads to reversal of wiping and scratch reflexes. (Based on Sperry.[286])

right and left hind feet of the rat, and interchanging of flaps of skin from the back of the frog. In both cases the crossed afferent nerve supply produced lasting misdirection of movement, where stimulation of the affected area on one side led to response localized to the other side. Neither the rat nor the frog corrected for these anatomical displacements by experience. Sperry's principal procedures to displace afferent stimulation are summarized in Figure 5-10.

Sperry rejected the "monopolistic status" of learning theory in accounting for the development of basic sensorimotor mechanisms, for these experiments on anatomical displacement showed that spatially organized behavior was affected not at all by experience. He went on to say that, inasmuch as the brain of man grows for years, learning is a forceful effect in imposing organization on higher levels of the nervous

system, although the exact nature of the learning process in bringing about this organization is not known.

To account for his experimental results, Sperry[288] fell back on an old theory of spatial specificity or "local sign" of receptor and nerve elements, interpreting it in neural and biochemical terms rather than in the mental and projectional terms of nineteenth century physiological psychology. He said that the "local sign" quality depends on very accurate matching of the central and peripheral connections of every one of thousands of neurons relating the receptor surface and the brain. During maturation, each receptor element acquires a unique chemical constitution. Each skin locus, for example, becomes marked by a given direction and position, which is expressed in the receptor and nerve processes in terms of biochemical properties. The contact of developing central neurons with these receptor loci imparts a specific biochemical status to the neuron terminal according to its attachment at the receptor. Furthermore, in embryonic development, both cortex and lower centers undergo a differentiation corresponding to that which occurs on the body surface, by means of which the central nervous system acquires a biochemical point-to-point map of the receptor surfaces. This differentiation of specific loci of function affects both sensory and motor mechanisms. Only in the very earliest stages of growth do these systems show any plasticity in correcting for anatomically displaced sensory or motor function. Later on, no amount of re-education and training can correct such functional disorientation.

Sperry proposed his new approach as providing a sound explanation for all built-in behavior mechanisms, from the simplest reflexes to the most complex genetically defined systems of response.

SUMMARY

1. Peterson and Peterson observed a subject who wore inverting-reversing lenses for 14 days, and reported that there were some specific motor adjustments but no complete or general perceptual adjustment. The specific learned changes were retained for eight months with very little loss.

2. A limited number of studies on animals have shown that a rhesus monkey was greatly disturbed by visual inversion, but adapted to some extent. In contrast, chickens showed no adaptation either to visual reversal or to a seven-degree lateral displacement of the line of sight.

3. Kohler carried out extensive studies over many years on many aspects of visual distortion, including inversion, reversal, and angular displacement. His

work was based on the assumption that experimental displacement returns the adult to the condition of incomplete perceptual development as found in the infant.

4. Although Kohler assumed that subjects would eventually adapt completely to experimental displacement, his own reports indicate that adaptation to reversal was not complete in 24 days or in 37 days, and that adaptation to inversion was not complete in 6, 9, or 10 days. Adaptation was dependent on learning specific coordinations, and thus perceptual adaptation was partial and variable. Successful adaptation was noted to lateral displacements no larger than 10 to 15 degrees, but not to larger angular displacements.

5. Kottenhoff attempted to correlate speed of visual movement perceived during visual reversal with extroversion-introversion. Introverts were said to have reported faster movement than extroverts.

6. Snyder and Pronko observed a subject who wore inverting-reversing lenses for 30 days, and was retested two years later. Data were obtained on general orientation tests and specific learning of four manipulative performances.

7. Task performances suffered from the visual displacement to varying degrees, depending on their visual requirements. Performance in mirror tracing and on the Purdue pegboard did not recover completely in 30 days time. After-effects were also more severe for tasks requiring more visual guidance.

8. After two years, these specific skills which had been learned under visual displacement were retained with very little loss.

9. Von Holst and Mittlestädt have shown that invertebrates and fish with anatomically displaced feedback (inverted eyes, and so forth) responded in a disoriented fashion and never recovered. Von Holst proposed a theory of

neural comparison of efferent and afferent activity to explain the regulation of motion.

10. Sperry carried out a series of studies of anatomically displaced afferent tracts, mainly in amphibia, which showed that the animals responded according to the original spatial organization of their sensory-neuromotor system and never adapted to the artificial disorientation. Sperry interpreted this in terms of a variation of "local sign" theory, postulating neural and biochemical coding of the sensory surfaces.

CHAPTER 6

CRITICAL SUMMARY OF DISPLACED VISION STUDIES

The prior studies of displaced vision reported in the last two chapters have employed many techniques, followed many procedures, and produced many results, often seemingly unrelated. In the present chapter, we shall take a critical second look at the various studies, trying to point out their similarities and differences, their strong points and weaknesses, and their significance in defining what we believe to be the important behavioral aspects and dimen-

sions of displaced vision. Our primary interest is not to prove or disprove the empirical theory of space perception, for we believe that the problem of innate versus learning factors cannot be settled in such a direct and unqualified way. At this point, we wish merely to analyze the experimental problems of defining the varied phenomena of displaced vision toward the end of improving methods of investigating these phenomena.

Any evaluation of studies on displaced vision must consider both methods and results. As described heretofore, the principal methods have consisted in fitting optical lens systems, mirrors, or prisms to the eyes and then observing the effects of wearing these devices for some time. Each of these optical systems has its own peculiarities which have influenced the observations on perceptual or motor adjustment. In addition, the types of performance situations used in analyzing the effects of perceptual disorientation are known to affect the results found. We shall start this survey of past experiments by considering the nature of some of the different methods used in the study of displaced vision.

EVALUATION OF EXPERIMENTAL METHODS

Figure 6-1 illustrates some of the techniques which have been used to produce either inversion or reversal of the field of vision by means of experimental spectacles or headgear. The lens system shown in Figure 6-1,A, is like those employed by Stratton,[295, 296] Ewert,[74] and Snyder and Pronko,[275] which both inverted and reversed the visual field. Prisms, such as shown in Figure 6-1,B, can be used either to invert or to reverse the visual field, depending on how they are arranged in spectacles. In his studies, Kohler[149-152] used totally reflecting prisms to reverse the visual field, and also used prisms of less than 90 degrees. The mirror headgear shown in Figure

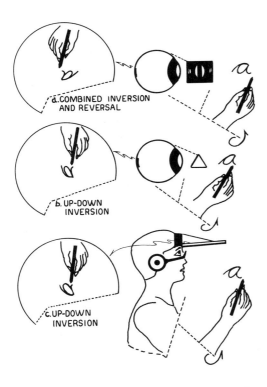

Figure 6-1. Types of optical displacing devices. A. Inverting and reversing lens. B. Inverting prism. C. Inverting mirror system.

6-1,C, shows one way that mirrors can be arranged to control the visual field. Such an arrangement, used by Kohler but credited to Erismann, vertically inverts the field of vision but does not reverse it right to left. Stratton[297] originated the use of mirrors to displace the locus of vision.

Experimental Spectacles

There are serious limitations in using experimental spectacles and headgear in displaced vision experiments, for these devices produce variations in stimulating conditions beyond the desired displacements of the visual field. The most significant limitations are the following ones.

a. The field of vision usually is greatly restricted. Stratton achieved a relatively wide monocular field of 45 degrees with his lens systems, but in Snyder and Pronko's study, the monocular field was reduced to 20 degrees. Kohler's observations with right-left reversing prisms involved a visual field of 30 to 35 degrees.

b. When binocular lens or telescope systems are worn, normal accommodation is destroyed, and the range of accommodation is greatly restricted. With such binocular systems, as in the study of Snyder and Pronko, telescopes must be adjusted to give a single image at a particular distance that, of course, cannot be varied. With binocular lens or prism systems, cues for depth and for convergence and divergence are reversed. Stratton resorted to monocular vision in order to avoid some of these binocular side effects, but restricting vision to one eye also is undesirable.

c. The various optical systems produce different conditions of visual displacement with different eye, head, and body movements. Thus, research with fitted spectacles, prisms, and mirror headgear really involves differential visual displacement in relation to different movement systems of the body, and many of the phenomena of wearing the optical systems may be due to the variable effects of different movements.

d. When we produce displacement of the visual field by means of prisms or mirrors attached to the head, every movement of the head causes apparent movement of the whole visual field, a condition which is often very disturbing to the subjects. The nausea, giddiness, and fainting which were reported by Kohler and others were undoubtedly caused in part by these unusual movement effects. Also, when displacing prisms are attached to the head, every sidewise tilt of the head changes the plane of the displacement.

e. With almost all of the optical systems, there are grave disturbances in the normal relationships between movements of eyes, head, and body. For example, when prisms are used to displace the line of sight, the eyes must move laterally with respect to the body to bring the fixated object to the fovea. As another example, Kohler's inverting mirror mounted out from the forehead required the subject to direct his gaze upward to observe his displaced visual field.

f. Because of the very great technical problems of designing good optical devices to fit into spectacles, the accuracy and flexibility of experimental procedures in the optical studies of displaced vision leave much to be desired. The experimental arrangements that have been tried are cumbersome, uncomfortable, and entail unavoidable errors of fitting when used with more than one subject.

g. Perhaps the gravest limitation of the optical methods is that it is not possible to invent devices which will produce different conditions of inversion, reversal, combined inversion and reversal, and angular displacement of the locus of vision or of the line of sight which are experimentally comparable.

Each device has its own limitations and introduces its own extraneous variables, so that the results of the various studies are not directly comparable.

Controlled Optical and Television Methods

The limitations of the methods of using experimental spectacles and headgear have led to efforts to utilize other procedures of producing displaced vision. Siipola[239] used different arrangements of mirrors to produce several conditions of displaced vision. The different conditions tested were roughly comparable, except for the fact that the subject had to assume somewhat different postures to observe his activity with the different mirror placements.

In our own first studies, we used fixed prisms to eliminate some of the secondary factors involved in the use of experimental spectacles and optical headgear.[217, 218] This technique eliminated the effects of head movements in producing apparent movement of the visual field, provided a relatively wide field of vision, and produced no disturbance in accommodation. Figure 6-2 illustrates how a fixed prism was mounted to study inversion of the visual field. The arrangement permitted considerable flexibility of manual performances to be tested without obstruction, and could have been used to study more than one type of displacement.

More recently, we have developed techniques of using closed-circuit television to displace the visual field.[274] Figure 6-3 diagrams a standard arrangement of television components and motion analysis equipment used for research on displaced vision. The television camera records the performance of the subject, which must be viewed by him in the television monitor. The televised image can be controlled either electronically or optically, so that different dimensions of inversion, reversal or

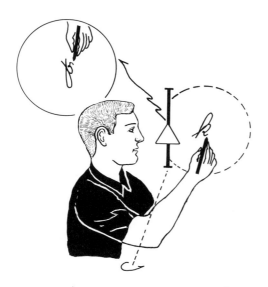

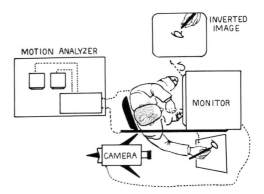

Figure 6-3. Using closed-circuit television to study displaced vision.

Figure 6-2. Using a fixed prism to study inverted vision.

angular displacement of the visual image can be obtained in the same performance situation. With this method, direct comparisons can be made between the effects of many different types of displacement.

BEHAVIORAL PHENOMENA OF DISPLACED VISION

Although the many different studies of displaced vision in man and lower animals have often been treated as equivalent in psychological literature, it is just as important to recognize their differences as their similarities. The visual field can be displaced in many ways, and the effects can be shown to be functions of the kind and degree of displacement. Thus, the primary interest of many earlier investigators in degree of adaptation to some generalized condition of perceptual disorientation has, for us, little meaning. Rather, we are concerned with differentiating among the various experimental variables to discover insofar as possible the effects of each on perceptual-motor integration. In this section we shall try to point out differential effects where possible, in addition to summarizing more general phenomena.

Organic and Emotional Disturbances

We know of no other experimental procedure ordinarily used in behavior research that produces such striking behavioral and organic disturbances as may accompany some conditions of displaced vision. These effects range from minor emotional disturbance and frustration, through dizziness, giddiness, faintness, to nausea and illness. Organized behavior is disrupted and sometimes blocked more or less completely, and at times human subjects appear almost as immobile as Foley's[91] monkey.

Aside from some systematic observations of Ewert,[74] the implications of the emotional and organic accompaniments of displaced vision have been dismissed for the most part as unfortunate side-effects. For example, Kohler[149] noted that an occasional subject could not stand up under the stress of the experimental procedures and situations, and thus was forced to discontinue his participation. Subjects who continued with the inverting mirror had to be watched continually at first, and cared for almost as invalids. Dizziness, nausea, discomfort in wearing the spectacles, and feelings of depression were mentioned as immediate effects, and dizziness and nausea as after-effects. However, Kohler did not analyze these effects further or comment on their significance.

As we have indicated above, some of these emotional and organic disturbances can be traced directly to the characteristics of experimental spectacles and headgear, which caused such effects as apparent movement of the visual field and disturbance of the normal relationships between eye and head movements. Ewert observed acceleration of apparent movement when his telescopic lenses were put on and again when they were taken off. He observed that dizziness occurred with movements of the eyes and head, leading to inhibition of normal eye-head coordinations so that the subjects moved around as stiff-necked as ramrods. There was considerable individual variation among the three subjects as to the length of time that the dizziness persisted during the course of the experiment.

Ewert described several conditions under which his subjects experienced no dizziness: when the eyes were open and the head and objects in the background were stationary, when the eyes were closed during head movements, when the eyes were open and only objects were moving, and when the head was moved very rapidly (as a dancer flings her head in rotation). Ewert also observed that directions were seen reversed during movement, and that this reversal could not be eliminated.

Gross anxiety and depression are not uncommon among subjects who try to wear inverting or reversing optics for even a short period of time. Our own experience is that many subjects respond with considerable apprehension to this type of situation even when it is controlled to eliminate the giddiness and the nausea. Their emotional reactions are not unlike those that sometimes occur in persons who are trying to learn to wear bifocal lenses that distort their established visual field. All in all, it is not surprising that a very limited number of subjects have participated in displaced vision experiments.

Although emotional and organic disturbances are intensified by some of the side-effects of wearing experimental optics, they can not be attributed entirely to these extraneous causes. Displacement of the visual field in itself can induce considerable discomfort and disturbance, and further disturbances are sometimes observed as after-effects after the displacement has been discontinued. The indications are that visual displacements seriously disrupt the intrinsic neuromotor regulatory systems of patterned behavior and accordingly impose severe stress on the individual. We do not believe that experimentally imposed visual displacement is at all comparable — as Kohler assumed — to the infant's predevelopmental state, but rather sets up conditions which are dynamically opposed to the basic movement systems of the body.

Degree of Perceptual Adaptation to Inverted and Reversed Vision

In his original study, Stratton[295] posed the question: What degree of visual adaptation will occur if the image on the retina is inverted in an up-down direction and reversed right to left? This same question was posed with different emphases and points of view in later studies of Ewert,[74] Peterson and Peterson,[208] Snyder and Pronko,[275] and Kohler.[149] The first four of these investigators produced combined inversion and reversal of the visual field by means of lens systems, while Kohler studied inversion and reversal of vision separately.

These studies of inversion and reversal also differed in regard to the procedures followed and nature of performances observed. Stratton wore a monocular system for eight days, Ewert's three subjects wore binocular lenses for 14 days, as did the subject observed by Peterson and Peterson, and Snyder and Pronko's one subject (Snyder) wore binocular lenses for 30 days. Kohler used long exposures, varying the times for different subjects. He wore reversing prisms himself for 24 days and his other subject wore them for 37 days. Three subjects wore the inverting mirror for 6, 9, and 10 days. Ewert's and Snyder and Pronko's studies emphasized practice in specific psychomotor tasks, whereas Stratton's, Peterson and Peterson's, and Kohler's studies stressed more general types of orientation and simple localizations.

Subjective judgments of perceptual orientation from these different experiments were fairly consistent, and all studies except Ewert's reported that some reorientation occurred, which might be described generally as of a consistent perceptual orientation with the displaced vision. All reports hedged on the pictorial quality of this judged orientation except that of Kohler, who described it with great precision. In their daily observations, Ewert's subjects reported no reorientation. Snyder and Pronko noted the comparative nature of the judgments made, and also noted that a critical attitude in the subject could cause his judgments to vary. One can say generally that if a subject with inverted or reversed vision were concentrating upon and performing some specific act of motor adaptation, he would report a consistent or even normal orientation.

The most significant fact about reported perceptual orientation in displaced vision is its dependence on and interaction with overt adaptive movements. Perceptual judgments at all stages of adaptation depended on the movements made in the situation. We believe that this fact provides direct evidence for the behavioral foundation of perceptual orientation. When one first views any kind of visually displaced field, it may look somewhat strange and disoriented, or it may not. It is only when dynamic motion occurs in the displaced field that the gross nature of disorientation is discovered and experienced. As Kohler has noted, this movement foundation of the discrepancies due to the displacement proceeds to the very last stages of adaptation, even during long exposure. As he stated it, the individual can tolerate some discrepancies in seeing, but he cannot tolerate even minor errors in performance of overt movements of locomotion, grasping, head turning, and so on.

The fact is that perceptual judgments of the orientation of the visual field are never absolute, but depend on many variables, including the motion factors of which we have just spoken. Kohler himself arranged an unusual demonstration of the equivocal nature of ordinary space perception. He conceived the idea of trying to investigate relative visual displacement by constructing an inverted environment, as shown by the photograph in Figure 6-4. The subject shown here is himself inverted in an inverted room, and maintains his position in the chair at the table by hanging on with his hands and legs. The results of investigations with this technique were, we understand, as equivocal as the subject's perceptions.

Our ordinary visual experiences make us aware that there is a very wide range of angles through which the image on the retina can be rotated or displaced without noticeably affecting the apparent orientation of the visual field. Even with more extreme displacements, as, for example, when one views his visual environment by bending over and look-

Figure 6-4. An inverted room constructed to study space perception. (Photograph courtesy of Ivo Kohler.)

ing through his legs or by lying down on his side, the sense of the vertical is not lost nor does it change appreciably. This "normalization" of the direction of the vertical has been studied in a number of different ways by producing displacements of the position of the eyes with respect to the visual environment.[6, 7, 214, 331–333] Such displacements can be produced by tilting the body in space or by holding the body constant and displacing or rotating the environment. There is no doubt that there is a range of relative visual displacement, varying for different individuals and conditions of observation, throughout which perceptual responses do not vary significantly. In one study of Witkin and Asch,[333] the visual environment was rotated as much as 75 degrees before some subjects reported deviation of the vertical.

We can demonstrate this wide range of tolerance for displacement by asking subjects to bend over and view a vertical writing board through their legs and then perform a task of writing. The subject usually compensates for the environmental inversion of his visual field by writing upside down, and to him everything still looks pretty normal as he views what he has done, even though this writing is reversed from his

(also still normal) perception of familiar objects around him. The point is that the individual can integrate different patterns of objects and motions oriented in quite different directions in the same visual space if we do not disturb the very critical geometric relationships between the eyes and the head.

Perception of the up-down dimension in space is also dependent on relative strength of visual, cutaneous and gravitational-postural effects in different situations, as has been demonstrated by Simons[243] in a study of directional perceptions during maneuvers of an aircraft that produced conditions of zero-gravity. A steel walkway was mounted on the ceiling of the cabin of a C-131b plane, as shown in Figure 6-5, and subjects (four in number, including Simons) used magnetic sandals to maintain attachment to this upside-down walkway when the plane went into the zero-gravity maneuver. In their inverted position, with no gravitational clues, all subjects perceived "down" as in the direction of attachment to the walking surface. One subject perceived the pilot of the plane as upside-down from his own inverted position. One subject who walked in magnetic contact with the walkway

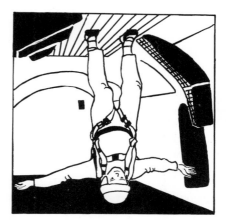

Figure 6-5. Walking on the ceiling of an aircraft during zero-gravity maneuver. (Based on Simons.[243])

while maintaining contact of his fingers with the floor of the plane reported that the feeling of "down" oscillated between floor and ceiling.

Many other observations and experiments could be cited to show how passive perceptual judgments of orientation vary because of their dependence on many different but interrelated factors. In view of these facts, we believe that the criterion of seeing the world upside-down or right-side up, which has been used in many of the inversion experiments, has little meaning, and that the variability and inconsistencies in perceptual judgments which have been reported were only to be expected. The orientation of the environment begins to have behavioral meaning to the individual when he reacts in it actively, trying to bring his own bodily movements into some degree of conformity with the perceived stimulus patterns.

The dependence of space perception on active motion was demonstrated strikingly by Kilpatrick[147] in his studies with distorted rooms. Subjects were able to judge or perceive the nature of the distortion only after actively exploring and moving within the distorted area. The recent work of Held and his associates[113, 114] has demonstrated specifically the differential roles of dynamic and passive movements in adapting to visual disorientation. They found that no significant degree of learning occurred in a displaced vision situation if the subject's hands or body were moved passively by some outside action. However, adaptation did occur when the subject reacted dynamically in the displaced field, by means of his own muscular responses. Results such as these support our general ideas of the essential unity of perceptual-motor integration, and provide further evidence that an individual must respond dynamically to changed stimulus relationships if new spatial coordinations are to be acquired. Significant adaptation in a displaced

visual world involves achieving — in Stratton's words — a new correspondence between touch and sight, or — in our own terms — new perceptual-motor integrations.

Specificity of Perceptual-Motor Adaptation

Another line of evidence for the motion basis of adaptation to displaced visual fields derives from the many observations of the specificity of the new adaptive reactions. All experiments on inverted and reversed vision, including those of Stratton, emphasized that the perceptual reorientation which did occur was dependent on prior motor adaptation and that the experiences or feelings of reorientation were restricted specifically to the objects and situations in which manipulative adaptation occurred. Kohler made this observation time and again in his reports, notwithstanding his emphasis on subjective introspective factors in describing his data and his implications that a general perceptual reorganization occurred which affected all psychomotor integration.

Snyder and Pronko made the most systematic observations on the course of learning specific perceptual-motor skills, not only during the displacement period but before and after it as well. They found the same sort of learning function — although perhaps at a different level — during displacement as during normal vision. Furthermore, these specific motion patterns were retained very effectively over a two-year period. When the subject put on his spectacles again after two years, his specific skills in the inverted field showed almost no loss.

The points of agreement on specificity of adaptation seem to be these: that subjects reported a normal visual orientation only in test situations or with objects in which prior effective motor adaptation had been achieved; that subjects might report effective reorientation only while performing the activities in which this prior motor adaptation had taken place; and that subjects might report shifts in orientation in different parts of the visual field during performance. Outside the situations in which effective motor adaptation (and accompanying perceptual orientation) had taken place, the individuals wearing inverting and reversing optics had a great deal of difficulty and reported inconsistencies in subjective judgments of perceptual orientation.

These findings on the specificity of motor and perceptual adaptation to displaced vision are generally contrary to the original theoretical expectations of the experimenters. For the most part, such experiments have been designed in the belief that some sort of general developmental reorientation of motor behavior and perception would occur, and that all activities and experiences would be affected by this developmental change-over. The findings seem to show clearly that no such general change-over occurred. The continuous wearing of the spectacles or headgear provided opportunity for adaptation in many different situations, but it appears that there was little carry-over from one situation to another. In other words, the effects of practice in different situations with inverted or reversed vision were very specific, as one might expect from observations on the specificity of psychomotor skills under normal circumstances.

Differential Effects of Inversion, Reversal, and Combined Inversion and Reversal of Vision

Stratton's first two experiments involved the use of a monocular lens system which both inverted and reversed the visual field. Studies by Ewert, Peterson and Peterson, and Snyder and Pronko reproduced this same general condition, but with binocular lens systems. In contrast, Kohler attempted to study inversion and reversal separately. It is of theoretical importance to compare these different conditions of systematic displacement, relative to their immediate effects on different types of movements and the degree to which individuals can adapt to them. The diagrams in Figure 6-6 illustrate the appearance of a performance field under the systematic conditions of inversion, reversal, and combined inversion-reversal, as well as with a lateral displacement of the line of sight.

Perhaps the first comparative data on inversion and reversal were those reported by Cox,[55] not from an optical displacement study, but from a study of maze tracing in two identical mazes which could be displaced relative to each other. Cox found that bimanual motion patterns which were reversed left-to-right were easier than when one pattern was rotated 180 degrees (both

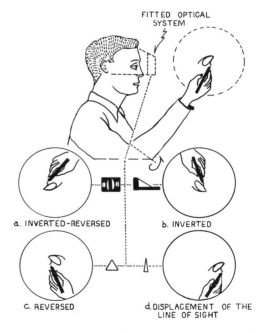

Figure 6-6. Types of visual displacement, and resulting appearance of the performance field.

inverted and reversed) relative to the other, and that both were easier than when one pattern was rotated just 90 degrees. However, no significance was attached to this particular finding.

Siipola[239] was the first to try to analyze systematically the relative effects of different conditions of inversion and reversal of vision. She used mirrors to produce depth inversions to the side, front, and front and side conditions combined. She found some differences between the displacement conditions, but attributed these differences to the relatively awkward positions subjects were required to assume when viewing the mirror located to the side of the performance field.

Kohler also attempted to compare the relative effects of inversion and reversal, but did not use the combined inversion and reversal condition because he thought it was so difficult that no real adaptation could occur. He expressed that belief even though Stratton and Ewert had reported significant behavioral adaptation with reversed and inverted vision. In regard to the relative effects of up-down inversion and right-left reversal, Kohler interpreted his observations to the effect that adaptation to inversion occurred faster. In spite of this observation, he believed that inversion was the more difficult condition, and that faster adaptation occurred with inversion because it induced greater effort in learning on the part of the subject than the right-left reversal. Actually, Kohler's methods did not permit direct comparisons of the two conditions of displacement. He used a mirror system attached to a headgear to invert the field and a binocular prism system to reverse it right to left. Each of these systems induced its own secondary effects, which varied greatly under different conditions. Further, the number of subjects was too limited for meaningful comparisons of the two conditions.

In general, the problem of comparing different conditions of displacement is extremely difficult when optical devices are used. The techniques of closed-circuit television, which we have used in the studies to be described in later chapters, provide new ways of dealing with this problem in controlled experiments.

Differential Effects of Angular Displacements of Vision

The visual field can be displaced in many ways besides systematic inversion or reversal, by means of several kinds of angular displacements of varying magnitudes. We distinguish between angular displacements of the line of sight, such as those produced with prisms by Wooster,[334] and angular displacements of the locus of vision, which involve shifting the relative origin or locus from which the field of vision is observed. This latter condition can be achieved with mirrors, as in Stratton's[297] third experiment, or—more effectively—with television. In addition to these displacements, the field of vision can be rotated to any desired angle. This was done by Brown[32] with prisms, and the entire visual environment of the observer was rotated in the experiments of Witkin and Asch.

There are still other special cases of angular displacement which have been studied. The field of vision of one eye can be displaced with a prism in procedures such as those used by oculists to determine breakdown and recovery angles of convergence and divergence for single vision. Or one part of the visual field can be displaced angularly while another part is not — a condition which was used by Kohler.

The effects of these various angular displacements of the field of vision, line of sight, and locus of vision are quite different from the effects of up-down inversion or right-left reversal of the visual field. Minor angular displacements produce no disturbance of perception or motion, and when disturbance does occur, its severity and the degree of adaptation depend on the type, the dimension, and the magnitude of the angular displacement. For some conditions of angular displacement, the disturbance is greater than with inversion or reversal.

In Brown's study, subjects wore prisms which rotated the visual field 75 degrees. One subject wore the prisms 7 days, and four other subjects wore them for half an hour each day for 16 days. Brown was interested primarily in depth perception, which was disturbed by the visual rotation and improved only slightly with practice. He noted that judgments of near distance, within range of manipulative objects, improved more than judgments of far distance. There was some recovery of motor coordination and perceptual orientation.

These observations of incomplete motor recovery to visual rotation can be compared to the findings of Witkin and Asch. As described earlier, they asked subjects to judge orientation of the vertical during rotation of the entire visual environment and found that some subjects reported no deviation with as much as 75 degrees of rotation. In other words, subjects who were asked to make passive judgments about the orientation of their visual field showed considerable tolerance for displacement, but Brown's subjects, who were required to perform in fields rotated 75 degrees, were disturbed considerably and did not adapt completely. Clearly, the effects of displacement depend in part on the behavior required in the displaced field.

Wooster studied manual localizing movements when the line of sight was displaced laterally by about 21 degrees. Although subjects improved their ability to localize true position even when no specific knowledge of error was given,

they improved faster and to a higher level of accuracy when they were allowed to check their errors by active touch or by sight. However, their adaptation was best if the target was one of their own hands, placed in front of them by the experimenters. Auditory cues were not very helpful.

Kohler made general observations of adaptation to varying degrees of displacement of line of sight, with both monocular and binocular vision. In general, his subjects adapted successfully to smaller displacements, up to about 10 to 15 degrees, but not very well to larger displacements. His studies on partial displacement (of half the visual field) showed that some adaptation to this discrepancy occurred.

In the first study of angular displacement of the locus of vision, Stratton observed that a very marked adaptation occurred in three days to the special displacement that he studied, so that the perceived disorientation between vision and movement gradually diminished. The lower parts of the body, which could be seen most easily, seemed reoriented first, while the head, shoulders, and chest yielded more slowly to the new orientation. Stratton thought that the new "harmony of touch and sight" progressed faster in relation to body parts which perform articulated movements. He speculated that, "If we were always to see our bodies a hundred yards away, we would probably also feel them there."

Although there are very few comparable observations on these various conditions of visual rotation, displaced line of sight, and displaced locus of vision, some general points can be made. First, we note that minor angular displacements may produce little if any disturbance. Second, the degree of disturbance appears to vary considerably with different types of performance. Third, as in the inversion and reversal studies, adaptation to displacement is aided by active movements and manipulations within the displaced field.

Normal Range of Angular Visual Displacement

These observations on limited angular displacements of vision are in agreement with an important concept about the regulation of perceptual motor behavior — that of the normal range of angular displacement. We know that our perceptions of direction and orientation remain fairly constant even when we assume many different bodily positions. We can move our head in many ways with respect to the body and with respect to the visual field without disturbing our passive perceptual reactions as to the orientation of that field. Even when we are performing complex patterns of motion monitored by vision we have considerable tolerance for relative displacement between vision and motion. For example, one can move the head into many different positions while writing on a stationary piece of paper without noting any disturbance of visual control.

We shall return to this concept of normal ranges of displacement later, presenting experimental confirmation and defining its significance more precisely. The phenomena of normal angular displacement represent one aspect of space constancy in perception and motion which we believe can be dealt with best in terms of some neurogeometric conception of the action of the nervous system. In brief, we believe that the central nervous system operates to detect and regulate specific directional differences in movement-produced patterns of stimulation and that the angular range within which the system operates normally will vary for different motion systems and reactions. These ranges of angular variation in visually organized responses represent normal displacements of vision, the limits of which are determined by central brain mechanisms. Beyond these normal limits, displacements of the visual field produce a great number of different effects in behavior, including different forms of adaptation.

Differential Effects of Displacement on Different Types of Motion

One of our own major interests in studying displaced vision has been to determine how displacements of different kinds affect various types of movements and behavior patterns. The earlier studies provide only a few general observations relating to this problem.

Stratton observed in his third study, involving mirror displacement, that locomotor movements adapted first, followed by manual movements, and only later by movements of head, upper torso, and shoulders. Kohler noted similarly that adaptation for locomotion, turning, and reaching was faster than for head movements.

Other general observations have indicated that movements are disturbed more if they involve a higher degree of visual guidance, as might be expected. Siipola found that movements in certain directions were disturbed more by a particular type of displacement than movements in other directions, although differences in posture imposed by her experimental conditions made comparisons difficult.

One generally unrecognized phenomenon of adaptation to displaced vision is the use by some subjects in some situations of compensatory movements to reduce or eliminate some of the effects of displacement. For example, a person writing in an inverted field might write inverted script that would have a normal upright appearance. Or a subject wearing rotating prisms might tip his head to one side to bring the rotated field into a more normal relationship with the position of the head and eyes. It is our belief that many such compensatory reactions probably were used by the subjects in displaced vision experiments, largely unnoticed and unrecorded by the experimenters.

It is very likely that some of the inconsistencies and shifts in perceptual judgments of displaced fields were due to the adoption of compensatory motor adjustments on the part of some of the subjects. Gibson's[99] study of changes in the apparent curvature of lines during and after sustained observation illustrates the sort of change that can be attributed to compensatory reactions. Gibson used prisms to induce apparent curvature in straight lines, and found that, with sustained observation, subjects perceived the lines as becoming progressively straighter. After the prisms were removed, there were perceptual after-effects causing the lines to appear curved in the direction opposite to that induced by the prisms. Although this effect was interpreted as demonstrating the lack of a point-to-point relationship between the retina and the phenomenal field, we think a more meaningful explanation is that the subjects adopted compensatory adjustments which first straightened out the lines in the prismatic field, and then induced after-effects of curvature in the normal field.

In our own studies, we have attempted to analyze some of the effects of using compensatory movements in displaced fields, and to compare them with the use of noncompensatory movements. We have also made many observations on the relative effects of displacements on movements of different types, complexity, and spatial characteristics. All of these effects will be described in later chapters.

Attitude and Motivation in Adaptation to Displacement

In the studies involving the wearing of experimental spectacles or headgear, there have been for the most part very few subjects, most of whom were professional people aware of the implications of the experiment. For this reason, it is difficult to assess the role of attitude or motivation in determining the speed or degree of adaptation. However, one gets the clear impression from reading the various accounts that adaptation to displaced vision is not dependent on knowledge of the nature of the displacement, any special attitudes about what should happen in the situation, or any external source of motivation.

The first point — that knowledge of the displacement conditions is not necessary for adaptation — is confirmed by those few experiments which employed naïve subjects. Wooster used 72 subjects, most of whom had no specific information about the nature of lateral displacement of the visual field, and some of whom were entirely naïve, aside from the fact that they could guess that "something" was wrong. Nothing in Wooster's results indicated that knowledge of the nature of the displacement significantly affected the course of adaptation. Further, her subjects adapted to the displacements to some extent, in the sense of improving localizing accuracy, even when given no specific knowledge of error. We can conclude only that the visual displacement produced imbalances and disturbances in normal perceptual-motor integrations which in themselves motivated the individual to adopt new response patterns. When the sensory feedback from these responses was limited, the accuracy of the new movement patterns was limited, but with adequate tactual, kinesthetic, or visual feedback, subjects achieved a high level of accuracy.

Siipola also was interested in the factor of knowledge of the conditions of displaced vision. After testing 60 subjects under three conditions of right-left, front-back, and combined reversal of vision, she questioned them to try to discover the extent of their knowledge of the particular condition under which they had been performing. Forty per cent of her subjects had no understanding of the nature of the displacement, but this lack of knowledge apparently did not affect their results.

Kohler recognized that adaptation to displaced vision must be guided by self-regulatory behavioral organization, and that knowledge of the nature of the displacement is not a critical factor. His subjects could not judge accurately what was going on without making many different active tests of the displacement situation. Kohler spoke of these problems as applying particularly to the intermediate and last phases of the adaptation. He said that the subject often did not know what the directional disorientation was and could only "feel" that a movement was correct or incorrect.

Some observations have been made about the effect of attitude on subjects' perceptual judgments of the orientation of the displaced field. For example, Snyder and Pronko reported that their subject noted that his visual field was unusual only when asked to make such a judgment. He had continued to learn specific perceptual-motor skills in the displaced field, even though he perceived, when asked, that the field was distorted.

All of these observations and many of our own confirm our belief that adaptation to displaced vision is self-regulatory in character, brought about by the experimentally imposed noncorrespondence between vision and motion. No extrinsic rewards or reinforcements are necessary to motivate the individual to realign his movements with the altered geometric space. The motivational process is inherent in the situation, and the rate and degree to which the individual is motivated to adapt, or can adapt, are defined by the type and magnitude of the displacement.

It is also clear that rate and degree of adaptation to displaced vision depend on the flexibility of the species in modifying its basic modes of perceptual-motor response. The limited information available on subhuman species suggest that only higher animal forms possess such flexibility.

After-Effects of Visual Displacement

Although most of the reports of displaced vision studies included some mention of after-effects, there were few attempts to make systematic measurements. Wooster tried to make controlled observations on the after-effects on localizing performance in the experimental set-up and elsewhere due to wearing the lateral displacing prisms. She concluded in general that localizing errors occurred for a brief period in situations where the subjects had practiced localizations while wearing the prisms, but probably did not transfer to other situations. Ewert tested for after-effects in each of his specific performance tasks, and reported that none was observed. Snyder and Pronko, however, reported after-effects in all of their performance tests. These effects disappeared after about a day, except in the mirror-tracing performance in which some interference effect was noted for two weeks after the lenses were removed. Other observations confirm these of Snyder and Pronko: that, for a given displacement condition, the most long-lasting after-effects occurred in performances which were most disturbed by the displacement and for which the adaptation period was longest.

Several reports mentioned perceptual after-effects, such as apparent movement of the visual field with head or eye movements. Kohler observed such effects for as long as two weeks after the displacement period. He also described long-lasting perceptual after-effects in his subjects who had worn lateral displacing prisms; the most persistent after-effects occurred with perceptual relationships (such as the perceived bending of straight lines) which had taken longest to adapt. Stratton reported no after-effects after his first three-day experiment, but after eight days reported both perceptual after-effects and motor interference, as well as some feelings of nausea, possibly related to perceived movement of the environment.

Both Peterson and Peterson and Snyder and Pronko reported almost perfect retention, for eight months and two years respectively, of specific performances learned under visual inversion.

All of these reports testify to the specificity of adaptation in displaced fields. Performances which were most disturbed by displacement were most disturbed by the return to normal vision. However, the retention tests show that an individual can learn a skill in a displaced field and retain it for long periods of time, while performing with normal vision in the retention interval.

It is perhaps significant that Foley's monkey, which apparently was more disturbed by inversion than human subjects, showed after-effects for three days after the displacement period in such ordinary locomotor responses as climbing and jumping. No human subject was disturbed in his gross bodily movements for so long a time.

COMPARATIVE PHENOMENA OF DISPLACED VISION

The few studies which have been carried out on displaced vision in sub-human animals were summarized in the last chapter. Pfister[209] found that chickens wearing reversing prisms made no effective adaptation to the displacement, as judged by pecking coordinations. Hess[119] found similarly that newly hatched chicks made no adjustment to a seven-degree lateral displacement of their line of sight. The chicks would have died without learning how to hit food particles in their displaced field. This latter study stands in particular contrast to observations on human subjects that have shown little or no disturbance to small angular displacements. Wooster[334] found that accurate localization could be achieved after a few days of practice with a displacement of 21 degrees.

Failure to adapt to displaced vision also has been reported in fish and flies by von Holst and Mittlestädt,[128, 129] and in amphibia by Sperry[286] and Stone.[294] Most of these observations have been made on animals in which the sensory displacement has been made anatomically by changing the orientation of the eyes or by rearranging neural pathways.

In contrast, Foley's[91] rhesus monkey made considerable progress in adapting to inverted vision within a week's time, although the initial effects apparently were more severe and the rate of adaptation seems to have been slower than with human subjects under comparable conditions. The differences in degree might be due in part to more profound emotional disturbances in the monkey, who, unlike human subjects, could have no understanding that the displacement was temporary and experimental. However, it is probably correct to say that the monkey's adaptation was less efficient than man's.

These comparative studies indicate that there is increasing flexibility in perceptual-motor control as we ascend the animal scale — a state of affairs which is consistent with our general knowledge of comparative animal behavior. Whether the ability to adapt fairly well to extreme sensory displacement is possessed by primates alone or whether it is a mammalian characteristic can be decided only after further study.

THEORETICAL INTERPRETATIONS OF DISPLACED VISION

Theoretical emphasis in studies of inversion, reversal, and other displacements of vision has followed the shifting interests and points of view in the behavior sciences since their first beginnings. With recognition of Helmholtz's theory of the empirical origin of space perception, Stratton[295, 296] saw in his experiments on inversion a test of the validity of the empirical theory. Later, interest was sustained in displacement experiments in behavioristic psychology because of the apparent support that the results gave to a general learning interpretation of behavior. In this period, data from studies of visual inversion and reversal often represented arguments against the interpretation of behavior in terms of gestalt variables and doctrines.

Aside from their use to bolster general learning theory, the facts of displaced vision, which represent some of the most dynamic aspects of behavior, have never been incorporated adequately into either psychological or physiological theory. In psychology, these facts have been discussed in terms of some single explanatory concept, usually that of learning, and in sensory physiology they have been labeled as "psychic" aspects of perception and thereafter ignored.

We subscribe to quite a different view concerning the significance of studies of displaced vision. We see in them a method for analyzing some of the critical factors in the space regulation of motion, and thus for revealing new truths about the neural regulatory systems of behavior.

Learning Interpretations

We have already discussed at some length the interpretations of displaced vision phenomena derived primarily from general learning doctrine. Stratton thought that his results confirmed the empirical theory of space perception, although he had not achieved complete adaptation. Ewert[74-76] confined himself more to specific results; although recognizing the great potential of the individual for adaptation, he reserved judgment about its final level. In Kohler's[151] analysis of the problem, the learning basis of perception seemed almost to be taken for granted while he tried to describe the stages leading up to fully developed, i.e., learned, perception. The assumption upon which all of these learning interpretations were based was stated unequivocally by Kohler, that by imposing conditions of displaced vision on an adult, we can return him to a state of incomplete perceptual development equivalent to that of the infant.

The preoccupation of displaced vision experimenters with the defense of learning theory is nowhere better illustrated than in the analysis of Snyder and Pronko,[275] based upon data obtained from their one subject. They felt that the course of infant perceptual development has been clarified by the course of adaptation of their adult subject in card sorting, pegboard performance, and walking a chalk line in an inverted-reversed visual field. They equated the differentiation of perception of space in the young child to this situational learning under displaced vision, and asserted that such perception is specifically learned through "object-person interactions."

Snyder and Pronko went on to say that their data showed that any type of perceptual orientation of space could be established through learning. They expressed the belief that the time will come when the "taken-for-granted-ness" of up-down, right-left, and near and far will go the way of Newton's space and time, and that seeing itself, as well as perceiving up and down and right and left, will be declared **absolutely** relative to the conditions obtaining during their genesis. Until objects and persons enter into interactions of learning, there is no perception. It is out of this interaction that relational reactions of up-down and right-left get elaborated. If this view is found to be correct, according to Snyder and Pronko, then an overhauling of theories of perception equivalent to the "Einsteinian revolution" in physics will be demanded.

It should be noted again that the belief that infant development can be reduced to learning is contrary to all we know about the course of maturation, either of visually controlled motion or of any other perceptual-motor behavior. Further, Snyder and Pronko's suggestion that perceptual development comes about through specialized patterns of object learning does not conform to what we know about the neural organization of the visual system and of the development of visual response patterns in man and higher mammals. We know from the work of McGinnis[182] that directionally controlled ocular movements develop in the infant independently of learning. In fact, the child develops highly coordinated visual responses, including using his eyes to follow moving objects, at an age when only the most limited learning apparently can occur. Also, comparative studies indicate that highly precise visual pursuit movements in mammals develop at an early age through maturational processes,[313] and are mediated through subcortical mechanisms of the thalamus and midbrain.[263, 265, 269] In view of these findings and many others, the assumptions of Snyder and Pronko, Kohler, and others that visually organized patterns of space perception are learned in infancy must be rejected.

In general, the learning interpretations of displaced vision are unsatisfactory in several ways in addition to their unfounded assumptions about perceptual learning in infancy. They do not explain why adaptation is almost impossible under some conditions, and incomplete under all conditions except the most minor angular displacements. They do not explain the differential effects of different types and degrees of displacement. Nor do they explain the phylogenetic differences in responses to displaced feedback — why it is that lower animals show no ability to adapt. Our knowledge of comparative behavior leads us to believe that there are no sharp breaks in manner of response organization in the animal scale but that the differences are gradual and of degree. Thus, we believe that if lower animals show no ability to learn unusual spatial coordinations, then it is reasonable to believe that learning is not the primary organizational process responsible for human space perception.

Neurological Interpretations

If one accepts the proposition that space perception does not depend originally on learning processes, then the question of the rate and degree to which an individual can learn to respond efficiently in a displaced visual field becomes of secondary importance. The primary problem is to understand the mechanisms that regulate space-structured motion, and the significance of the displaced vision experiments depends on what they can tell us about these mechanisms. Some few investigators of displaced vision phenomena have made this emphasis, and accordingly have been interested primarily in neurological interpretations.

One such analysis is that of von Holst,[128] whose work was described in the last chapter. His experiments and observations have been carried out almost entirely with invertebrates and lower vertebrates, so that the question of adaptation to artificially displaced visual feedback could be dismissed; in these lower animal forms, no adaptation has been observed. Von Holst's theory is based on the idea of neural comparison in the central nervous system of afferent and efferent activity. Movement is initiated (by brain command) when there is an imbalance between the two.

This general idea is diagrammed in Figure 6-7, which indicates an ocular movement initiated by a moving object. The stimulus movement to the right produces visual exafference leading to a brain command, or motor impulse, to a lower efferent center to move the eye. This situation produces an "efference copy" in the lower center. The actual movement of the eye to the right produces a visual reafference which returns to the lower center to negate the efference copy. If the two effects are equal, no further movement occurs.

Now if the visual field is artificially reversed, either anatomically or by experimental optics, a stimulus movement to the right produces a motor impulse reversed in sign, to leave an

efference copy of "left-movement." However, because of the optical reversal, the visual reafference indicates "right-movement" and cannot cancel out the efference copy. The continued imbalance then leads to spinning or rotatory responses, which were described in flies and fish.

We believe that von Holst's emphases on the feedback principle (reafference) and on the idea of neural detection of differences are significant contributions to theory of perceptual-motor integration. However, his theory is weak in that he makes no attempt to reconcile his descriptions with known facts of neurophysiology. He insists, for example, that the organism must be able to distinguish between stimuli produced by its own movements and those due to movements of the environment, without indicating how this distinction is made. Further, his tendency to localize "perceptions," "intents," etc., in the higher brain centers solves no problems.

The other major neurological analysis of the displacement phenomena is that of Sperry, whose studies involving anatomical displacement of afferent paths represent an outstanding contribution to physiological psychology. We have already summarized some of his ideas about biochemical local sign in Chapter 5. In brief, he proposes that the central nervous system acquires a point-to-point map of the sensory surfaces of the body during embryonic development. When such a map is distorted by anatomical displacement of afferent signals, the sensorimotor coordinations (in lower animals, at least) are permanently disoriented. These studies indicate further that perceptual-motor responses are organized primarily according to the properties of the neuromotor system. The organism does not respond automatically according to the actual arrangement of stimuli impinging upon the sensory surfaces, but according to

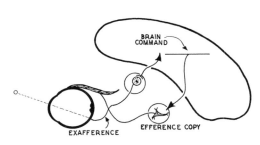

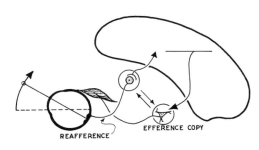

Figure 6-7. Von Holst's[128] principle of reafference.

the intrinsic organization of the response mechanisms.

Although there are very few neurological observations on human individuals bearing on these general problems of displaced sensory signals, one study of our own is relevant.[255] A number of epileptic patients who had submitted to complete or nearly complete section of the corpus callosum (in an effort to reduce the severity of seizures[307]) were trained in a mirror-tracing task and then tested for transfer of training from the preferred to the nonpreferred hand. Their performance in original learning and subsequent transfer did not differ from the performance of a group of normal subjects. In other words, the elimination of the large band of fibers between the brain hemispheres, which have been assumed to be associative fibers, neither retarded learning of a skill in a displaced visual field nor reduced the amount of transfer from one side of the body to the other. The implication is that such complex perceptual-motor adaptation depends on intrinsic reorganizational effects at all levels of sensorimotor control, and is not necessarily a higher level cortical associative process.

Corroborative evidence for this point of view comes from further studies by Sperry[289] involving surgical section of both the corpus callosum and optic chiasm in cats and monkeys. Although these split-brain animals failed to transfer some learned form discriminations from one eye to the other, they were able to transfer learned brightness discriminations and certain simple spatial habits. Thus it appears that while the collosal fibers may mediate specific bilateral response patterns, they do not serve generalized transfer or integrative functions. Space-structured motions are organized intrinsically on a reactive basis, whether mediated by lower neural centers or by the higher cortical pathways.

One more type of evidence for the basic nature of spatially organized responses can be cited. Welford[322] has reported that in persons over 65 years of age, movement patterns involving reversal of perceptual space relationships are learned much more slowly than any other type of skill — a finding which suggests that human flexibility in adapting to highly unusual spatial relationships declines with age more rapidly than ability to learn more normal perceptual-motor patterns.

In these first few chapters, we have pointed out some of the diversified aspects of the science of perception and motion, and some of the provocative questions they raise. We have centered our interest on the study of displaced vision, because we believe that this experimental procedure promises to contribute significantly to our understanding of how motion is made to conform to the spatial requirements of the environment. In the remaining chapters of the book, we shall present our own hypotheses of motion organization and its neural regulatory mechanisms, and describe our experiments on displaced visual feedback designed to test these hypotheses.

SUMMARY

1. Experimental spectacles and headgear using lenses, prisms, and mirrors to displace the visual field have a number of characteristics which limit their usefulness, including restricting the field of vision; disturbing normal accommodation, convergence, and divergence; inducing apparent movement with movements of the eyes, head, or body; and distorting normal relationships between eyes, head, and body. Effects of different types of displacement are not directly comparable when produced by different kinds of devices.

2. Experimental displacement produced general emotional and organic disturbances in addition to those produced by extraneous variables, undoubtedly because displacement disturbs basic regulatory systems.

3. Perceptual adaptation in inversion-reversal studies was partial, variable, incomplete, and dependent on motor adaptation in specific situations. These effects might be expected in view of the relative nature of passive perceptual judgments, which vary with many interrelated sensory and motor factors.

4. The motion basis of perception also was indicated by the specificity of adaptation to visual displacement. Very little transfer occurred from one situation to another.

5. No good comparisons were made between inversion, reversal, and inversion-reversal combined. Kohler thought inversion was more difficult, although his subjects adapted more slowly to reversal.

6. Adaptation to angular displacements of the visual field or locus of vision was very effective with small displacements, much less so with larger angles. Active manipulation and movement aided adaptation. These effects conform with our concept of normal ranges of angular displacement between vision and motion, within which performance is not disturbed.

7. The effects of displacement varied with different types of motion. The use of compensatory movements could change the nature of the adaptation.

8. Adaptation to displaced vision was not affected significantly by lack of knowledge of the conditions. Adaptation is apparently self-regulatory, motivated by the imposed noncorrespondence between vision and motion.

9. The most long-lasting after-effects of displacement occurred in relation to performances which had been most disturbed initially. Specific skills learned under displacement were retained almost perfectly for as long as two years.

10. Although a subhuman primate adapted fairly well to visual inversion, adaptation has never been observed in any other lower animal.

11. There are both learning and neurological interpretations of the phenomena of displaced vision. Learning interpretations stress the adaptation that takes place, but are weak in equating this experimentally induced process with original perceptual development in the infant. Neurological interpretations stress the nonadaptive nature of perceptual-motor coordinations in lower animals, and suggest that these processes are primarily genetically determined, in man as well as animals.

CHAPTER 7

EXPERIMENTAL FOUNDATIONS OF NEUROGEO-METRIC THEORY

In this chapter we shall introduce the main concepts of neurogeometric theory of perceptual-motor integration, and indicate some of the principal experimental findings that have helped define it. In the latter part of the chapter we shall describe our first experiments on behavior in displaced visual fields, which were designed to test some of our hypotheses. In these first experiments, visual inversion was achieved by using fixed prisms. Much more flexible experimental designs were possible in later studies carried out with closed-circuit television techniques.

NEUROGEOMETRIC THEORY

The set of concepts which we refer to as neurogeometric theory has been developed gradually over a number of years as an alternative to standard psychological descriptions of behavior organization in animals and man. We have felt for a long time that there were a number of serious inadequacies in orthodox behavior theory. For one thing, there never has been a satisfactory account of the spatial organization of motion. All the years of theorizing about the nature and origins of space perception have not yielded one good concrete idea about how it is possible for a man or an animal to follow with its eyes, hands, head, or body an object moving across its field of vision. An apparently simple movement such as this can be made with great precision, and is subject to continual corrective adjustments to make the motion pattern conform with the stimulus pattern. To explain such space-structured motion, standard behavior theory has nothing to offer except the concepts of reflex psychology, with its sequential linking of in-line stimulus-response arcs. We are convinced that the temporally organized reflex model does not fit the spatially organized motions that we observe.

Another problem in psychology is the general inadequacy of animal-based learning theory when we attempt to apply it to human behavior organization. Human perceptual-motor skills are specifically organized and infinitely variable. They are multidimensional, in the sense that they are made up of movements of different types, and can be described and understood only when we know something of the properties of these different components and how they interact in organized motion patterns. It is unrealistic to say that man acquires all of his complex response patterns through step-by-step learning or conditioning processes, made effective by discrete reinforcements. Yet this is the dead end to which learning psychology leads us, for it offers no organizational principles other than the concepts of association, conditioning, and time-coded reinforcement.

A third problem which has influenced our thinking is to account for the distinctive specialization of motion in the human system. We have felt that the make-up of man differs sufficiently from that of other animals to warrant more in the way of research designs and theoretical interpretations than those derived from the behavior of rats or dogs or pigeons. By no stretch of the imagination can we believe that highly precise and highly articulated human behavior is organized according to the effects of extrinsic rewards or reinforcements or chance contiguity of stimuli and responses. On the contrary, we believe that the significant patterns of human behavior are organized intrinsically according to the spatial requirements of the environment and are motivated primarily by these same requirements. The facts of learning and reinforcement do no more than suggest conditions under which perceptual-motor coordinations will be reorganized or integrated with physiological needs; these facts do not define the original regulatory mechanisms of patterned behavior.

Finally, we have felt that a theory of motion is not complete unless it can be related to a meaningful description of the sensori-neuromotor system. In this connection, we have been impressed with the very limited relationships that can be demonstrated between the so-called associative mechanisms of the brain and specific properties of response. For a number of reasons we have been led to reject the concept of the cerebral cortex as an associative system and to think of it as primarily a reactive or neuromotor system, organized relative to the spatial patterns of the sensory surfaces. We believe that the cortex represents one of several levels of motion regulation, and that its growth and proliferation in the human species was correlated with man's progressively more complex perceptually controlled manipulations in the use of tools and related symbolic operations.

With this general orientation to the problems of perception and motion, we have formulated a number of basic propositions:

1. The spatial organization of motion depends on the ability of the living system to react to differences in stimulation between specific points. These might be two points on the same receptor surface, two points located on two different receptors, or one point associated with an effector and another associated with a receptor. To carry out this function, the internuncial neurons of the central nervous system are associated at their dendrite endings with two specific points, and react only when a difference in neural activity exists between these two points. Thus the basic mode of action of internuncial neurons is that of differential detection instead of simple conduction.

2. The temporal organization of motion – its changes in spatial patterning in time – depends on the continuous barrage of sensory feedback signals from the various receptors of the body, which compare a motion and its effects with stimulus patterns of the environment. This monitoring function of the feedback mechanisms provides an element of self-regulation in motion organization which accounts for both its flexibility and its precision.

3. Motion is multidimensional; it is made up of three primary movement components – posture, transport, and manipulation – which are integrated into complex motion patterns. These components are differentially controlled at different levels of the nervous system, and in relation to different types of stimuli. Posture is regulated by gravitational stimulation; transport movements, by differences in stimulation between the two sides of the body; and manipulative movements, by the properties of hard space (objects, surfaces). In addition, motion integration demands that each component be regulated relative to the other components.

4. Behavior is motivated primarily by the demands of its motion systems. Differences in stimulation lead to response, and responses generate further differences in stimulation. Moreover, the reciprocal musculature controlling the members of the body and specialized receptors such as the eyes do not fixate a member rigidly, but rather generate continuous minimal movements which provide the sensory surfaces with the differential patterns necessary for response. When any marked displacement occurs between sensory patterns and patterns of motion, the individual is highly motivated to adjust its motions to achieve some degree of conformity with the environment. Further, even those behavior patterns that satisfy physiological needs are defined not by the drive states alone but by the nature of the motion systems as well; for example, eating and drinking responses are quite different in different animal species. Thus the patterning of behavior represents an integrated effect of physiological and perceptual-motor variables.

5. Tool-using behavior in man represents an extension of unaided motion, and is regulated equivalently by the neurogeometric detectors and the sensory feedback mechanisms of the body according to the spatial requirements of the environment.

6. The neurogeometric detectors of the brain are the heritable anatomical units which account for genetically determined behavior. In the process of evolution, the procedures of natural selection have favored neurogeometric neurons that are highly sensitive to differences in stimuli, so that we see progressively greater efficiency in articulating body movements to conform to stimulus patterns. Thus the behavior patterns that are characteristic of man do not depend on progressive refinement of the receptor systems; the eyes and the ears, for example, are highly developed in many subhuman forms. Rather, human behavior patterns depend on refinement of interrelated neuromotor systems so that sensory discriminations can be translated into highly differentiated and precisely integrated responses.

Neurogeometric Detector Neurons

The notion that there are specific neurons in the brain which detect spatial differences in patterns of stimulation and regulate movement accordingly is based on the results of many different types of experiments. The idea was derived originally from a series of studies of visual tracking and orientation in animals,[250–254, 262, 263, 266, 269, 313] some of which, particularly the study of Smith and Bridgman,[263] led us to hypothesize that in the midbrain of animals there are neurons that specifically con-

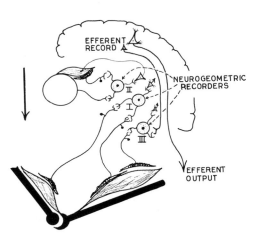

Figure 7-1. Types of neurogeometric detector neurons. Three types are assumed: intrareceptor (I), interreceptor (II), and efferent-afferent (III) detectors.

trol direction of response in relation to direction of stimulus movement in the visual field.

The primary assumption of neurogeometric theory is that the internuncial neurons of the central nervous system are organized so as to detect differences in stimulation between two points on the body. We assume that these detector neurons are anatomically related at their dendrite endings with two specific pathways, related to two loci of stimulation. When there is a difference in excitation at the two input points, the neurogeometric detector is excited. When there is no difference, the neuron does not respond. We further postulate three types of such neurogeometric detectors, as indicated in Figure 7-1. Type I are intrareceptor detectors, which record differences in stimulation between two points on the same receptor surface, such as the eye or skin. Type II are interreceptor detectors, which react to differences in stimulation existing between two points in two different receptor systems, such as the eye and skin, or skin and kinesthetic system. The Type

II detectors shown in the diagram detect differences between specific loci of stimulation on the retina and in the kinesthetic receptors of the eye muscles. Type III are efferent-afferent detectors, which compare differences between an efferent impulse leading to a given muscular response and a sensory feedback impulse resulting from that response.

Evidence for Neurogeometric Systems

The existence of neurogeometric detectors was demonstrated indirectly by a series of experiments on visual nystagmus movements in the guinea pig.[263] Figure 7-2 diagrams the critical stages of this study. The pig, with one eye

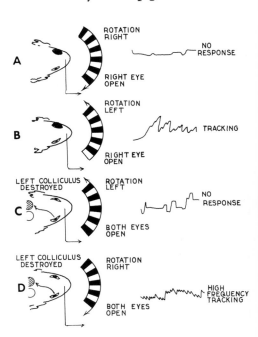

Figure 7-2. Neurological study of optical pursuit reactions in the guinea pig. A. With the left eye covered and rotation of the visual field to the right, no tracking responses are given. B. With the left eye covered and rotation to the left, tracking occurs. C. With the left colliculus destroyed and rotation to the left, no tracking occurs. D. With the left colliculus destroyed and rotation to the right, high frequency tracking responses occur.

covered, was placed in a rotating cylinder lined with a pattern of black and white stripes. When this striated field was moved toward the side of the seeing eye, no patterned response occurred. But when the stripes were rotated toward the side of the covered eye (in the diagram, toward the left), we observed precise tracking motions of the head (head nystagmus), as indicated by the movement record in Figure 7-2,B. In other words, a guinea pig with monocular vision tracked stimuli moving in one direction but not in the other; one eye controlled tracking movements in only one direction.

The next stage of the study was to produce surgical lesions in one superior colliculus. Because each colliculus receives fibers mainly from the eye on the opposite side, destroying the left colliculus, as shown in Figure 7-2,C, had the effect of almost completely blinding the right eye. Now stimulus movement toward the left produced no patterned response, but movement toward the right produced high frequency tracking responses. Each colliculus contains specific neurons that control tracking movements toward that side. From studies on decorticate guinea pigs, we know that the differential sensitivity of these midbrain neurons that control directional head tracking is very refined — so refined, in fact, that we suspect that single central neurogeometric detectors define the limits of visual acuity.[252]

While we believe that the slow pursuit phase of visual nystagmus is regulated by Type I detectors, associated with adjacent retinal points, we believe that the patterning of the responses shown in Figure 7-2 offers presumptive evidence of the action of Type II or Type III detectors. The nystagmus recorded from the pig with one eye covered was quite normal, showing the slow pursuit phase with the saccadic returns interspersed at normal intervals. When nystagmus was elicited from pigs

with collicular lesions, however, the pattern was quite different, as shown in Figure 7-2,D. In this case, the frequency of the saccadic jerks was greatly increased. Destruction of the midbrain nucleus had effected a change that was not entirely visual, for it was not produced by covering one eye.

There is good evidence that the mechanisms controlling the slow and fast phases of nystagmus are quite distinct, and that the fast phase is triggered centrally.[70] We believe that the central regulatory mechanism is a detector cell that makes comparisons across the midline of the body, either of two sources of afferent stimulation or of one afferent source and an efferent record of motor impulses. When one nucleus was destroyed in the guinea pig, one source of stimulation was eliminated, resulting in more frequent discharges from the Type II or Type III detectors controlling the saccadic jerks. This assumption is borne out by the fact that these fast discrete movements occurred in both directions in the record shown in Figure 7-2,C, even though there were no pursuit movements in that record.

There are many other observations showing that spatially organized visual responses are regulated by lower visual centers. Both cats and guinea pigs showed a high degree of visual acuity after the visual areas of the cortex were removed.[251, 254, 266, 269] They reacted to moving visual stimuli with as high a degree of precision as normal animals. Further, these decorticate animals reacted to apparent movement of the visual field, produced by stroboscopic illumination.[253, 265] The critical condition for these directionally controlled responses is for a pattern of spatial stimulus differences to exist. The decorticate animals did not distinguish between a continually presented pattern and an intermittent one, supplied stroboscopically. We believe that the best explanation for these effects is that there are neurons in the visual centers which are sensitive to differences between specific spatial points. There is some direct neurological evidence for this conclusion in the work of Lettvin, Maturana, McCulloch, and Pitts,[164] who found neurons in the frog's brain that responded only to moving visual stimuli, and others that were sensitive to border and contrast effects in visual stimulation. The implication is that internuncial neurons in the visual centers do not respond automatically when a certain receptor cell (or a group of cells) is stimulated, but rather react only when a stimulus difference exists between two retinal points.

There are a number of other sensorimotor phenomena that to us indicate the existence of neural mechanisms that make bilateral sensory comparisons, mechanisms that we have called Type II neurogeometric detectors. For example, continuously controlled movements of symmetrical members, such as the hands or eyes, can be performed simultaneously only if the two movement patterns are parallel or mirror images. The old trick of patting the head with one hand while rubbing the stomach with the other can be performed by some individuals only because the pats are discrete movements that can be integrated to some extent with the more continuously controlled rubbing movements. We assume that symmetrical movements are regulated by Type II neurons associated with points on both sides of the body, which detect angular displacements of sensory feedback to control the symmetry. Another example deals with bilateral sensory transfer and adaptation effects, when stimulation of a point on one side of the body results in changes in sensitivity at the corresponding point on the other side. A third example is the high precision of the ocular system in detecting binocular space differences; convergence movements are initiated by binocular dis-

crepancies smaller than a single retinal receptor.

Direct evidence for the existence of Type II detectors comes from the work of Galambos,[95] who has demonstrated that there are neurons in the auditory centers of the medulla that are exquisitely sensitive to differences in time or phase of sound stimuli activating the two ears. Such central detection would provide the basis for auditory localization. It is known that auditory localization depends on continuous minimal head movements, to avoid adaptation effects that would eliminate the binaural differences. This situation exemplifies the central concept of neurogeometric theory — that the organism patterns its movements spatially by reacting to spatial differences in stimulation, and also generates movements continually to provide further differences in stimulation.

We assume that the integration of high-speed transport movements (such as those found in walking, running, jumping, righting movements, and so on) with postural support movements is regulated by detector neurons that compare bilateral differences in stimulation. These complex coordinate and compensatory interactions are of genetic origin, and depend on integration of sensory effects from the optical, vestibular, and somesthetic systems. We believe that the central neural mechanisms responsible for these interactions — for the starting and stopping of ballistic transport and acceleratory movements, and their interactions with postural dynamics — are neurogeometric detector cells related to the different sensory systems that develop in the course of maturation. These transport-postural interactions are much more inflexible in lower animals than in higher. For example, the effects of vision on postural reactions become less pronounced and more variable as one ascends the animal scale. Also, the asymmetries in posture and patterned motion that result from unilateral injuries to receptor systems are more demonstrable in lower animals.

Our assumption that there are efferent-afferent (Type III) neurogeometric detectors is based on both behavioral and neurological observations. As an example of the latter, Magni, Melzack, Moruzzi, and Smith[172] have demonstrated that activity in the pyramidal system of the cat's brain has direct electroneural effects in the dorsal column sensory nuclei. Jabbur and Towe[139] have reported similar observations. We would conclude that neurons of the sort that we have described as Type III detectors are involved, to compare an efferent record with afferent sensory feedback.

The basic hypothesis underlying all of these more specific assumptions is that of differential neural function, which we propose as an alternative to the general idea that neural integration is accomplished at the synapse. No one has ever demonstrated how the blank spaces between neurons could facilitate some impulses and inhibit others with the precision and speed demanded by ordinary perceptual-motor responses. Precision and speed of motion patterns do not depend on learning, but are characteristics of motion that are genetically determined. To account for the development of such patterns in the normal course of maturation, we need a mechanism of definite anatomic structure which can develop in evolution and is subject to the processes of natural selection. It is our belief that a differential neuron fulfills these requirements better than a synapse. An internuncial cell can be assumed to have a specific evolutionary history related to its precision in detecting space differences in stimulation on the receptor surfaces of the body and in regulating the direction of motion in terms of such detected differences. Evolutionary progress has been marked by the elaboration and refinement of the neurogeometric detection systems of the brain.

Although the emphasis in this book is on experimental analyses of displaced vision, this is but one type of problem that can be related to neurogeometric theory. There are many questions about motion and its neural regulatory mechanisms which are not dealt with satisfactorily by synaptic and reflex doctrines and would benefit from a new approach. For example, how is the cerebral cortex related to motion? Why do the boundaries of the motor cortex and of the sensory cortex reflect bodily structure in the special functional but distorted pattern that has been mapped out? Why are there multiple sensory and motor mechanisms of the cortex? Why are there multiple projection systems related to the retina and to the cochlea? (To regulate different movement systems and their interactions?) Why do the various sensory projection areas of the cortex vary in size in different animals, not according to the size or precision of the various receptor systems, but as a function of the motility of the animal and its ability to articulate spatially organized movements? How are the motor systems of the cortex related to the basic postural and gravity-controlled movements of subcortical mechanisms? What is the meaning of the bilateral symmetry of the brain in relation to motion, and why would a bilaterally symmetrical brain system evolve if its dynamics were based only on synaptic interchanges? How do we account for the structural differentiation of the internuncial cells of the brain, and why is it that the dendrite pattern of such cells is so highly variable?

While we can not answer these questions in detail, we think that a reasonable first assumption is that the anatomical plan of the brain reflects the functional space organization of the body as a motion system, and is so organized to regulate such motion by neurogeometric differential detectors. Further, the functional organization of motion can best be described in terms of the postural, transport, and manipulative movement components which are integrated to make up all the different motion patterns of the body.

Types of Movements and Their Neurogeometric Regulation

Some of our first serious thinking about the nature of patterned motion was motivated by the necessity during World War II of designing special operational and training equipment which would optimize the pattern of behavior of the performing individual. Prior to those years, little attention had been paid in psychology to the make-up and regulation of motion, other than the analyses of Dodge[66] and Stetson[291] of tense and ballistic movements and their variations. Faced with the very real problems of providing workable and efficient perceptual displays and motion-machine systems for military devices, some of us turned away from association and learning psychology, which contributed little to the solution of our problems, and tried to develop new concepts about the fundamental organization of human behavior.

It became apparent to us that motion is multidimensional, and that the dynamics of perceptual-motor patterns depend on the regulation of the different components and their interactions in the patterns. We also were convinced that all movement components are space-structured, and that they are differentially controlled in terms of different patterns of stimulation. The analysis worked out, which has proved useful in research and meaningful in theorizing, describes motion as made up of postural, transport, and manipulative components, controlled respectively by gravitational stimulation, bilateral differences in stimulation on the two sides of the body,

and the spatial properties of hard space — objects, surfaces, and so on. Gravitational control in the vertical axis and bilateral control in the right-left axis provide the basis for the many axial effects we see in movement organization. Some of these will be described later in connection with our studies of displaced vision.

According to our neurogeometric theory, the brain mechanisms of motion have evolved from primitive postural and body transport systems, as first formed in primitive limbless animals. As the higher animals with limbs, mobile head and face have evolved, systems of refined transport and manipulative movements have been differentiated from these primitive posturally organized mechanisms. Further, we believe that the course of evolution of prehistoric man in the use of tools further elaborated the space-organized motion systems to produce the specialized brain of modern man. We view the mammalian brain as a multidimensional motion system organized for the differential regulation of space-structured postural, transport, and manipulative movements. Even the higher cortical centers — which have long been described as associative centers — we believe to be primarily motion centers, organized relative to the sensory surfaces.

The drawing in Figure 7-3 indicates the three movement components, and the levels of the central nervous system where each is controlled. We believe that posture is controlled through the older subcortical mechanisms of the medulla, midbrain, and cerebellum. Transport mechanisms are bilaterally differentiated from these postural mechanisms and are regulated by the new cerebellum and parts of the cortex. Also, there are neurogeometric systems in the cerebellum that integrate the transport movements with posture, and others in the cortex which integrate transport with manipulation. Manipulative move-

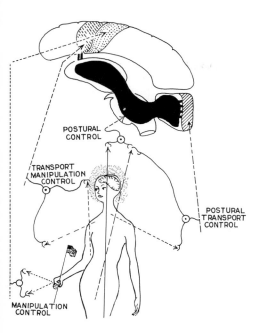

Figure 7-3. Three levels of neurogeometric differentiation and integration of motion. Posture is regulated by older subcortical structures, transport by bilateral structures of the new cerebellum and cortex, and manipulation by the cortex. Cerebellar mechanisms integrate posture with transport, and cortical mechanisms integrate transport with manipulation.

ments are regulated specifically by the cerebral cortex and are relatively independent of the postural system. They depend on differential control of space-organized motions of receptor systems for their precision and organization.

CONTROLLED OPTICAL STUDIES OF INVERTED VISION

In the remainder of this chapter, we shall describe our first experiments on displaced vision, in which we used fixed prisms to invert the visual field. These experiments have been reported in part by Rhule and Smith.[217, 218] Although many different kinds of experiments and observations had contributed

to the development of our theory, we looked upon the displaced vision experiment as an exceptionally good technique for testing some of our ideas about the spatial organization of motion. We were interested in analyzing quantitatively the effects of visual inversion on different types of motion, and determining whether complete adaptation could be achieved — a point which had never been settled satisfactorily. We wanted to compare the course of adaptation under continuous exposure to inversion with adaptation under intermittent exposure, in order to determine whether periods of normal vision interfered with adaptation to inverted vision. We wanted to know whether inversion had differential effects on motions of different complexity, on the travel and manipulative components, and on direct and compensatory motions. We planned to test for after-effects of the visual inversion as assessed by means of transfer phenomena. Finally, we wanted to determine whether perceptual pretraining in reading in an inverted field would facilitate learning to write in the inverted field.

Procedures

In order to study the effects of visual inversion without the side-effects induced by the wearing of experimental spectacles, we limited the study to handwriting performances which the subject could view through an inverting prism fixed in a frame above the writing surface. The six-inch tank prism provided an undistorted inverted visual field 50 to 60 degrees wide, which was not affected by movements of the subject except for minor changes in size of the field. In order to measure travel and manipulative movements separately, an electronic handwriting analyzer was used. The arrangement of the optical system and the analyzer is diagrammed in Figure 7-4.

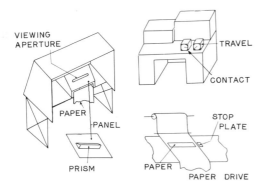

Figure 7-4. Diagram of the electronic motion-analysis instrumentation and prism arrangement for studying inverted writing.

The handwriting analyzer used in these studies was an adaptation of the electronic analyzers described in Chapter 1. The subject wrote with an electrically conductive pencil on Teledeltos conductive paper, which was passed under a plastic plate containing a two-inch wide writing aperture. When the subject made contact with the paper, a subthreshold electric current passed through his body, the pencil, and the paper, activating a time clock which measured contact time. When the pencil was lifted between letters or symbols, the contact time clock stopped and a travel time clock was activated. At the end of one line of writing, the subject touched a stop plate which stopped both clocks. With this device, very accurate measures were obtained of total contact time and total travel time for each line of writing.

A photograph of the work booth, writing unit, and inverting prism used in these experiments is shown in Figure 7-5. The subject shown here is holding his pencil somewhat below the writing aperture. During experimental trials, the black cloth shown thrown over the top of the booth was dropped behind the subject to produce a black enclosed work space, the walls of which were but dimly visible. The writing surface was illuminated by a light mounted under the panel containing the prism.

Three separate experiments were carried out, two involving approximately the same total exposure time to inverted vision, and the third designed to assess the effects of perceptual pretraining. In the first study, subjects worked almost continuously for 12 hours performing drawing and writing tasks in an inverted visual field. In the second experiment, subjects worked one-half hour per day for 20 days in the same tasks. In the third study, 12 subjects were trained for one-half hour per day for five days to read material seen through the inverting prism, and then were trained to write in the inverted field. A control group of 12 subjects practiced writing in the inverted field without the pretraining in reading.

The tasks used were writing lines of *a*'s, drawing lines of triangles, and making lines of dots, in each case making eight characters to a line. The writing paper was moved forward after each line to present a fresh writing surface. Each experimental trial included three lines of each character, with the order of tasks within trials randomized by trials. Half of the subjects in each of the first two experiments wrote in their

Figure 7-5. Photograph of the arrangement of inverting prism and electronic handwriting analyzer used to study the effects of inverting the visual field on the component movements of dotting, writing, and drawing motions.

normal fashion, so that the characters appeared inverted (triangles appeared point down) in the inverted visual field. The other half wrote in a compensatory way, that is, they wrote upside-down *a*'s and point-down triangles so that they would appear upright in the inverted field.

In the 12-hour study, six graduate and undergraduate student subjects worked from 7:30 A.M. to 10:30 P.M. in one day, with one-half hour off for lunch and again for dinner, during which periods they were blindfolded. During the rest of the day, 12 hours in all, they remained in the work booth performing blocks of about five trials separated by rest periods. Three performed direct movements, and three, compensatory.

In the 20-day study, 12 student subjects worked for one-half hour each day for 20 days. Six of these subjects used direct movements that appeared inverted, and six used compensatory movements that appeared upright. Half of each group were male, and half, female; the groups also were balanced approximately for age and college class. After completion of the 20 training days, the subjects in this experiment were run for an extra period on the twenty-first day to test for transfer effects between direct and compensatory performances. Those who had trained with upright movements were tested for performance with compensatory movements, and those who had trained with compensatory were tested with upright.

In all experiments, undergraduate subjects were given extra points toward their final achievement level in psychology courses for their participation. All subjects were instructed to try to achieve a normal level of legibility and quality in writing and drawing, and were asked to judge the quality of their work as they performed. The 20-day subjects wrote at least one *a* and drew at least one triangle with normal vision prior to each day's experimental trials, and then

were asked to try to achieve this level of legibility with inverted vision. During their working trials, they were given periodic instructions to produce characters equal in quality to their normal writing.

In order to obtain quantitative measures of normal travel and contact times in the tasks used, six subjects were tested each day for ten days with normal vision. Each day they wrote three lines of *a*'s, drew three lines of triangles, and made three lines of dots.

For purposes of data analysis, each subject's median contact and travel times in each task were used for his scores for a particular trial. In each case, this would mean selecting the median contact and travel times from the measures obtained from three lines of writing or drawing. To indicate performance in blocks of trials or of groups of subjects, the means of these median scores were used.

Perceptual Reorientation

This study is one of the first investigations of sustained exposure to inverted vision in which the subjects did not have to overcome geometric discrepancies in head and eye movements that hinder the establishment of space constancy. Our expectations were that some perceptual reorientation would be achieved in relatively brief exposure times, if these movement discrepancies during inversion were prevented.

The results of both the 12-hour and 20-day experiments showed that all subjects but two achieved a very high quality of performance in the allotted practice time. Figure 7-6 compares performance on the first day and the last day of two typical subjects in the 20-day experiment. One wrote upright characters, and one wrote inverted. On the first day of the experiment, the patterns of writing both triangles and *a*'s were disorganized, with the attempts at

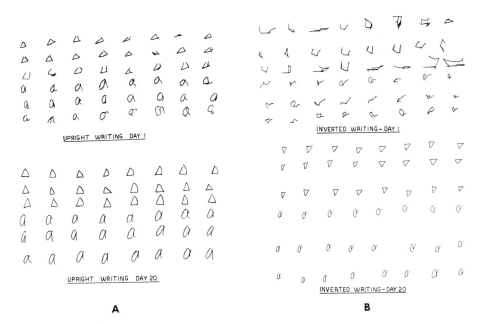

Figure 7-6. Samples of writing and drawing in two subjects on the first and last days of the 20-day experiment. A. Upright performance. B. Inverted performance.

inverted writing showing much the greater disturbance. By the twentieth day, both subjects were writing and drawing in a fairly reputable manner.

The subjects in the continuous 12-hour study were asked to make general reports on "how they were doing" and "what they observed" during the course of the work day. The gist of these reports are summarized here.

Subject 1 (upright writing and drawing):

"More difficulty with triangles than *a*'s and dots; worried about effect of inversion on school work; want to work continuously; (noon) still having trouble with triangles."

Subject 2 (upright writing and drawing):

"Triangles a lot harder to draw; interference experienced first with *a*'s and then with triangles; do not seem to be fatigued; *a*'s harder at first, but now triangles; triangles are getting sloppy; take more effort; (2:10 P.M.) seem to be governed by what I see now; (4:45 P.M.) seem to be less troubled with triangles and

more with *a*'s; some sort of conflict between visual cues and how I feel; at first drew as they were supposed to be, now am beginning to draw as I see them; had a lot of trouble with *a*'s at first, then all of a sudden they seemed to get better."

Subject 3 (upright writing and drawing):

"Triangles are bad; it seems as if the movement used in drawing triangles is different from that used normally."

Subject 4 (compensatory writing and drawing):

"Letter *a* causes the most trouble; some confusion in drawing triangles and writing *a*'s; (late in day) seem to be writing with the left hand."

Subject 5 (compensatory writing and drawing):

"Trouble and confusion in drawing: (afternoon break) forget how to make characters."

Subject 6 (compensatory writing and drawing):

"Confusion with both *a*'s and triangles; (11 A.M.) sense of vertical direction lost while drawing; (6 P.M.) triangles now easier to draw than *a*'s."

Some of the comments made by subjects in the 20-day study who used upright writing are as follows:

"Thinking about how to draw slows me up; sometimes I feel like I am not writing *a*'s but something else; the first *a* of the line causes trouble; I feel like I am just watching the *a*'s, my hand is doing it; I have a feeling I am in control of making dots, not so with *a*'s and triangles; with these, I expect the movement to make upside down symbols; most of the time I feel like I am watching the symbols being drawn rather than drawing them myself; if I make a mistake, it takes a while to correct it; where the pencil goes the wrong way, I have difficulty in correcting it; it's not a matter of right or wrong, I expect to see what I draw as inverted."

Comments of the six subjects who used compensatory writing and drawing are as follows:

"Symbols are more automatic and easier to draw when I first start; a slight speedup in drawing motion helps, but one can't go too fast; (on the last day of the study) not much confusion anymore; have to slow up occasionally to improve quality of what I draw; (fifteenth day) frustrated at first, now feel organized; (last day) feels like I am drawing with the other hand; drawing now very automatic, never get confused; though I know I am drawing *backwards*, the symbols appear natural; (last day) once in a while I still get confused, occasionally make an error, but it seems quite natural, almost automatic; am still aware that I am drawing upside-down though the symbols look normal, kinesthetic sense becoming associated with vision; now it seems the symbols drawn under the prism are more natural than what I normally draw and perceive as a triangle."

From these limited reports, it appears that the subjects who used compensatory writing and drawing achieved a better perceptual reorientation than those who wrote upright characters. Only one subject of the latter group (Subject 2 of the 12-hour study) reported experiencing some reorientation, when he said he reached a point of drawing

the characters as he saw them. Two of the subjects of the 12-hour study and three of the 20-day study who used compensatory movements reported that everything looked natural even though they knew they were writing upside-down (or backwards).

We judge from these reports that it is possible to achieve some perceptual reorientation in the specific performance field with controlled conditions of inverted vision within 10 to 12 hours of exposure, whether it is continuous or intermittent. This effect apparently occurs faster and more decisively when compensatory patterns of motion are used.

In both of these studies, we obtained reports to the effect that the subject felt that he did not own or control his own movement; that he got a feeling of disembodied movement; or that he was writing or drawing with the other side of his body. Apparently the disturbance of geometric organization of motion patterns affected all levels of neural interaction including those concerned with body integration and body image.

Individual Differences in Adaptation

We have been interested in examining some of the individual differences that occur in adaptation to displaced vision because of the limited number of subjects observed in most of the earlier studies. We shall present here individual data from the six subjects in the 12-hour study. These subjects saw nothing except the inverted performance field during the entire study, and the major portion of their manual movements during that time, except for eating movements, were timed.

The learning curves shown in Figures 7-7, 7-8, 7-9, and 7-10 indicate individual performance throughout the experimental day. These graphs indicate, respectively, contact times for writing *a*'s, travel times for writing *a*'s, contact

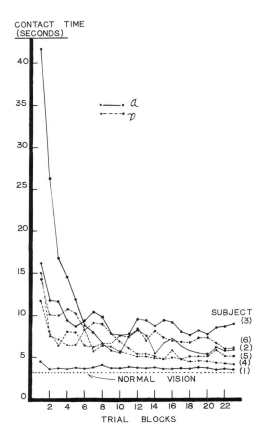

CONTACT TIME
(SECONDS)

Figure 7-7. Learning curves showing duration
of contact movements in writing *a*'s for six
subjects in the 12-hour experiment.

subjects were slowest for all tasks and
both types of movement. However, the
subject who was extremely slow initially (Subject 2) was not the slowest at
the end of the day. The relative position
of subjects at the end of the day was
very nearly the same in all of these
graphs. One of the subjects (Subject 1)
showed very little disturbance in performance times throughout the course
of the experiment. His scores sometimes were faster than the normal means
established by the six subjects working
with normal vision. Several of the subjects approached normal performance
time in these writing and drawing tasks
by the end of the day, and all six of
them were making dots faster (both
contact and travel times) at the end of
the 12 hours practice than the established normal mean.

In general these curves are typical
learning curves, showing progressive increase in speed and tending to level off
during the allotted practice time. These
observations confirm Snyder and Pron-

times for drawing triangles, and travel
times for drawing triangles. It should
be noted that the ordinates are scaled
differently for contact times and travel
times. The broken horizontal line drawn
through each graph indicates the level
achieved by subjects tested with normal
vision. Each point plotted on these
graphs indicates the mean of a block of
six trials.

These graphs show a wide range of
individual variation in initial performance which gradually decreased throughout the day. At first there was more
variation shown in writing *a*'s, but at
the end of the day, the triangle task
showed greater variability. The slowest

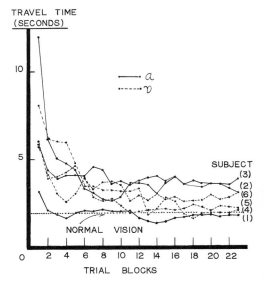

TRAVEL TIME
(SECONDS)

Figure 7-8. Learning curves showing duration
of travel movements in writing *a*'s for six subjects in the 12-hour experiment.

ko's[275] findings that their subject became progressively more efficient at performing manual tasks during the period of inverted vision. There are no sudden shifts in our learning curves that would indicate that a sudden or general perceptual reorientation took place. Some subjects adapted faster than others, and some showed considerably more variability than others, but all showed a general increase in efficiency from the beginning of the day to the end.

One person who started to act as a subject in this 12-hour experiment was dismissed because of inability to perform. He stated that he just could not do the task. He did not appear to be over-emotional, but his performance was seriously disorganized. No other sub-

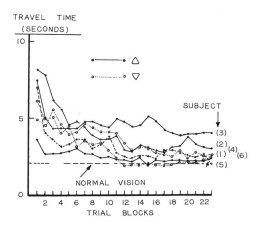

Figure 7-10. Learning curves showing duration of travel movements in drawing triangles for six subjects in the 12-hour experiment.

jects became ill or particularly disturbed, notwithstanding the grueling nature of the 12-hour study. At times some of the subjects showed the effects of boredom and fatigue, but recovered from these let-downs within the short rest periods allowed. The fact that they kept on and became more efficient testifies to the general motivating conditions of the experimental task.

Adaptation with Continuous and Intermittent Inversion

Most of the prior studies of displaced vision have been based on the assumption that continuous exposure would lead to faster adaptation because periods of normal vision would interfere with the learning process in displaced visual fields. Not all experimenters made this assumption. Wooster,[334] for example, felt that intermittent practice was quite satisfactory. Our own expectation was that intermittent exposure to displaced vision would produce the same general level of adaptation as an equal period of continuous exposure. This expectation was based on the assumed specificity of the directional and geometric properties of

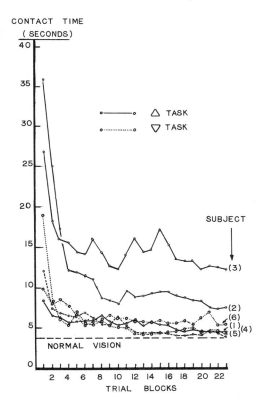

Figure 7-9. Learning curves showing duration of contact movements in drawing triangles for six subjects in the 12-hour experiment.

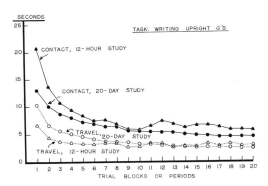

Figure 7-11. Learning curves for duration of contact and travel movements in writing *a*'s upright in the 12-hour and 20-day experiments.

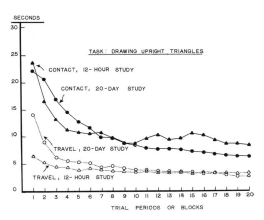

Figure 7-12. Learning curves for duration of contact and travel movements in drawing upright (point up) triangles in the 12-hour and 20-day experiments.

the movements to be learned in the displaced visual field.

The pertinent comparisons to be made here are between the curves of learning for the continuous 12-hour exposure, and for the 20-day intermittent exposure. Figures 7-11, 7-12, 7-13, and 7-14 compare the mean durations of contact and travel movements for successive blocks of trials in the two studies. For the 12-hour study, each point is the mean of six trials, which represented approximately one-half hour exposure time. Only the first 20 of these values have

been plotted. The points plotted for the 20-day study represent the mean durations of movements in different tasks during each daily half-hour exposure period. While the number of trials completed during a period was not fixed, it did not vary much from six. The curves in Figures 7-11 and 7-12 show mean contact and travel times for writ-

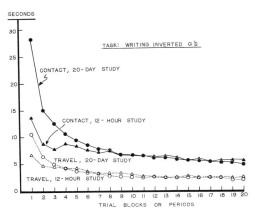

Figure 7-13. Learning curves for duration of contact and travel movements in writing inverted *a*'s in the 12-hour and 20-day experiments.

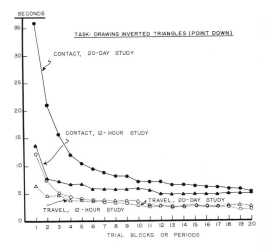

Figure 7-14. Learning curves for duration of contact and travel movements in drawing inverted (point down) triangles in the 12-hour and 20-day experiments.

ing *a*'s and drawing triangles upright in the inverted field, and the second two sets show mean times for making compensatory movements. The top pair of curves in each graph represent contact movements, and the bottom pair, travel movements.

In general, there were no consistent differences in the course of adaptation related to the type of exposure. In some cases, the 12-hour group performed faster, and in other cases, the 20-day group. The curves for the two conditions tended to level off at approximately the same level after the initial learning period. Because these learning curves for the 12-hour study were based on the performance of only three subjects (three for direct and three for compensatory movements), we replotted the data using the medians of the three values instead of the means, but the general nature of the curves was not altered significantly.

We judge from these comparisons that the adaptation to displaced vision is not interfered with by periods of normal vision alternating with practice in the inverted field. This is an argument against describing the process as one of general perceptual reorganization. Rather, the nature of the adaptation seems to be highly specific to the situation involved. The critical sensory and movement factors determine behavioral and perceptual adaptation in much the same way in both continuous and intermittent exposure to displacement. This specificity is consistent with our neurogeometric predictions.

Adaptation to Tasks of Different Complexity

One of our theoretical predictions was that visual inversion would have differential effects upon motions of different complexity. We define motion complexity in terms of the number of relative space discrepancies that must be resolved in order to perform the motion. Accordingly, simple motions, such as making dots, should be affected much less than more complex motions under comparable conditions of displaced vision.

The comparisons between the tasks of different complexity are presented in Figures 7-15 and 7-16, which plot the course of adaptation to inverted vision in terms of contact and travel times for the three different tasks. These data were taken from the 20-day study. The normal means for contact movements in writing *a*'s, drawing triangles, and making dots are shown by the small bars to the right in Figure 7-15, and the normal range for travel movements in all three tasks is shown by the dotted lines to the left in Figure 7-16. Normal travel movement means for the three tasks were almost identical.

These data comparing motions of different complexity are quite clear. Simple motions involving no compound change in direction were affected less by inversion of the visual field than more complex motions, and showed a more complete recovery from the effects of the inversion. Performance in making dots was slowed down only to a very limited degree, and recovered beyond the level we had established for normal vision. In contrast, performance in writing *a*'s and drawing triangles was greatly disturbed and leveled off above the normal level for contact movements, and approximately at normal level for travel movements.

One might wonder why the travel movements are affected by inversion of the visual field as much as they are, particularly the travel movements for making dots. These movements are not inverted in direction by the prism because they are made laterally across the field. However, all the travel movement curves showed an initial disturbance and a distinct recovery function. This effect was due in part to the localizing

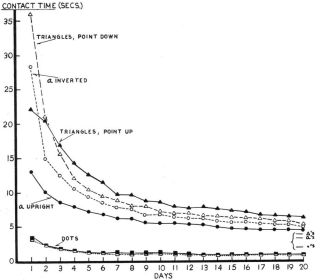

Figure 7-15. Learning curves for duration of contact movements of dotting, writing, and drawing tasks in the 20-day experiment. Normal means are shown at right.

precision needed in making each symbol. Even the dots had to be placed fairly accurately on the paper. Also, we know from many experimental analyses of motion that the different movement components are not independent but show the effects of interaction with other components. Thus a condition which would disturb one component would very likely have some effect on other components.

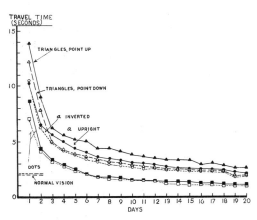

Figure 7-16. Learning curves for duration of travel movements of dotting, writing, and drawing tasks of the 20-day experiment. Normal range is shown at left.

Differential Effects of Inversion on Different Movements

In general, we predict that particular movements will be differentially affected by displacement of the visual field in terms of their relative directional properties and in terms of the geometric precision involved in them. In writing *a*'s or drawing triangles, we would expect a greater effect of visual inversion on the contact movements, inasmuch as these movements require more precise geometric control and vary more in direction than the travel movements. In making dots, however, we would expect a greater disturbance of the travel movements because the only precise control involved is in localizing.

The curves already presented in Figures 7-11, 7-12, 7-13, 7-14, 7-15, and 7-16 provide rough comparisons of the relative effects of inversion on contact and travel movements, as observed both in the 12-hour and 20-day studies. In writing *a*'s and drawing triangles, the initial effects of the inversion were greater and the recovery was slower and less complete for the contact movements than for travel movements. In making dots, the travel movements were more disturbed initially, although they recovered completely.

Statistical analyses were carried out on the data from the 20-day study to determine whether these relative effects were statistically significant. It was found that contact movements on the first day of inversion were significantly slower than normal contact movements for writing a's and drawing triangles, but not for making dots. The same relative effects were found for travel movements. That is, the observed elevation of the travel movements for making dots on the first experimental day was not statistically significant, although the travel movements for the other tasks were significantly slower. On the last experimental day, the contact movements for a's and triangles were still significantly slower than normal, but none of the travel movements were. In other words, our statistical summary permits us to say that contact movements for the two more complex tasks did not recover completely, but all of the travel movements did recover to normal level.

Comparison of Direct and Compensatory Movements

One of our original predictions was that compensatory movements would show greater initial disturbances in the inverted visual field, because the subjects using these reactions were not only adapting to distorted visual relationships, but were using unfamiliar motion patterns as well. However, we believed that the use of such compensatory reactions might aid the course of adaptation in the long run, because such patterns appear normal in the displaced field.

The data summarized in Figures 7-15 and 7-16 give a direct comparison of the use of direct and compensatory movements in the 20-day study. No consistent differences were found between the two types of response. In some cases, direct movements were faster, and in other cases, compensatory were faster. In the 12-hour study, two subjects using direct movements were extremely slow, but because there were only three subjects in each group, the differences between groups were not significant.

In spite of these equivocal results, we believe that compensatory reactions to displaced vision are critical in determining the nature of perceptual-motor adaptation. At this late date, we can not assess the role of compensatory movements in defining the observed results of the older studies of inversion and other displacements. We feel sure, however, that this role was of some significance, and that careful experimentation is necessary to clarify how compensatory reactions affect adaptation to displaced vision.

Degree of Final Adaptation

One of our interests in displaced vision experimentation is to determine the final level of adaptation that can be achieved. Many of the earlier investigators assumed that adaptation would eventually be general and complete, but none of the studies has ever proved this point conclusively. As a matter of fact, one general point of agreement among most observers has been that adaptation was still incomplete at the termination of the period of displacement.

Our own answer to this question from the limited data of these studies is that the degree of adaptation depends not only on the nature of the displacement, but on the nature of the motion, its complexity, direction and orientation. Simple motions may recover completely with but slight practice, but complex behavior patterns apparently may never recover. After 20 days of practice in an inverted field, our subjects had learned to write a's and draw triangles with considerable efficiency, but their contact times had leveled off at a level significantly higher than the normal mean.

We believe that Kohler[151] and Snyder and Pronko[275] were wrong in assuming that complete adaptation could be achieved. Their results as well as ours show that adaptation is specific to the situation, and variable according to the nature of the situation. In later chapters we shall present much more evidence to substantiate this view, and to clarify its details.

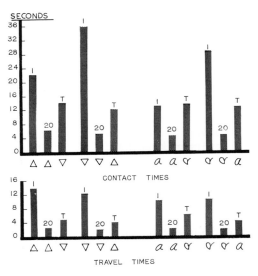

Figure 7-17. Transfer of training from direct to compensatory writing and from compensatory to direct writing in the different tasks of the 20-day experiment. Mean contact and travel times are shown for first day (1), twentieth day (20), and transfer test (T).

After-Effects and Transfer Effects

In our summary of reported after-effects of visual displacement in Chapter 6, we pointed out that such effects appear to be specific to particular performance situations, of generally limited duration, but more long-lasting in those performances that showed more disturbance under the displacement condition. In these studies of inverted writing, we observed no interference from the experimental practice with writing in normal visual fields. One subject in the 12-hour study who reported some perceptual reorientation during the day could write *a*'s and triangles with normal vision as soon as the experiment was over with apparently no interference.

One way to study after-effects is to test for transfer at the end of the period of practice with displaced vision. In our 20-day study, we tested all subjects on the twenty-first day for transfer effects from the movements they had been using to movements oriented in the opposite direction. That is, subjects who had trained with direct or upright movements were tested with compensatory movements, and those who had trained with compensatory were tested with upright. We wanted to know whether we would find interference (negative transfer) between the two types of performance, positive transfer, or no effect.

The transfer data are given in Figure 7-17. Three different measures are given

for each of the different conditions, as indicated by the sets of three bars: level of performance on Day 1, level of performance on Day 20, and transfer score. Contact times are given in the upper sets of bars, and travel times in the lower. Separate measures are given for upright and inverted triangles, and upright and inverted *a*'s. For example, the first three bars at the upper left indicate mean contact time for making upright triangles on the first day of inversion, and on the twentieth day of inversion, and the score for that same group of subjects in making inverted triangles on the twenty-first day. The second group of three bars indicates mean contact times on the first and twentieth days for the group that trained on inverted triangles and then their score when they transferred to upright triangles.

To interpret transfer effects, we need to compare the transfer score of one group with the initial and final scores of the group that trained on that same type of movement. That is, because the transfer test in the first group of bars is for inverted triangles, we should compare it with training scores in inverted triangles in the second group of bars to determine whether any saving resulted from another kind of training. When we make these reciprocal comparisons, we find that there was some positive transfer in all cases except for contact movements in making upright *a*'s. Training in making inverted *a*'s did not have any positive transfer to the making of upright *a*'s, as far as contact times were concerned, for the transfer test of this group was at the same level as initial performance of the group that trained in making upright *a*'s. In general, there was more positive transfer between upright and inverted movements in making triangles than in writing *a*'s. We would expect this, because the directional specificity of the triangle is less than that of the symbol *a*. No interference (negative transfer) effects occurred.

These results indicate that practice in inverted visual fields has only limited transfer effects for very similar motion patterns. This confirms our other observations of specificity of adaptation to conditions of visual displacement.

Effect of Perceptual Pretraining in Inverted Visual Fields

We have stated repeatedly in our discussion of displaced vision studies that the specific results do not warrant the conclusion that general perceptual reorganization occurs in disoriented visual fields, more or less independently of motor learning. This point of view is not shared by every one, either in the displaced vision field or in psychology generally. Snyder and Pronko's theory of perceptual learning, Ivo Kohler's theory of sensory conditioning, Wolfgang Köhler's[153] theory of gestalt reorganization, Kilpatrick's[147] theory of

attitudinal reorganization — all of these have been proposed to deal with the problems of perceptual-behavioral relationships, and all would assume that the significant adaptation to inverted vision is one of general perceptual reorganization.

The general validity of this assumption can be tested by determining whether a period of perceptual pretraining in a displaced visual field will facilitate adaptation of other modes of response under the same displacement condition. Siipola[239] reported such an experiment in her study of mirror drawing. She found that subjects who were permitted to observe the performance of other subjects in the mirror drawing task did better initially in the task than subjects who had no such perceptual pretraining. No other comparable experiments have been reported.

We carried out an experiment in which one group of 12 subjects were trained for one-half hour per day for five days in inverted reading under the inverting prism. A reading trainer was used to present printed matter in a controlled way, and quantitative data were obtained on improvement in performance during the five days. After this pretraining period, these subjects were trained in writing *a*'s, drawing triangles, and making dots in the same sort of inverted visual field. A control group of 12 subjects were trained in writing and drawing without the preliminary perceptual (reading) training. Our expectation was that only the most limited transfer would occur from the reading training to the writing tasks, because the two tasks involve entirely different systems of neurogeometric control.

The graph shown in Figure 7-18 illustrates the progress made in five days by the experimental group in learning to read inverted letters and words. The total number of units read correctly approximately doubled from the first

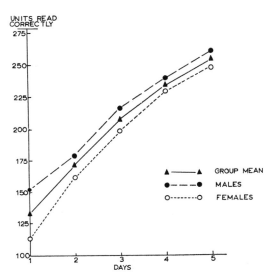

Figure 7-18. Learning curves for reading inverted letters and words.

day to the fifth. It is interesting that the male subjects did significantly better than the female subjects on the first day, and scored consistently better on every succeeding day.

When the experimental group and the control group were trained in writing and drawing tasks with inverted vision, it was found that the group that had been pretrained in reading did no better than the group that had not. As a matter of fact, the control group's scores were slightly better throughout the first few days of practice, but the differences were not statistically significant. The preliminary training in one perceptual-motor skill had absolutely no positive effect on learning another skill, even though reading and writing generally are assumed to be related activities.

Siipola's positive findings as to the effects of perceptual pretraining probably were due to the fact that her pretraining involved observation of the actual skill which the subjects later performed. We do not believe that these results contradict our own, for both can be interpreted as testifying to the specificity of perceptual-motor skills, in displaced visual fields as elsewhere.

SUMMARY

1. Neurogeometric theory is proposed as an alternative to standard psychological interpretations of behavior organization, in terms of the concepts of reflex arcs, association, conditioning, and reinforcement.

2. Neurogeometric theory proposes that the spatial organization of motion depends on differential neural function, that its temporal organization depends on sensory feedback regulation, and that there are three basic movement components — posture, transport, and manipulation — differentially regulated at different integrative levels of the brain. These motion systems provide a primary source of behavior motivation.

3. The evolution of man has been marked by the development of progressively more refined and interrelated neuromotor systems.

4. Evidence for differential neurogeometric detector neurons is derived in part from studies of head and eye nystagmus in animals. In guinea pigs, visual pursuit movements to one side are controlled by the superior colliculus on that same side and the opposite eye. We assume the existence of Type I (intrareceptor) detectors for that type of control. The fast or saccadic phase of nystagmus is controlled differently, presumably by Type II (interreceptor) or Type III (efferent-afferent) detector neurons, with connections across the midline.

5. Cells in the frog's brain which are sensitive only to visual movement, or to border and contrast effects, and cells in the cat's auditory centers which are sensitive to time differences in stimulation at the two ears function differen-

tially, providing evidence for our general concept of central neural function.

6. Differential function of internuncial neurons is a more useful concept in dealing with many problems of motion than the concept of integration at the synapse. The brain is structured according to the functional space organization of the body as a motion system, and even at the cortical level can be considered more a reactive system than an associative one.

7. Postural movements are controlled primarily by gravitational stimulation; transport movements, by bilateral differences in stimulation; and manipulative movements, by the geometric properties of hard space. Each system is regulated at different brain levels, and there are also centers for integrating transport with posture and with manipulation.

8. In a series of experiments, subjects performed writing and drawing tasks in a performance field seen through a fixed inverting prism. Six subjects worked almost steadily for 12 hours in one day, and 12 worked one-half hour per day for 20 days. Another 12 were given pretraining in inverted reading, and their performance in inverted writing compared with a control group. Contact time and travel time of handwriting were measured separately.

9. Some perceptual reorientation occurred during the exposures used, whether continuous or intermittent. Subjects using compensatory movements seemed to report more successful reorientation.

10. There were wide individual differences in performance under inversion, but all subjects showed progressive decreases in performance times, resembling standard learning curves. One subject had to be dismissed from the 12-hour study because of inability to perform. No others were particularly disturbed.

11. Adaptation with intermittent exposure was equivalent to adaptation with continuous exposure.

12. Disturbance varied with the complexity of the task. Making dots was disturbed very little in comparison with writing a's and drawing triangles. Contact movements were disturbed generally more than travel movements, except in making dots. Travel movements and the contact movements for making dots all recovered to normal levels. The degree of final adaptation depended on the type and complexity of movements.

13. No consistent differences were found in course of adaptation between subjects using direct movements and those using compensatory movements.

14. No disturbing after-effects were noted after the inversion was discontinued. Some positive transfer occurred between direct and compensatory movements, when tested after the 20-day study.

15. Perceptual pretraining in inverted reading had no effect on subsequent training in inverted writing.

CHAPTER 8

THE USE OF TELEVISION IN BEHAVIOR RESEARCH

Television has been adapted to many uses in science, the arts, education, and technology. Its use as an educational aid and teaching device is increasing yearly. It has become a relatively common tool of remote observation and control in many areas — for example, in missile guidance, aircraft control, and handling lethal chemical and biological materials. Closed-circuit television, in particular, is being used ever more widely for purposes of communication, observation, and control. But as a basic scientific tool for behavior research, the potential of television has been ignored almost entirely. Our interest in this technique was excited by the possibility of being able to vary both spatial and temporal dimensions of the behavioral field with unmatched speed and flexibility. In this chapter, we shall describe some of our first exploratory television studies as well as general experimental instrumentation and research designs that we have developed in our applications of television to behavior science.

As we have emphasized before, our primary theoretical interest has been in evaluating neurogeometric theory of motion. We have suggested the importance of our general concept of displaced perceptual feedback in the mechanisms of perceptual-motor integration, and the significance of the displaced vision studies to this theory of behavior and brain function. Television offered the first truly new method of displacing visual feedback of human motion since Stratton's[295-297] studies with lenses and mirrors. Thus the major part of our television research to date has involved visual displacement of some sort — either spatial or temporal displacement — or some other form of visual distortion. In addition, we have explored the use of television techniques in research on infant and animal behavior, in the investigation of the visual feedback process of tool using, in studies of perceptual motivation in human learning and performance, and in observation of the perceptual feedback processes of artistic performance. We believe that the information which can be gained from research of this nature has significance not only for limited interpretations of perception and motion, but for all aspects of behavior, including motivation, learning, early development in the infant and child, and the behavioral problems of illness and medical diagnosis.

In the past few years, we have designed and built a fairly extensive television laboratory of behavior research, which has been arranged to make possible flexible adaptation of television instrumentation to different problems of human motion and perception. Our basic instrument is the closed-circuit television chain. We have also explored the use of linked closed-circuit camera-monitor systems, videotape recorders, and stereoscopic television in different aspects of motion and motivation research.

The theoretical orientation that has guided these television studies has also suggested a number of ideas about behavior recording and motion analysis in man, leading to the development of a new technique for human motion analysis. We have used our electronic behavior recorders and motion analyzers in conjunction with television set-ups for systematic analyses of the spatial and temporal feedback characteristics of a number of different types of performance.

Special Features of Television Methodology

Television has a number of special characteristics which make it a distinc-

tive scientific tool for behavior study. Of prime importance to us are those features of television which make it a unique method of displacing the visual field. It is an instrument of remote vision, unlike any other remote vision device. The television camera can be placed almost anywhere, and the effective image can be received and transmitted under entirely different circumstances of observation. Thus we have a movable eye which provides a source of displaced vision that no type of optical device can duplicate. Video systems can be thought of as selective mirrors, in which the incident light can be divorced physically from the reflected beams. Thus the individual observer need not put himself in a special position before the reflecting system in order to observe himself. He can observe himself from any angle or any distance.

Video systems provide a means of electronic variation of all the psychological dimensions of visual stimuli. Accordingly, many new innovations in the visual sciences of psychophysiology and perception of color, space, and form are made possible by closed-circuit camera-monitor chains, videotape techniques, and three-dimensional television. All of the critical space, time, form, and color dimensions of visual perception can be controlled rapidly and flexibly for either binocular or monocular vision. There is no doubt that television will become an indispensable device in the study of perception.

Unlike other forms of visual reproduction, the television image can be reproduced immediately or placed in permanent record by means of videotape. Thus the visual feedback of performance can be delayed by almost any desired interval, making possible systematic analyses of the visual feedback relationships in perceptual-motor integration. The recorded visual image of performance also can be used in learning studies to give information feedback at any desired time.

Video systems make possible the study of the time and space relations of visual and auditory stimulation and perception in language and music.

Using multiple camera systems, the visual feedback of performance of two or more persons can be interlocked, so that the performance of one can serve as the guiding visual stimulus for the performance of a second. Thus video methods can be applied to various fundamental problems of nonverbal social communication.

INITIAL STUDIES

Our original work applying closed-circuit television to the study of displaced vision involved a comparison of the relative effects of 30, 90, and 180-degree horizontal displacement of the locus of vision on handwriting.[274] As illustrated in Figure 8-1, the visual field of performance was not seen directly by the subject, but was observed in the television monitor. A horizontal opaque screen, mounted chest-high before the subject, shielded from his view his writing hand. This screen, however, did not obstruct clear vision of the monitor, which was located directly in front of the performance field. The camera was mounted on a movable tripod that could be placed in any desired position behind the subject's shoulder, to his side, or out in front just above the monitor. As suggested by the drawing, the tilt of the camera was adjusted to correspond to the normal angle of line of sight with respect to the performance field. Writing and drawing performance was tested in eight individuals. The subject was seated comfortably in front of the writing table without the screen and told to write his name. The opaque screen was then adjusted, and the subject was

told to write at normal speed while guiding his writing by watching the monitor. All subjects were tested first with the camera adjusted to the 30-degree position, as shown in Figure 8-1. After samples of writing had been obtained at this displacement angle, the camera was moved to the 90-degree and the 180-degree positions. The order of using these latter two positions was varied with different subjects.

Some of the first writing samples obtained from several subjects are shown in Figure 8-2. The camera displacements for each set of samples are indicated. The appearance of the writing as well as observations made at the time indicate that the 30-degree position caused the subjects only minor disturbance in writing. There was some decrease in legibility when words were written at normal speed, but no real breakdown in performance. Even unusual words could be written with 30-degree visual displacement by all of the individuals observed.

The effects of the 90-degree and 180-degree displacements on writing per-

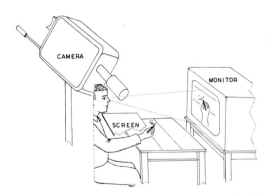

Figure 8-1. Diagram of the original television instrumentation used to study writing and drawing performance with spatially displaced televised feedback. The screen hides the subject's movements from his direct vision. The substitute image of these movements, on the monitor, can be displaced in many different ways by moving the camera or by means of optical and electronic control of the televised image.

30°   90°

180°

Figure 8-2. Effects of different angular displacements of the locus of vision on handwriting accuracy and orientation.

formance were much more pronounced. The only way that any of the subjects could write at the 90-degree position was to ignore the visual feedback of motion and write by means of kinesthetic and cutaneous guidance. The one legible sample of writing shown for the 90-degree displacement was produced by means of this method of control. At least three of the subjects blocked completely in their efforts at writing or drawing with the 90-degree displacement, while the writing efforts of the other subjects were almost completely illegible. Two subjects practiced for well over four hours trying to trace a complex form with the 90-degree displacement angle, and showed very little, if any, learning. During the practice, the pattern was rotated so that the subjects could not learn the pattern kinesthetically.

The 180-degree displacement also produced very marked disturbance of

writing and drawing performance, but not as severe as the 90-degree displacement. With 180-degree displacement, we made our first observations of spontaneous compensatory writing and drawing movements. As the 180-degree samples in Figure 8-2 show, some individuals wrote right-side up, some reversed, and some upside-down. The samples of writing were generally poor, but far better than the attempts with 90-degree displacement.

Marked individual differences were observed in the subjects. A few individuals were fairly relaxed under the different conditions of displacement, whether or not their performance was good. But to most of the subjects, the experience of not being able to control their own movements was one of considerable frustration and apparent embarrassment. At least two of the subjects spoke of the experience as one of the most frustrating that they could remember.

Overall, the results of this first experiment on motion in displaced televised visual fields confirmed the usefulness of television as a scientific instrument, particularly for analyzing the effects of displaced vision. Compared with optical methods of displacing the visual field, the television camera proved more flexible in providing precise experimental control, and in permitting displacement in many different dimensions. These preliminary results, as well as the results of a similar study of simple tracking behavior reported by Martindale and Lowe,[177] showed clearly that the effects of one specific displacement condition cannot be generalized to other conditions as has sometimes been assumed. Television provided a long-sought method for comparing different conditions of inversion, reversal, combined inversion and reversal, and angular displacement of the visual field while secondary factors are controlled.

Change in Position of the Monitor

One of our first exploratory studies on the general applicability of television attempted to determine the effect on writing and drawing performance of moving the monitor to various positions about the subject, and to various distances. Different angular positions of the monitor had no significant effect on writing when the camera was located so as to give a nearly normal angular view of the performance field. With the camera at some distance, subjects could still write with normal legibility, even though the absolute size of the image of their writing varied greatly. Subjects could draw forms reasonably well (if a good black drawing line was used) even when their visual guide of performance was located some 50 feet away.

Nonsystematic Displacement of the Visual Field

In these initial studies, some observations were made on combining different conditions of displacement. The monitor image of writing performance was angularly displaced and reversed, or displaced at obtuse angles and inverted and changed in size. The effects of these combined dimensional displacements were very marked. In some subjects, performance of tasks requiring continuous visual control was almost completely blocked.

Observations of Children

In exploratory studies of young children, we found that children could perform in televised visual fields as well as adults. Young school children who had just learned to write wrote legibly at small displacement angles and showed some of the same disturbances of motion at large displacement angles that we had found in adults. Although no systematic studies were done to compare

adaptation of children and adults to displaced visual fields, it was observed in these limited studies that some children of six and seven years of age responded to displaced visual fields in a well organized manner.

Exploratory studies were made of the reactions of children to their own body images as viewed on a television monitor. When the camera was placed in unusual positions, children maneuvered to get a normal, straight-on view of their own face in the monitor. Even when such a feat was impossible — for example, when the camera was moved to give only a partial view of the face — the children went through various contortions trying to achieve a "normal" image. With an upside-down image, they would try to get an upright view of their face. We tried reversing the facial image right to left on a fairly large number of young hospitalized children (4 to 10 years) and found none who failed to recognize themselves. Such observations suggested many interesting new ways of evaluating both perceptual-motor organization and motivation in the young child.

Observations on Animals

Some observations were made on the effects of a televised image on animals. One question we tried to answer was whether the fighting fish (*Betta splendens*) would show the fighting reaction to a black and white televised image of itself, or whether color and form are both necessary to induce the reaction. We tested three fighting fish, each of which would show the typical fighting colors and movements to their own mirror images. None of them showed a fighting reaction to any monitor image that we could produce. Perhaps a critical test of fidelity in television may be the achievement of a monitor image that the fighting fish will confuse with her adversaries in the real world.

TELEVISION METHODOLOGY

We soon learned that successful use of television in behavior research requires careful organization of laboratory facilities. Because of the size of the camera units and the particular requirements for viewing demanded in studies of displaced vision, we found it necessary to design special laboratory mounts and supports. For our various studies of displaced vision, we have arranged laboratory set-ups with vidicon systems of different size, the large image-orthicon broadcasting camera, the stereoscopic television system, and the Ampex video-tape recorder.

Displaced Vision Laboratory

The Displaced Vision Laboratory has been designed to explore many different aspects of spatially and temporally displaced visual feedback. Figure 8-3 diagrams one main section of this laboratory, which is equipped with an overhead camera carriage system, performance booths, motion analyzers, and accessory equipment for observing the behavior of the subject. The overhead carriage system for camera control consists of a double track system carrying a camera mount that is adjustable in height over a distance of about four feet. The carriage can be moved back and forth in both horizontal dimensions as well, so that the camera can be located at any point over a large area of the experimental room. The direction of sight and tilt of the camera also are adjustable.

With such a flexible camera mount, we have achieved quick and accurate control of the direction and position of the camera relative to the subject's performance field. Many of the experiments of space-displaced vision are concerned primarily with this relative orientation of the subject's motion and camera direction. As shown in Figure 8-3, the

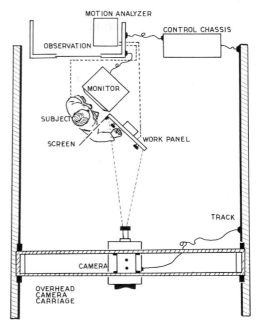

Figure 8-3. Instrumentation of a laboratory for systematic study of space-displaced and size-distorted visual feedback.

camera-monitor system provides him with visual feedback of his motions, but from a point of view displaced from the normal line of sight. Because very rapid changes can be made in the camera orientation, viewing conditions can be changed readily from trial period to trial period to conform to preplanned experimental designs. Moreover, the overhead mount makes possible the use of different performance situations, inasmuch as there is no need to adjust the design of work panels and tables to the camera support.

We study many of the phenomena of displaced vision in terms of systematic motion analysis procedures. Our electronic motion analyzers[270] time the component movements of different types of performance, including object assembly motion,[249] panel control operations,[112] dial-setting movements,[108, 109] and drawing and handwriting.[261] The timing circuits are connected to the subject and to the performance devices, and measure the duration of the different movement components separately.

Camera Instrumentation and Techniques

A photograph of one general arrangement of the camera carriage, performance situation, subject's booth, and motion analysis devices appears in Figure 8-4. The task that the subject must perform is to trace a star pattern on a writing surface located just to the right but outside of the black cloth booth in which she is sitting. The camera views the subject's hand as it traces the star and transmits this image to the monitor. With this particular camera, inversion and right-left reversal of the image can

Figure 8-5. The image-orthicon camera, showing the variable lens arrangements of the optical system. (Photograph courtesy of Univ. of Wisconsin Television Laboratory.)

be produced simultaneously or separately by means of switches located on the outside of the camera. Thus the subject's visual feedback of her own motions can be inverted by throwing one switch, reversed by throwing the other, or both inverted and reversed.

In the situation pictured in Figure 8-4, analysis of performance involves determining the accuracy of response, and timing the durations of movements in different directions by means of the motion analyzer located on the desk. The analyzer shown here has four clocks, each of which is connected to two opposite sides of the eight-sided star. The duration of contact of the subject's stylus with each segment of the star is registered separately on one of the four clocks. The experimenter can record each time and reset the clock to register the opposite side, or he can allow the paired durations to summate on the clocks to give total durations for movements in the four different dimensions — horizontal, vertical, and two different diagonals.

We have used several types of television camera-monitor systems in our studies of displaced vision. Work to be described in this book has been carried out with the large British-made image-orthicon camera (Figure 8-5), the RCA

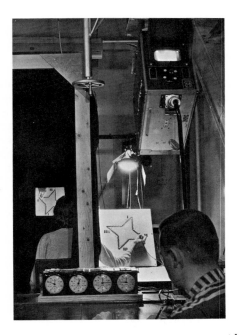

Figure 8-4. Subject tracing a star pattern with televised visual feedback of motion. The two small switches on the left side of the television camera permit independent electronic control of the vertical and horizontal orientation of the monitor image.

studio vidicon camera (Type TK-15), which is pictured in Figure 8-4, miniaturized RCA vidicon cameras (TV-Eye), and the Dage industrial television camera (Model 100 BN). These cameras differ both in size and in special features. The image-orthicon cameras are of limited value in experimental research because the camera tube will "burn" if exposed for any period of time to a relatively bright light source. This burn leaves a permanent image of the exposed area on the tube and makes it unsuitable for further use. Because these camera tubes cost in excess of one thousand dollars, the calculated cost of sustained experimentation with these cameras is large.

The vidicon camera is of almost unlimited utility as an experimental device. These cameras have the disadvantage of requiring a relatively large amount of light to produce a high quality image, but the image so obtained is more than satisfactory for research purposes. The studio vidicon camera is smaller than the image-orthicon unit, but is equipped with equivalent lenses. The smaller miniaturized and industrial type of vidicon cameras have the very great advantages of portability and ease of mounting and control.

As shown by the view of the image-orthicon camera in Figure 8-5, the television camera is equipped with a rotating head which permits rapid change of lens size, and thus rapid control of the relative size of the visual feedback image. In addition, the rotating camera head makes possible flexible control of many of the visual characteristics of the image, such as the amount and kind of visual feedback, color, brightness, blurring, and so on. Special "zoomar" lens systems are available which permit direct control over the size of the image with continuous control of focus.

It is readily apparent that the tele-vision camera is an unmatched instrument for use in displaced vision studies because of the many ways it can be used to control and vary the visual image. The subject's view of his own motions can be inverted, reversed, or both inverted and reversed in any one of several ways, i.e., by controlling the directional characteristics of the camera signal or of the monitor signal, by adjusting the position of the camera or monitor in space, or by putting lens or prism systems in the camera head which will invert or reverse the visual image. By using appropriate dove prisms, the camera image can be rotated to any desired angle. Lenses of different sizes change the apparent size of the image. Masks and filters can be used to screen out parts of the visual field and thus control the amount and kind of visual feedback. Or the camera can be moved about to different positions with respect to the performance field of the subject, much as if the eyes were moved about the room independently of the body.

Against these advantages must be weighed the disadvantage imposed by television techniques — that of limiting the scope of movement of the subject. In order to maintain controlled conditions of observation, the subject's performance must remain within the field of the camera, and he himself must be in a position to watch the monitor. These conditions are admittedly different from the freedom of movement permitted a subject who wears his visual displacing systems on his head. However, the many disturbing side-effects of the optical systems, plus the fact that the effects of the different systems can not be compared directly, have precluded the kind of precise experimental control that makes television techniques so valuable for studies of visual displacement. We have willingly sacrificed unrestricted mobility of the subject in order to achieve this control.

Stereoscopic Television Facilities

The closed-circuit video system also can be arranged to provide a controlled three-dimensional or stereoscopic feedback of the visual field. This three-dimensional display is achieved by the use of two miniaturized vidicon cameras which give the appropriate disparate images of the subject's performance field. Visual integration of the separate images can be accomplished in two ways — by color separation on the monitor that is resolved by wearing color filters,[186] or by space separation of monitor images for each eye, which is resolved by prisms which permit fusion of these separate images. In our preliminary observations with stereoscopic television, the color separation technique was used.

The general arrangement of our stereoscopic television laboratory is shown in Figure 8-6. The large monitor shown in this figure is a color kinescope, in which two color channels (red and blue) are operative. The camera corresponding to the right eye gives a red image of the performance situation, and that corresponding to the left eye, a blue image. The two color images are viewed by means of glasses or goggles equipped with red and blue filters, which maintain the color separation for the two eyes but permit fusion of the images for depth vision.

With this set-up, we hope to explore some of the basic problems of space displacement of the two retinal images in relation to both perception and motion. In addition, we are using stereoscopic television to compare the effects of three-dimensional and two-dimensional visual feedback on various types of performance. In the future, we hope to equip this laboratory with delay circuits and recording systems essential for analyzing the time relationships involved in binocular and stereoscopic vision.

Delayed Vision Facilities

Another major type of control of the visual feedback of motion made possible by television is to delay the image of

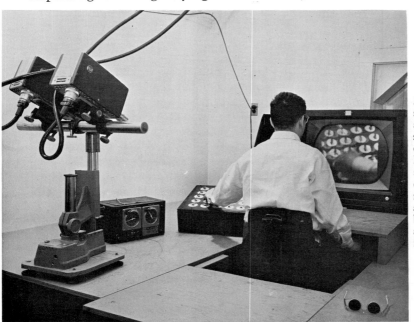

Figure 8-6. A stereoscopic television system and motion-analysis instrumentation. The dual-camera system at left transmits two color-separated images to the color monitor, which must be viewed by appropriate red and blue spectacles to give a three-dimensional image.

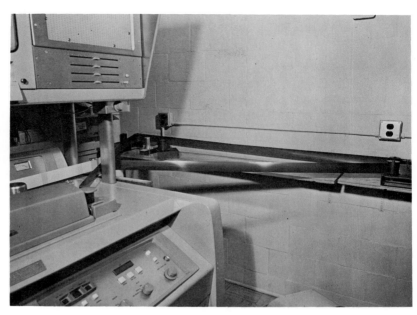

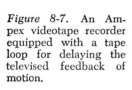

Figure 8-7. An Ampex videotape recorder equipped with a tape loop for delaying the televised feedback of motion.

performance. We have used two types of delayed televised visual feedback. With one technique, the subject is given a delayed television image of performance while he continues to perform.[273] To achieve this, two videotape recorders are needed — one to record the televised image of performance and one to play back this record after a short delay interval to the monitor, while the subject is still performing. A second type of delayed feedback can be achieved with one tape recorder. During performance, the subject sees nothing while a record of the televised image is being made. After the task has been finished, the recorded image is played back to the subject's monitor.

The instrumentation for this second type of delayed feedback is shown by the photograph in Figure 8-7. An Ampex tape recorder is tied in with a camera-monitor chain to record the televised image of performance. The videotape is then run through a tape loop, which is adjusted in length to correspond approximately to the duration of the task. When the task is completed and the tape has run its course, a switch is thrown to shift from recording to playback, and the visual image of the subject's performance is played back to him. In other words, the subject has seen nothing on his monitor while he is performing, but after a controlled delay he is shown what he has been doing.

The tape-recording equipment is arranged so that conditions of delayed vision can be combined with conditions of space-displaced visual feedback, either with standard or with stereoscopic television. Plans for future experimentation call for close integration of all of these special television procedures for controlled observations on many of the critical spatial and temporal relationships in perceptual-motor integration.

Infant Behavior Laboratory

A small television laboratory has been set up in the Pediatrics Hospital of the University of Wisconsin Medical School for the purpose of systematic experiments on visually motivated behavior in infants and children. The main television techniques used in the displaced vision laboratory are adapted here for studies of infant behavior. In addition, a number of special motivating and recording devices have been developed for the infant studies.

The diagrams in Figure 8-8 illustrate two set-ups developed to analyze infant behavior in terms of the development of space-organized motion. In the circular playpen arrangement, the child's motions

in orienting toward a televised image of his mother or of other persons or situations are measured. The playpen rotates continuously and thus continuous head, eye, and body movements are required of the child if he is to maintain vision of the monitor image. The other set-up is arranged to test visual orientation and motivation in very young children. A television monitor is located so that an infant lying in a crib can watch the televised image — of parents, strangers, objects, and so on — with or without sound. A small screen, arranged so as to

A

Figure 8-8. Studying perceptual motivation and control in infants with television. A. In a continuously rotating playpen, the child must keep shifting his position to watch a televised image. B. With a television monitor in a crib, the infant's orientation can be observed directly, or he can be required to move a small screen in order to see the monitor.

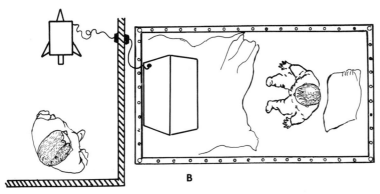

B

block the infant's view of the monitor, can be removed by touch. In this situation direct observations are made of the direction of the infant's gaze, and of his manual actions in displacing the screen.

Television research in infant behavior has objectives other than a general theoretical analysis of motion. Such research is a possible new approach to assessment of intelligent behavior in babies younger than two years. Also, these studies have defined some new techniques which may prove useful in helping the sick or injured child adapt to the hospital environment. Our observations show that television and other devices have potent motivational value for very young children, and can be employed effectively in maintaining organization of the behavioral environment of the newly hospitalized child. These techniques provide a means of determining to what extent the ability to control the perceived environment can help children in their normal development, or in adjusting to illness or other unusual situations.

EXPERIMENTAL DESIGN IN TELEVISION STUDIES

Two general types of experimental design have been used in our studies of displaced visual feedback. In experiments involving fairly extensive or long-term practice in different conditions of displaced vision, we have ordinarily employed group designs, training randomly selected groups under the different conditions. When the objective of the experiment has been to compare as precisely as possible a fairly large number of conditions, we have used experimental plans in which each subject acts as his own control, i.e., the same subjects are run under varied conditions with the order of presentation varied so as to control the effect of order. When-

ever possible, we have carried out experiments according to preplanned statistical design and have evaluated observed differences by means of widely used tests of reliability of data.

Comparison of Performance under Televised and Direct Viewing

In most of our studies, we have not been concerned with comparing performance under conditions of televised feedback with performance carried out with normal direct vision. In some initial exploratory experiments, however, we made such comparisons in order to determine whether the use of television seriously hampered the efficiency of performance. In a study of tracking behavior, we used a closed-circuit camera-monitor system of limited visual resolution. The Dage industrial television camera used in this study provided a monitor picture of 250 scan lines to the inch, considerably less than the scanning frequency of 600 lines to the inch provided by the vidicon cameras used in most of our experiments. All television images are characterized by some blurring and distortion, particularly near the outside border. Some depth distortion also occurs. The experiment described here indicates that even a relatively poor monitor image does not affect tracking performance seriously.

The tracking device shown in Figure 8-9[168] was used to compare performance with direct and televised vision. The subject's task was to align his cursor (the narrow white line in the circular panel in the background) with a target bar that moved in a circular path of about 270 degrees. The target is the white bar at the 12:00 o'clock position in the circular panel. The handwheel control can be seen vaguely as a circular disc at the subject's right hand. The target was activated in an irregular circular path by means of a mechanical-

Figure 8-9. Tracking a moving target by means of television viewing.

electrical target-generator system, and followed a path which varied greatly in speed and direction. There were nine reversals of direction in the path employed. The gear ratio between hand-wheel and cursor was 6 to 1, a ratio that has been found to give optimal accuracy with this particular apparatus. Two viewing conditions were used. The target and cursor were observed directly, or in the television monitor, where 300 degrees of the panel could be seen. For television viewing, the camera was directed at the target and cursor at an angle equivalent to normal line of sight. The monitor was located directly in front of the subject, 18 inches from his eyes. The clarity of the monitor picture in the experiment was much better than that shown in the photograph, inasmuch as the photographic lights enhanced the blurring.

Ten subjects were used in the experiment. Five used direct vision and five used televised viewing, performing ten trials a day for four days. On the fifth day, the television trackers performed with direct vision and the direct vision group, with television. A graphic error recorder gave a continuous record of error in tracking, and each subject was shown his record each day. A quantitative measurement of error was obtained by summating the heights of the graphi-

cal error oscillations of selected trials on each day.

The learning data for this experiment are shown in Figure 8-10. Mean errors for direct-vision tracking were below those for television tracking on all four days. However, an analysis of variance showed that the differences between these means were not statistically significant. The relatively limited learning effect was about the same for the two conditions of tracking. It should be noted also that when the two groups exchanged viewing conditions on the fifth day, the difference between them was not significant.

The results of the study show that the distortion due to a limited resolution in a television system did not significantly reduce the efficiency of tracking performance. This is not to say that significant differences would not occur with more prolonged training of the subjects, or with more difficult tracking conditions. Also, some tasks undoubtedly are degraded more by television viewing than others, depending on the complexity of the motion patterns and the nature of the work devices. However, in general, we feel that televising the visual

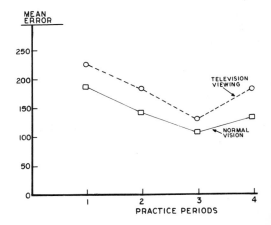

Figure 8-10. Tracking accuracy as a function of practice with direct and television viewing of the target-cursor display.

feedback of performance does not affect seriously the efficiency of motion.

Differential Effects of Displaced Visual Feedback on Motion Components

Because of our theoretical orientation to the problems of motion organization, much of our research is based on analysis of the various component movements in visually controlled motion instead of on a general evaluation of performance. Consequently, one of our first television studies of displaced vision was concerned with the effects of displacement on the component movements of an assembly task. We describe that experiment here to illustrate our motion analysis procedures as well as to demonstrate the differential effects of displaced visual feedback on different types of movements. In this study, we were concerned with the effects of inversion and reversal of the visual field on each of the four component movements of pin-assembly motion – grasp, loaded travel, place, and nonloaded travel.

According to our theoretical concepts of motion, every movement of the human body is considered to have a certain degree of spatial or geometric differentiation, which determines in part the effect upon it of a particular condition of visual displacement. In general, eye movements are most highly differentiated, movements of the legs and torso, the least. Movements of the hands have a relatively higher degree of such differentiation than movements of the arm. Applying this set of ideas to the assembly movements studied here, we expected the greatest effect of the displacement on the component movements that have the most precise spatial organization. In the pin-assembly task, the assembly component – the task of placing the pin in the hole – and the loaded travel movement are the most precisely patterned. The nonloaded travel and grasp movements involve rather general

orientation to the pins and do not demand as accurate localization. Accordingly, we expected the greatest effects of visual displacement on the assembly and loaded travel components.

The electronic motion analyzer shown in Figure 8-11 records separately the duration of the four component movements – grasp, loaded travel, place, and nonloaded travel – making up the assembly task. As described earlier, this technique involves passing a very low-level electric current through the subject's body, and using the contact of the subject with performance objects to control relay circuits and timing clocks. A four-channel electronic relay system is used in this analyzer. When the subject grasps a pin in the assembly bin, he closes the bin relay and starts the grasp-time clock. When he lifts a pin and thus breaks contact with the bin, the grasp clock stops and the loaded-travel clock starts. This relay action in timing the travel movement is accomplished by means of a special flip-flop circuit linking the contact and travel circuits of the relay. A similar flip-flop circuit connects the bin relay and the assembly-plate relay. Thus, when the subject places the pin in contact with the assembly plate, the loaded-travel

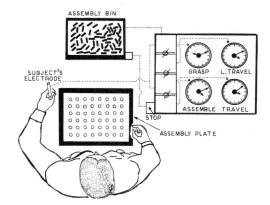

Figure 8-11. Using a four-channel electronic motion analyzer to time separately the four movements of an assembly task.

clock stops and the assembly clock starts. Finally, when the subject releases the pin in the assembly plate, the assembly clock stops and the nonloaded travel clock runs until contact is made once again with a pin in the assembly bin. The four clocks summate times (accurate to 0.01 sec.) for the four movement components until the task is complete. A fifth clock gives the total time of the assembly cycle while a counter registers the number of cycles performed.

A photograph of the entire set-up and a close-up of the assembly operation are shown in Figure 8-12. For an experimental trial, the subject sat at the table

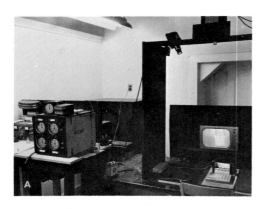

Figure 8-12. A. Experimental set-up used to analyze the effects of displaced televised feedback of performance on the component movements of an assembly task. B. Close-up of the performance area and monitor.

before the assembly plate, lifted metal pins, about one-half inch in length, one at a time from the small aluminum bin, and inserted them into the 48 holes of the assembly plate in a systematic order. For television viewing, he watched his own performance in the television monitor mounted in the black screen behind the assembly table. A slanting opaque screen mounted at chest level in front of the subject prevented his seeing the assembly bin and plate directly. The television camera was mounted directly above the assembly table in a wooden support.

In this study, direct viewing of performance was contrasted with two conditions of televised viewing. In the first television condition, the camera was oriented directly above the assembly plate, with a normal orientation, i.e., the view was as the subject would see it from directly above, with the up-down and left-right dimensions normal. In this so-called normal orientation of television viewing, the line of sight was actually displaced somewhat from that used in direct viewing of performance. In the second television condition, the camera was rotated 180° so that the televised image was both reversed from right to left and inverted. The monitor image seen in Figure 8-12,B, was obtained with normal orientation of the camera. Thirty undergraduate student subjects were divided randomly into three groups. One group performed with direct vision, the second group with the normally oriented television image, and the third group with the inverted-reversed television image of the assembly performance. Each subject performed the assembly task once a day for four days.

The mean durations of the four component movements for each of the three viewing conditions, as recorded on the fourth day of practice, are shown in Figure 8-13. It will be observed that marked differences in time due to viewing conditions are found only for the assemble movement — putting the pins into the assembly plate. For this component, the duration for the normally oriented television viewing was about double that for direct vision, but not much more than half that for the inverted-reversed condition. Less marked variations for the three viewing conditions were found for the grasp, carry, and nonloaded travel movements.

The most marked learning effect over the four days of practice was found for the inverted-reversed viewing condition. The progressive changes in duration of the four movement components with inverted-reversed viewing are shown in the learning curves in Figure 8-14. Here it can be seen that the movement component showing the greatest learning change is the assemble movement. In Figure 8-15 are shown learning curves for the assemble movement for the three different conditions of viewing. It should be remembered that we are primarily

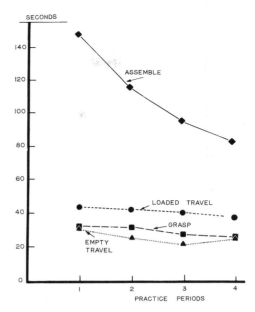

Figure 8-14. Learning curves for duration of different component movements with inverted-reversed visual feedback.

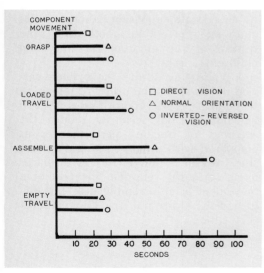

Figure 8-13. Relative durations of different component movements in assembly operation with direct vision, normally oriented televised viewing, and inverted-reversed televised feedback. The assemble movement is the most severely affected by the space displacements.

interested in the differences in the data related to the two television conditions. We would expect performance with direct viewing to be superior, not only because of the blurring and distortion always present in the television image but also because neither television condition duplicated the normal angular line of sight.

Analyses of variance were carried out on the data from all four days of practice, and Duncan range tests were applied to determine which differences were significant. Only the assemble component gave highly reliable differences. For this movement, all the differences in duration related to viewing conditions were significant at the 1 per cent level. The grasp component showed differences between direct viewing and normally oriented television and between the two television conditions which were significant at the 5 per cent level. The loaded travel movement varied signifi-

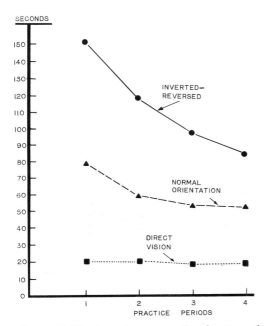

Figure 8-15. Learning curves for duration of the assemble component with different conditions of visual feedback.

cantly (at the 5 per cent level) in duration only between direct vision and inverted-reversed television, while the nonloaded travel movement showed no significant variations related to viewing conditions. These results confirmed our original expectations only in part. The highly differentiated assemble movement, as predicted, was affected the most by inversion and reversal of the visual field, and the less highly precise nonloaded travel movement, as predicted, was affected the least. The results on the other two components showed moderate disturbance.

SUMMARY

1. Television is a significant new scientific tool adaptable to many kinds of basic research in behavior science. Its distinctive features that make possible the spatial and temporal separation of the reception and display of visual patterns make it a particularly valuable device for studies of displaced vision.

2. In a first study of handwriting with displaced televised visual feedback, the camera was displaced horizontally 30, 90, and 180 degrees from behind the subject. The 30-degree displacement caused little disturbance, but the larger ones seriously disrupted behavior. The 90-degree displacement was more disturbing than 180 degrees.

3. Laboratory facilities have been developed for displacing visual feedback by electronic means, by varying camera position, by using different lenses and prisms, and by introducing a videotape recording system into the camera-monitor circuit. Stereoscopic television facilities have been developed, as well as a separate television laboratory for studying perceptual motivation and control of the environment in young children.

4. Validating studies have been carried out to assess the utility of television techniques. It was found that television viewing did not seriously reduce the accuracy of tracking performances as compared with direct viewing. Another study revealed that television displacement seriously retarded the assemble movement of an assembly task, but disturbed the grasp and travel components very little.

CHAPTER 9

TELEVISED INVERSION AND REVERSAL OF VISUAL FEEDBACK

We deal in this chapter with the classical problem of displaced vision, i.e., the effects on perception and motion of inversion and reversal of the retinal image. Earlier, in surveying and interpreting the events of inversion and reversal as aspects of the more general problem of space-displaced vision, we referred to these conditions as "systematic" displacement, as contrasted with other degrees of angular displacement or "nonsystematic" dislocation of vision.

In reviewing the high points of earlier studies in this field, we told how Stratton[295, 296] at first failed to observe clearcut perceptual adaptation to inverted vision, how later studies of Ewert[74] confirmed Stratton's main findings, how Siipola[239] made the first comparisons between different kinds of inverted and reversed vision, and how the more recent investigations of Snyder and Pronko[275] and Kohler[149-152] confirmed earlier work about the importance of overt motor reorganization in perceptual adaptation to inverted and reversed vision.

One of the main problems of systematically displaced vision — that of determining the relative effects of different conditions of inversion and reversal — has not yielded to study by means of experimental spectacles or other optical methods. Such optical techniques introduce variable secondary distortions of vision that affect behavior and thus obscure the primary effects of inversion and reversal. As noted above, Siipola initiated experiments on this problem. Kohler attempted to compare right-left reversal of the visual image, produced by prism spectacles, with up-down inversion produced by wearing a horizontally oriented mirror on the forehead. He thought that inversion was more difficult than reversal, and explained away the fact that subjects adapted more rapidly to inversion by assuming that they were more highly motivated because of the difficulty. Kohler believed that the condition of combined inversion and reversal of vision was so difficult that it could not be studied without danger to the subject who would be required to wear the experimental devices — a conclusion not warranted in view of Stratton's original observations to the contrary.

The technical problems involved in comparing the effects of inversion, reversal, and combined inversion-reversal can be surmounted by using the television camera to displace the field of vision. With television, we can invert and reverse electronically the effective visual feedback of motion without introducing secondary factors which distort the experimental comparisons to be made. The research described in this chapter is concerned principally with comparing the effects on behavior of inversion, reversal and combined inversion and reversal of the visual field by means of closed-circuit television. Planning our experiments according to the specific concepts of neurogeometric theory, we have studied several different types of performance and patterns of motion. In addition, we have investigated for the first time the effects of different conditions of systematic displacement upon movements oriented in different directions.

Theoretical Predictions

Our neurogeometric theory of motion has some direct implications concerning the differential effects of inverted and reversed vision. We assume that neural mechanisms of postural and transport movements, besides regulating these

movement components, function as neurogeometric reference systems to compute the directions of all movements, including manipulative. Figure 9-1 illustrates some applications of this theory to the problem of specifying the relative effects of inversion and reversal. Here are diagrammed three conditions of systematic displacement of the visual field — up-down inversion, right-left reversal, and combined inversion and reversal of the image of movement in drawing a vase. According to neurogeometric theory, inversion would affect principally the gravitational-postural system, and reversal would affect the bilaterally controlled transport system of movement. However, since the spatial orientation of all movements, including learned and unlearned manipulative movements, is defined in terms of these two reference systems, both inversion and reversal of the visual field would affect all types of motion to some degree.

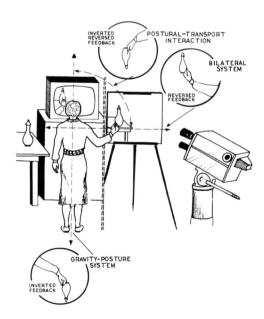

Figure 9-1. Neurogeometric interpretation of the relative effects of visual inversion and reversal.

Because the postural reference system is more primitive and probably based upon several distinct neurogeometric feedback systems (vestibular, kinesthetic, cutaneous, and visual), we would expect that organized motion would be more severely disturbed and that the rate and degree of adaptation would be less with inversion than with reversal. Further, since the postural and transport control systems are integrated by neurogeometric mechanisms, we would expect more severe disturbance from inverting the visual feedback of a motion than from combined inversion and reversal. With inversion, we disturb the geometric relation of a movement to its postural base as well as the postural-transport interactions. Combined inversion-reversal maintains the intrinsic relationships of the field of vision and thus would not disturb the postural-transport interactions seriously. Thus we would expect generally that visual inversion would disturb performance more seriously than combined inversion and reversal.

We would expect that right-left reversal of the entire visual field would cause very limited disturbances to perceptual-motor integration, and that these effects would show up most prominently in individuals of strong lateral dominance (right-handed or left-handed). The reversal effects should be limited for the most part to complex motion patterns, and in general would be less serious than the effects of inversion or of inversion-reversal.

A further prediction of neurogeometric theory is that the effect of the displacement of stimulus feedback is a function of the space properties of the motion pattern involved relative to the dimension of displacement. The degree of disturbance, and the rate and degree of adaptation would depend in part on the spatial complexity of the motion pattern or of any movement component, either transport or manipulative. The more complex the movement, the greater

the effect of displacement. With respect to directional orientation of motion, movements in the reference planes would be affected less by a systematic displacement than movements in diagonal directions, inasmuch as the latter involve continuous nonsystematic relations to the reference systems of movement.

In investigations of performance in displaced visual fields, we distinguish between direct reactions, in which the pattern of motion is oriented normally, and compensatory reactions, in which the motion pattern is reoriented so that the resultant trace looks normal to the subject. For example, in an inverted visual field, a direct reaction is performed normally but looks inverted; a compensatory reaction is performed in an inverted manner so that it looks normal. We would predict that movements which compensate for the displacement condition may be disturbed more initially than noncompensatory (noncorrective) movements, but we would expect no basic differences between direct and compensatory motion in determining the final degree of adaptation. Further, differential effects of different displacement conditions may be less pronounced when compensatory reactions are used, due to the normally appearing orientation of the performance.

The relative effects of any displacement condition upon transport and manipulative movements can be predicted only in part. We look upon transport movements as having a maturational organization largely uninfluenced by specific training, whereas the spatial integration of manipulative movements is very flexible and defined by situational practice. Generally, therefore, we expect a greater degree of adaptation of manipulative movements than of travel movements to displacement of the visual feedback of motion. But, since manipulative movements are often far more complex spatially than travel movements (as, for example, in handwriting), we would expect that manipulative movements sometimes would be disturbed more severely than travel movements by inversion or reversal of the visual field.

TELEVISION INSTRUMENTATION

The use of television to displace the visual field has the advantage of eliminating secondary factors that disturb perceptual-motor integration, and also the great advantages of speed and accuracy of control of the primary experimental variables. The orientation of a televised visual field can be controlled in several ways — by shifting the position or directional orientation of the television camera or monitor, by changing or adjusting lenses, or by varying electronic circuits.

When the systematic displacement conditions of inversion and reversal of the visual image are to be studied, the most effective and rapid control is by electronic means, as shown by the photographs in Figure 9-2. The camera shown here has been modified and equipped with external switches to invert or reverse instantaneously the orientation of the monitor image. The small switch seen on the left side of the camera controls the vertical orientation of the image, and a similar switch inside this side cover controls the horizontal orientation. When the outside switch is thrown, the monitor image is inverted, and when the inside switch is thrown, the monitor image is reversed from right to left. The four photographs in Figure 9-2 show monitor images that are normal, reversed, inverted, and inverted-reversed. All other conditions in the experimental situation, e.g., the motor task relationships and the posture of the subject, remain the same while the visual

image of performance is changed from one orientation to another.

One of the demands of analytic experimental study is flexibility of control of the conditions or treatments to be investigated, so that rapid changes can be made from trial to trial, or from subject to subject. The video system described here provides us with this rapidity and flexibility of adjustment, and was used for most of the experiments to be reported in this chapter. Using this arrangement, experiments of balanced design could be carried out without difficulty.

DIRECT REACTIONS TO INVERTED AND REVERSED VISION

In a first series of experiments, the subjects were required to perform direct reactions in inverted, reversed, and inverted-reversed visual fields. Three different types of performance were investigated: handwriting motions, maze tracing, and target tapping.

The experimental set-up is shown in Figure 9-3. The subject sat in a black cloth booth, facing a partially masked television monitor. He extended his arm through a slit in the cloth in order to perform the required task. The television camera, mounted on an overhead adjustable dolly system, was arranged to give a view of the subject's hand equivalent to the normal line of sight. Switches on the camera were then used to invert, reverse, or both invert and reverse, the monitor image. Handwriting and tracing tasks were performed in a restricted writing area on electrically conductive paper. The target-tapping task was performed on a glass surface in which were embedded twelve ¼-inch brass contact plates, arranged three inches apart in a hollow square. Durations of contact and travel movements were recorded separately, accurate to hundredths of a sec-

Figure 9-2. Photographs of television instrumentation for controlling systematic inversion and reversal of the visual feedback of motion. A. Normal televised feedback. B. Right-left reversal. C. Up-down inversion. D. Combined inversion and reversal.

ond, by an electronic motion analyzer, shown on the table in the figure. The analyzer was connected to the subject and either to the conductive paper for the writing and tracing tasks or to the contacts of the tapping panel.

Handwriting

Twenty-four subjects performed three different handwriting tasks with normal visual feedback and under three conditions of systematic displacement — up-down inversion, right-left reversal, and combined inversion and reversal. Each subject acted as his own control, performing under all four conditions. To rule out the effects of order, each subject was presented the four different conditions in a different sequence. Two days training were given in three different writing and drawing tasks: making a series of six dots in a horizontal line; writing six *a*'s in a horizontal line; and drawing six right-angle triangles with the perpendicular side to the left. Each task was performed twice, and the order of tasks was the same for all subjects. The series of six rows of symbols was repeated for the four viewing conditions, making a total of 24 lines of symbols in a daily session.

The data of the experiment consisted of the duration values for the three

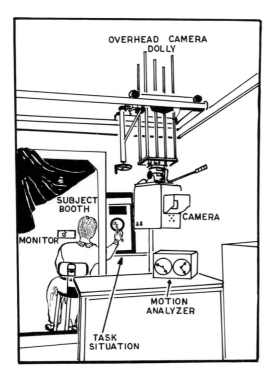

Figure 9-3. Diagram of television and motion-analysis instrumentation for studies of systematic inversion and reversal of the visual feedback of different types of human motions.

different tasks under the four conditions of systematic displacement of the visual field of motion. The data were subjected to analyses of variance, and the reliability of the differences in performance related to both displacement conditions and type of task was determined by range tests of the significance of differences between means.

Mean performance times for the first day are shown in Figure 9-4, which presents bar graphs for mean contact and travel times for all three tasks combined, under all four viewing conditions. Mean contact times are represented by the bars at the left, and travel times, those at the right. Normal, reversed, inverted, and inverted-reversed vision are indicated by the letters N, R, I, and IR. These data show that, on the first

day, the inverted feedback condition had the most deleterious effect on performance, the combined inverted-reversed condition, the next, and the reversed condition, the least effect. These same relative effects were found also on the second day.

When the data were analyzed separately for the different tasks, different degrees of disturbance were found depending on the nature of the performance. The data from the second day are graphed according to task and viewing condition for contact times in Figure 9-5 and for travel times in Figure 9-6. It can be seen in these figures that, for the simple task of making dots, the differences in performance times for the various viewing conditions appeared slight, and did not follow the same pattern as that described above. For the more complicated tasks of writing *a*'s and drawing triangles, however, the same relative effects were found as were

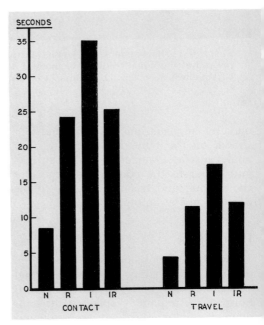

Figure 9-4. Durations of contact and travel movements of handwriting with normal, reversed, inverted, and inverted-reversed vision.

shown in Figure 9-4, i.e., movement time was slowest with inverted viewing, next slowest with inverted-reversed, and most nearly normal with reversed viewing. These effects were consistent for both contact and travel movements.

Analyses of variance showed that there were reliable differences in the means related both to viewing conditions and to tasks. Duncan range tests were then applied to determine which means were significantly different from others. With respect to viewing conditions, mean contact and travel times with normal viewing were significantly different at the 1 per cent level from those with all other viewing conditions for each of the three tasks. Few other differences were significant at the 1 per cent level, but many were significant

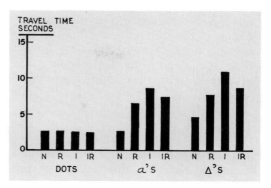

Figure 9-6. Durations of travel movements of dotting, writing, and drawing tasks with normal, reversed, inverted, and inverted-reversed vision.

at the 5 per cent level of significance, summarized in Table 9-1. In this table, the four viewing conditions are indicated by the letters N (normal), R (reversed), IR (inverted-reversed), and I (inverted). Any two conditions which did not produce mean durations significantly different at the 5 per cent level are underlined by a common line. This table shows that the normal means differed significantly from the other conditions in all cases. Means for inverted viewing differed significantly from all others in three out of six cases, and from reversed viewing in four out of six. Differences between reversed and inverted-reversed performance were not usually significant.

Table 9-1. Summary of Significant Differences in Mean Durations of Handwriting Tasks*

	CONTACT TIMES				TRAVEL TIMES			
Dots	N	IR	R	I	N	R	I	IR
a's	N	R	IR	I	N	R	IR	I
△'s	N	R	IR	I	N	R	IR	I

* Mean performance times increase from left to right. Any two conditions not underlined by a common line are significantly different from each other at the 5 per cent level of significance.

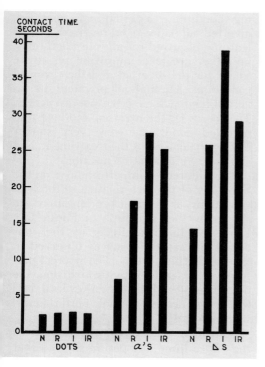

Figure 9-5. Durations of contact movements of dotting, writing, and drawing tasks with normal, reversed, inverted, and inverted-reversed vision.

This experiment generally confirmed our prediction concerning the relative effects of the different conditions of systematic displacement, and also showed that the degree of disturbance was greater with more complex movement patterns.

Maze Tracing

The type of experiment just described was repeated with the task of tracing the maze diagrammed at the top of Figure 9-7. The maze path was made of metal foil, ¼ inch wide, arranged in a pattern measuring two by eight inches over all. The task of the subject was to trace this path with a metal stylus from the circle to the square. The motion

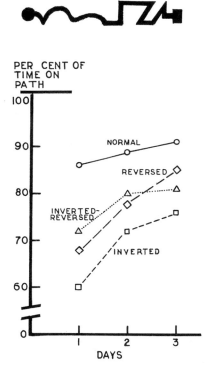

Figure 9-7. Learning curves of maze tracing with normal, reversed, inverted, and inverted-reversed vision.

analyzer recorded contact time on the path, and time spent off the course.

Again in this experiment, each subject acted as his own control. Twenty-four subjects were assigned different orders of the four viewing conditions, which they kept throughout the experiment. Each subject performed under the four viewing conditions three times per day, for three successive days. The percentage of total performance time that the stylus stayed in contact with the maze path was determined for each trial, and the median percentage for each group of three daily trials for a given viewing condition was used for a daily score. Thus, each subject had four scores per day, one for each viewing condition.

The learning data for this experiment are shown in Figure 9-7. These four learning curves plot daily mean scores for the 24 subjects under the four viewing conditions, i.e., normal, reversed, inverted and inverted-reversed. Some learning occurred for all four conditions, but the greatest improvements were found for the inverted and the reversed conditions. Throughout practice, the inverted feedback gave the poorest scores. The scores for the reversed and inverted-reversed conditions were very similar during the course of the experiment, and shifted once in relative position.

The differences in performance on the third day of practice relative to the four conditions of feedback orientation are shown by the bar graph in Figure 9-8. Here the relative effects of the four conditions are the same as observed in the handwriting study. The poorest performance was found with inversion, the next poorest with inversion-reversal, and the most nearly normal performance, with reversal.

Statistical analyses of the data from the entire three-day period showed that normal performance differed significantly at the 1 per cent level from performance with all of the other three viewing conditions. Similarly, perform-

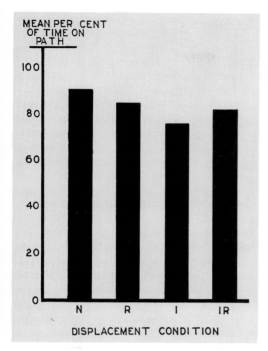

Figure 9-8. Maze-tracing accuracy on the third day with normal, reversed, inverted, and inverted-reversed vision.

ance with inverted feedback differed significantly from all others, but performances with reversed and inverted-reversed viewing were not significantly different. Analyses of data from the third day only showed similar results, except that the inverted condition did not differ significantly from the inverted-reversed on the last day.

Target Tapping

The tapping panel used in this experiment was a glass plate into which twelve ¼-inch square brass contacts were embedded flush with the surface. The contacts were arranged three inches apart in a hollow square. The subject's task was to tap each contact cleanly with a metal stylus as fast as possible, starting with the upper left contact and proceeding in a clockwise direction. One trial consisted of two complete circuits of the square, ending on the contact just below the starting point. A four-channel motion analyzer was used to record contact and travel times for the horizontal and vertical sides of the square separately, so that two values were obtained for contact movements and two for travel movements for each trial. A fifth clock recorded the total time for a trial.

In this experiment, a group design was used. Thirty-two subjects were divided randomly into four groups of eight subjects each, one group for each of the four viewing conditions — normal, reversed, inverted, and inverted-reversed. On a preliminary test, all subjects performed three trials with normal orientation of the visual field, and, on the basis of their performance in these three trials, were divided into subgroups of fast and slow performers. On the succeeding four days, the subjects performed three experimental trials per day with their assigned viewing condition. Only the data from the experimental trials were used, and the data from fast and slow performers were analyzed separately.

Learning curves for the four days' practice are shown in Figure 9-9. The values plotted here are mean contact and travel times for the entire task, combining the data for vertical and horizontal movements. The curves to the left give the data for fast performers, and those to the right, for slow performers. Travel times are plotted at the top, and contact times at the bottom. Viewing conditions are indicated by the letters N (normal), R (reversed), I (inverted), and IR (inverted-reversed). These results follow a somewhat different pattern from that found in the handwriting and maze-tracing studies. First, the contact times showed little variation relative either to days or viewing conditions. This consistency might be expected, because the contact movement in this task was simply a tap, once the contact had been located by means of a travel movement. The second difference to be noted in this experiment is that travel movements were slowest with inverted-reversed viewing and less disturbed by inverted viewing. This difference is more clearcut with the fast performers. Both of these displacement conditions were more disturbing than reversal.

There was marked individual variation in performance in this experiment. The dots in Figure 9-10 represent individual performance time on the last day,

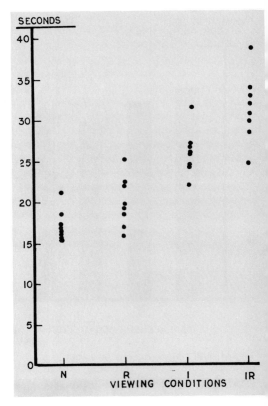

Figure 9-10. Individual differences in target-tapping performance time on the last day with normal, reversed, inverted, and inverted-reversed vision.

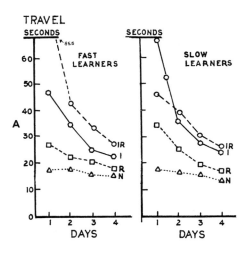

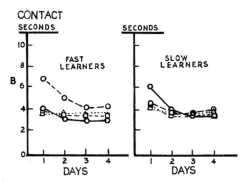

Figure 9-9. Learning curves of target-tapping motion for normal, reversed, inverted, and inverted-reversed vision. Curves for initially fast performers are given to the left, those for initially slow performers to the right. A. Travel time curves. B. Contact time curves.

contact and travel movements combined, for the four different conditions of displacement. It is apparent that the more disturbing viewing conditions led to increased variability of scores.

Complete analyses of variance were made of the data of this experiment, and Duncan range tests were applied where reliable differences were indicated. With respect to the days of practice and the four different viewing conditions, the significant differences between various performance means are summarized in Table 9-2, where the means for fast and slow performers are given separately. The means not underlined by a common line are significantly different at the 5 per cent level. This table shows that, whereas all conditions were significantly different on the first day of practice, there were fewer and fewer reliable differences on succeeding days. The differences between the inverted-reversed condition and the inverted condition were marked with the fast performers, but equivocal with the slow group. The reversed condition of visual feedback did not disturb performance significantly after the first two days of practice, at least when the data are analyzed separately for the subgroups.

Table 9-2. Summary of Significant Differences in Mean Durations of Target-tapping Task*

Day	FAST PERFORMERS				SLOW PERFORMERS			
	N	R	I	IR	N	R	I	IR
1	21.5	30.5	50.6	92.2	21.3	40.9	68.1	56.5
2	21.6	24.7	37.6	47.5	20.0	28.8	39.3	43.0
3	19.3	23.2	27.7	37.3	19.0	23.1	30.9	34.2
4	18.8	20.8	24.6	32.3	17.3	20.8	27.0	30.2

* Any two conditions not underlined by a common line are significantly different from each other at the 5 per cent level of significance.

In this experiment, we attempted to analyze the effects of two variables which were not a consideration in the handwriting and maze-tracing studies. The first was individual performance speed, as measured by the three preliminary trials with normal orientation of the visual field. Overall, the separate analyses of data for "fast" and "slow" performers added little to our understanding of the experimental results. In many cases the "slow" performers actually performed the task faster than the "fast" group during the four days of practice with displaced visual feedback. In view of the marked individual variation in performance shown in this experiment, the distinction between fast and slow initial performance probably

had no significance for the experimental trials.

The second variable analyzed in this experiment but not in the handwriting or maze-tracing experiments was direction of movement within the total task pattern. Performance times were recorded separately for the horizontal and vertical segments of the target-location task. No significant differences were found relative to the different directions of movement.

In this experiment, poorest performance was found with inverted-reversed orientation of the visual field, instead of with inverted orientation, as in the other experiments. To account for this finding, we can speculate that a task requiring travel movements in four directions was affected differently by the various conditions of displaced vision than the more customary left-to-right tasks. However, another investigation of the effects of inversion and reversal on a task involving movements in different directions, to be described later in the chapter, showed the greatest disturbance resulting from inversion, not inversion-reversal as found here. We have no immediate explanation for this discrepancy.

In general, the three experiments described in this section show that there are very marked differences in the overall effects of different conditions of displaced visual feedback, and that these effects depend in part on the pattern of motion and the movement components under consideration. For the most part, the differences observed follow the specific predictions of neurogeometric theory of perceptual-motor integration. Of the systematic displacement conditions studied, inversion of the visual field generally was associated with the greatest disturbance of behavior and the most limited level of adaptation. Reversal of the visual field generally caused the least disturbance, and inversion-reversal usually caused an effect intermediate between the others. Learning occurred with practice in the displaced visual fields, but usually not enough to overcome the differences in performance related to displacement conditions.

COMPENSATORY REACTIONS TO INVERTED AND REVERSED VISION

In a second series of experiments, the performance of compensatory reactions to displaced visual feedback was analyzed and compared to the performance of direct reactions. It will be remembered that compensatory reactions are movements oriented so as to compensate for the displacement of the visual field. The movement pattern itself is displaced so that the resulting trace looks normal in the displaced field.

Compensatory Handwriting

This experiment repeated most of the conditions of the handwriting experiment reported in the last section, except that the subjects were required to perform in a compensatory way in the displaced visual fields. In a reversed field, they reversed the orientation of the symbols; in an inverted field, they used inverted symbols; and in an inverted-reversed field, they both inverted and reversed the symbols. In all cases, the symbols were supposed to look normal in the displaced field. These various patterns of performance are illustrated in Figure 9-11, along with normal writing in a normal visual field.

Three writing and drawing tasks were used, as in the previously reported experiment — making dots, writing *a*'s, and drawing right-angle triangles. Contact and travel times were recorded separately. Twenty-four subjects performed all three tasks under the four viewing conditions (normal, reversed, inverted, and inverted-reversed), but each of the subjects was presented with the viewing conditions in a different order. One trial consisted of making a row of six characters, and two trials were given per day for each task under each condition of visual feedback. Experimental sessions were continued for five consecutive days.

Mean performance times of all subjects on the last (fifth) day of the experiment are shown in Figure 9-12. In these bar graphs, the data for contact movements are given at the left, and those for travel movements, at the right. The three groups of bars represent the three tasks: dots, *a*'s, and triangles. The four viewing conditions are indicated by the letters N (normal), R (reversed), I (inverted), and IR (inverted-reversed). It is evident from these results that, by the fifth day of training, requiring the subjects to make compensatory reactions more or less negated the differential effects of the displacement conditions. Even the normal condition seems to have been affected to some extent by the overall change in performance requirements. Travel movements, in particular, were much the same for all viewing conditions. The contact data for making dots and drawing triangles also showed the equalizing effect of using compensatory reactions. After five days of practice, contact times for drawing triangles were similar for all viewing conditions; in fact, the longest mean contact time was found for normal performance in the normally oriented field. Differences between the contact means for writing *a*'s, however, were statistically significant.

When the data from all five days of practice in this experiment were analyzed, we found that changing the condition of visual feedback did not cause significant variation in the dotting task, but did for the other two tasks. Significant learning effects occurred for both contact and travel movements in all three tasks.

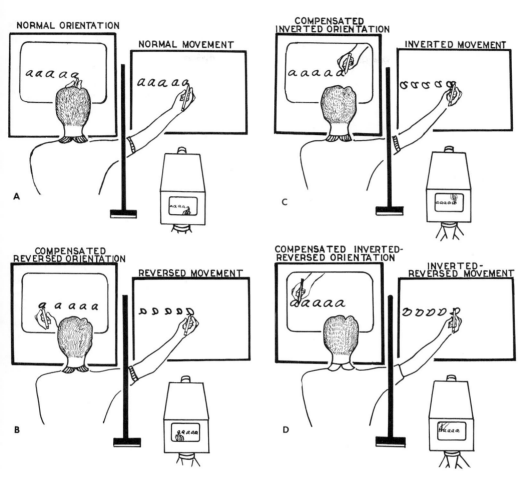

Figure 9-11. Diagrams showing normal performance with normal televised viewing and compensatory performance with reversed, inverted, and inverted-reversed vision.

Direct and Compensatory Handwriting Compared

In another experiment, direct comparisons were made between compensatory and direct reactions to inverted and reversed visual feedback. A group-control plan was used, with 24 subjects divided into four groups of six subjects each. Two groups performed direct reactions, one group with the condition of visual reversal and one with visual inversion. The other two groups performed compensatory reactions, one group with visual reversal and one with visual inversion. We designate the four groups with the letters DR (direct-reversed), DI (direct-inverted), CR (compensatory-reversed), and CI (compensatory-inverted). Subjects performed the three handwriting tasks used in the experiment just described: making dots, writing *a*'s, and drawing triangles. Two trials per day were run for each task, and the experiment was continued for eight days in order to bring performances to a fairly stable level.

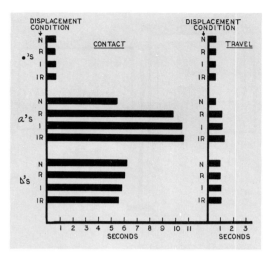

Figure 9-12. Durations of contact and travel movements of compensatory handwriting on the fifth day of practice with normal, reversed, inverted, and inverted-reversed vision.

The learning curves for the triangle task are shown in Figure 9-13. The top four curves represent the mean contact times for the four groups, and the bottom four curves represent the mean

travel times. The triangle task produced the longest contact and travel times of the three tasks, but reached a stable level of performance after about five practice sessions. Of the four experimental groups, those performing with compensatory reactions in an inverted visual field (CI) gave the slowest contact time values.

Performance data for the four different experimental conditions on the last day of practice are summarized in Figure 9-14. The bar graph to the left shows mean contact times for all four experimental groups and for the three different tasks. The bar graph to the right gives mean travel times. In general, these data confirm our expectations concerning the relative effects of inversion and reversal of visual feedback, because inversion usually slowed performance time more than did reversal. The direct-inverted (DI) condition produced slower movement times than the direct-reversed (DR) condition in five out of six cases. The compensatory-inverted (CI) condition gave slower

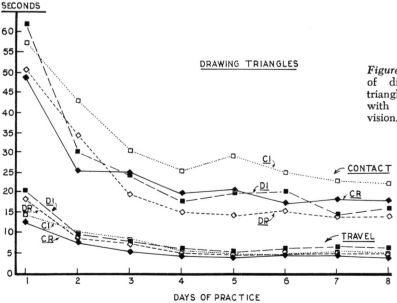

Figure 9-13. Learning curves of direct and compensatory triangle-drawing performance with reversed and inverted vision.

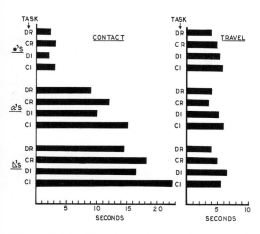

Figure 9-14. Durations of contact and travel movements on the eighth day of practice for direct and compensatory performance with reversed and inverted visual feedback. The movement times for the dotting, writing, and drawing motions are shown separately.

movement times than the compensatory-reversed (CR) condition in all six cases. After eight days, compensatory movements were slower than direct movements with comparable conditions of visual feedback in all but one of the twelve paired cases. The differences reported here for contact movements in the writing and drawing tasks are statistically significant at the 5 per cent level.

Long-Term Adaptation to Inverted Vision with Direct and Compensatory Reactions

We have been interested in comparing the relative level of adaptation with compensatory and direct reactions after prolonged exposure to a displaced visual field. According to our theory, adaptation of compensatory performance should be more limited than direct, because it involves both visual and kinesthetic displacement. In reorienting movement to correct for displaced visual feedback, the individual must not only resolve the visual displacement, but must also modify established movement patterns

with their kinesthetic feedback. These considerations would apply particularly to motions such as handwriting which have an anisotropy established by practice, and would apply less to motions in which specific directional orientation has not been established. However, the relative efficiency of compensatory and direct reactions is probably influenced as well by the factor of perceptual compensation. Because the compensatory type of reaction with displaced vision gives nearly normal visual feedback of the effects of performance, we would assume that it would facilitate adaptation to the displacement.

Relevant here are some of the data presented in Chapter 7 comparing direct and compensatory reactions in inverted visual fields for relatively long exposure periods. In this study, inversion was accomplished by means of a fixed prism. Subjects were trained in three handwriting tasks (making dots, *a*'s, and triangles) for 30 minutes per day for 20 days. Half of the subjects used direct reactions, and half used compensatory. As can be seen in Figures 7-15 and 7-16, after some days of training there were but minor differences between the two groups. After 20 days of practice, the differences between compensatory and direct reactions were not statistically significant, although both methods of writing *a*'s and drawing triangles in the inverted visual field were still significantly slower than comparable performance in a normal visual field.

A few general conclusions can be drawn from these various studies on compensatory reactions to displaced vision. Although compensatory performance is usually poor initially, the prism inversion study indicates that adaptation to visual inversion is eventually just as effective with compensatory reactions as with direct reactions. However, the use of compensatory reactions tends to equalize to some extent the differential effects of the various conditions of displaced visual feedback. We have observed that compensatory reactions sometimes have the effect of making the individual unaware that he is performing in a displaced visual world, inasmuch as his motion patterns appear to be normally oriented.

These phenomena of compensatory adaptation to inverted and reversed vision throw some light on the results of earlier workers, particularly Snyder and Pronko[275] and Kohler,[151] relative to perceptual adaptation to inverted and reversed vision. We believe it possible that in these earlier experiments the use of compensatory movements contributed to the subjects' normal perceptual orientation. If this were true, the assumed processes of perceptual rehabituation to displaced vision might in fact have involved to an important degree the use in particular situations of compensatory reactions, which would have had the effect of making the inverted or reversed visual field appear normally oriented in space.

EFFECTS OF DISPLACED FEEDBACK ON MOVEMENTS IN DIFFERENT DIRECTIONS

According to our theoretical assumptions, the relative effect of any condition of visual displacement depends not only on the dimension of displacement, but on the direction of movement as well. Movements can be made in the normal reference dimensions of motion and perception, i.e., up-down and right-left, or can be made diagonally. We would predict that with systematic inversion or reversal of vision, up-down and right-left movements would be affected less than diagonal movements, because the latter would involve not only the systematic displacement of a particular reference system, but also

disturbance of the interactions of the reference systems. We would still assume that, among the systematic conditions of displacement, inversion would cause the most severe disturbances. The present experiment was designed to test these assumptions with respect to a task involving movements in eight directions.

A television set-up was used to test the effects of normal, reversed, inverted, and inverted-reversed vision on a maze-tracing performance. A four-pointed star maze was used, as shown in Figure 9-15. In tracing around the star with a metal stylus, movements were made in eight directions: up, down, right, left, and four diagonal directions. Each segment of the maze path was connected separately to a channel of an electronic motion analyzer, so that the contact time in each direction could be timed independently. The maze path itself was designed with small, circular culs-de-sac along each side, which would trap the stylus momentarily if contact with the

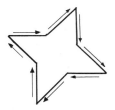

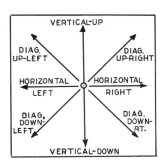

Figure 9-15. Star maze used for tracing, and pattern showing eight directions of movement.

side were made. Thus, efficient performance required accurate guidance of the
stylus within the main pathway. One
trip around the maze represented one
trial.

Thirty-two subjects were assigned
randomly to four groups of eight, and
each group performed under a different
viewing condition — normal, reversed,
inverted, or inverted-reversed. Each subject performed 24 trials per day for four
days. The starting point in tracing the
maze was varied systematically by subject, and changed for each subject after
eight trials. In half of each block of
eight trials, the maze was traced clockwise, and in the other half, counterclockwise, with the order varied systematically among the subjects. For each
trial, eight time scores were obtained
for movement in the eight directions,
which could be summed to give total
performance time for that trial.

The learning curves in Figure 9-16
show mean total performance times for
each group, averaged for each block of
eight trials. It can be seen that the
inversion condition had by far the most
severe effect on performance time, with
inversion-reversal the next most severe.
Performance with reversed visual feedback was practically identical with normal throughout the four days.

Performance scores for movements in
different directions are summarized in
Figures 9-17 and 9-18, which show respectively the data for all four days,
and for the last day alone. Each group
of four bars represents the means for
the four viewing conditions for a particular direction of movement. These
directions are indicated by arrows at
the left. It can be seen that, without
exception, inverted visual feedback
resulted in the slowest performance,
followed by inverted-reversed feedback.
None of the mean scores for reversal
differs to any marked degree from normal performance; performance with
these two conditions was roughly twice

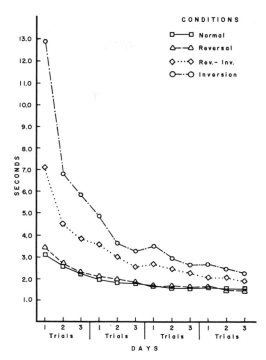

Figure 9-16. Learning curves of mean performance times in star tracing for normal,
reversed, inverted, and inverted-reversed vision.

as fast as with inversion. These relationships hold for the combined four-day
means, and for performance on the
fourth day. When we compare the scores
for the different directions of movement,
we find that the group with inverted
vision generally moved more slowly in
diagonal directions than horizontally and
vertically, but the other groups showed
but minor differences for movements in
different directions.

Analyses of variance determined that
there were reliable differences in
performance related to the viewing
conditions, and Duncan range tests
determined which differences were significant. Table 9-3 summarizes these
data for every direction of movement.
Those conditions in the table not underlined by a common line were significantly different at the 1 per cent level.

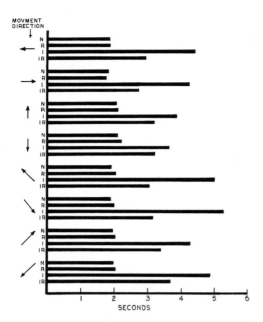

Figure 9-17. Mean performance times over four days practice for movements in different directions, with normal, reversed, inverted, and inverted-reversed vision.

The differences between the normal condition and the reversed condition were not usually significant, either for the four-day data or for the fourth day, but all other differences were significant.

Before carrying out experiments of the sort described here, we had thought that movements in a particular dimension might be disturbed the most by visual displacement in that dimension. That is, we had speculated that movements to the right or left might be disturbed the most by right-left reversal of the visual field, while movements up and down would be disturbed the most by visual inversion. This experiment and others have shown conclusively that such is not the case. Figures 9-17 and 9-18 show no marked differences between horizontal and vertical movements, no matter what the displacement condition. As a matter of fact, with inverted visual

feedback, horizontal movements were slower than vertical.

Another expectation that was only partially fulfilled was that movements in diagonal directions would be significantly slower than movements in the horizontal and vertical reference planes. This was true only for the group who performed with inverted vision. For the other groups, vertical movements were about as slow as diagonal movements — in some cases slower.

This experiment confirmed the most consistent finding of all our studies of systematic displacements: namely, that inversion of the visual field is almost invariably more disturbing than either reversal or inversion-reversal. We believe that this results from the disturbance of the up-down reference system, related to the gravitational control of motion.

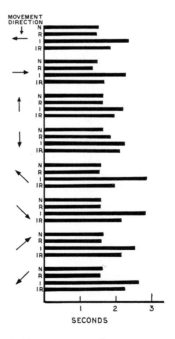

Figure 9-18. Mean performance times on fourth day of practice for movements in different directions, with normal, reversed, inverted, and inverted-reversed vision.

Table 9-3. Summary of Significant Differences in Mean Durations of Movements in Different Directions, Relative to Four Viewing Conditions*

MOVEMENT DIRECTION	DATA SAMPLE	DISPLACEMENT CONDITIONS			
Horizontal, Left	4 days	N	R	IR	I
	Last day	N	R	IR	I
Horizontal, Right	4 days	N	R	IR	I
	Last day	N	R	IR	I
Vertical, Up	4 days	N	R	IR	I
	Last day	N	R	IR	I
Vertical, Down	4 days	N	R	IR	I
	Last day	N	R	IR	I
Diagonal, Up Left	4 days	N	R	IR	I
	Last day	N	R	IR	I
Diagonal, Down Right	4 days	N	R	IR	I
	Last day	N	R	IR	I
Diagonal, Up Right	4 days	N	R	IR	I
	Last day	N	R	IR	I
Diagonal, Down Left	4 days	N	R	IR	I
	Last day	N	R	IR	I

* Those conditions not underlined by a common line are significantly different at the 1 per cent level of significance.

SUMMARY

1. The problem of the relative effects of inversion and reversal of vision has never been resolved. Kohler believed that inversion was more difficult than reversal, although his subjects appeared to adapt more quickly to inversion. He also believed that combined inversion and reversal would be extremely difficult, perhaps dangerous to the subject.

2. Television methods permit comparisons of reversal, inversion, and combined inversion-reversal without introducing secondary differences in the experimental conditions.

3. Neurogeometric theory would predict more severe disturbance from visual inversion than from either reversal or combined inversion-reversal, because inversion disturbs the more primitive up-down reference system and further disturbs the intrinsic relationships of the visual field. We would expect the degree of disturbance to vary with the com-plexity of movements, and would expect diagonal movements to be affected more than up-down or right-left movements.

4. In a series of experiments on handwriting, maze tracing, and target tapping, durations of contact and travel movements were recorded for normal, reversed, inverted, and inverted-reversed televised viewing of the performance field.

5. In handwriting, durations of both contact and travel movements were longest for inverted vision, next longest for inversion-reversal, most nearly normal for reversed vision. These differences were most pronounced for the more complicated movements involved in writing *a*'s and drawing triangles, and relatively very slight for the simple task of making dots.

6. Maze-tracing performance was significantly slowest with inverted vision; performance times with reversed and inverted-reversed vision were not signif-

icantly different. Performance improved markedly over three days' practice periods.

7. In target tapping, inverted-reversed vision generally slowed down performance the most, and inverted vision next, with reversed vision giving scores most nearly normal. The fact that the relative effects of the displacement conditions differed in this experiment from the other experiments is not accounted for. Travel movements became markedly faster over four days' practice for all displacement conditions; contact movements (taps) were consistently fast from the start and showed little change. There were no significant differences between durations of horizontal and vertical movements.

8. In another handwriting experiment, subjects were required to make compensatory reactions, i.e., to write symbols in such a way that they appeared correct in the displaced visual field. Significant learning effects occurred in five days. On the fifth day, performance was almost equivalent for dotting and making triangles under all conditions; for writing *a*'s, performance was much the fastest with normal vision, slower with reversed, inverted, and inverted-reversed, in that order. Differences between the displacement conditions were less than when direct reactions were used.

9. In an experiment comparing direct with compensatory handwriting under conditions of inverted and reversed vision, learning occurred over about five days, after which performance stabilized. By the eighth day, performance was generally slower with inversion than with reversal, and generally slower with compensatory than with direct reactions. These differences were significant for contact movements but not for travel movements.

10. A long-term study of adaptation to inverted vision (produced optically) showed that differences between direct

and compensatory handwriting were not significant after 20 days, although both kinds of performance in an inverted field were still slower than normal performance in a normal field.

11. Movements in eight different directions in a star maze were compared for duration under conditions of normal, reversed, inverted, and inverted-reversed vision. The group with inverted vision generally moved more slowly in diagonal directions than horizontally or vertically. The other groups showed no consistent differences between vertical and diagonal movements, and only a slight advantage for horizontal movements. Overall, performance was slowest with inversion, next slow with inversion-reversal, and next with reversal of vision.

12. The experiments on systematic displacement of vision showed that inversion is definitely more disturbing than reversal, and usually more disturbing than combined inversion and reversal. The degree of disturbance varies with motion pattern and movement component, and is greater for movements of increasing complexity. The use of compensatory movements increases the initial disturbance, but does not greatly affect the final level of adaptation. However, the use of compensatory movements tends to reduce the differential effects of different displacement conditions, probably because compensatory performance has the appearance of normality. Diagonal movements were shown to be affected more than horizontal or vertical movements by inverted vision, but not by reversed or inverted-reversed vision. Subjects performing under any of the systematic displacement conditions show a marked learning effect over the first few days' practice, but, except with the simplest tasks, appear not to achieve a normal level of efficiency. Performance with reversed vision approximates normal more readily than performance with inverted or inverted-reversed vision.

CHAPTER 10

TELEVISED ANGULAR DISPLACEMENT OF VISUAL FEEDBACK

In the present series of experiments, we are concerned with nonsystematic displacement of the visual feedback of motion, i.e., displacement in some dimension other than up-down inversion or right-left reversal. In keeping with our geometric principles of perceptual-motor integration, we propose to show that such nonsystematic displacement of vision and motion has quite different effects from the systematic inversions and reversals of the visual field described in the last chapter.

There are a number of different types of visual displacement besides systematic *inversion* and *reversal*, in which the visual field is flipped upside-down, or right-to-left. There is *rotation* of the visual field, to any angle from 0 to 360 degrees. When the visual field is rotated just 180 degrees, we have combined inversion and reversal, the condition first studied by Stratton,[295, 296] and used as one of our standard conditions of systematic displacement. In all of these conditions, the central point of fixation remains constant, while the visual field is flipped over or rotated about it. A type of displacement more complex behaviorally is angular *displacement of the line of sight*, in which the orientation of the visual field remains the same but its apparent position with respect to the viewer shifts in some direction. This type of displacement is illustrated in Figure 10-1, A. Another type of angular displacement, which can be produced with mirrors or with television methods, is *displacement of the locus of vision*. This dislocation, illustrated in Figure 10-1, B, achieves the effect of shifting the eyes from their

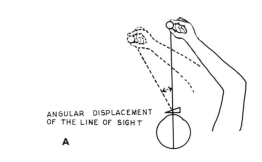

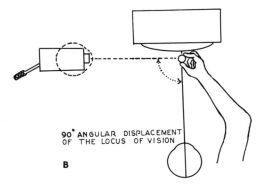

ANGULAR DISPLACEMENT
OF THE LINE OF SIGHT

A

90° ANGULAR DISPLACEMENT
OF THE LOCUS OF VISION

B

Figure 10-1. Two types of nonsystematic displacement of vision. A. Angular displacement of the line of sight by means of a prism. B. Angular displacement of the locus of vision, using the television camera.

normal position in the body to some other locus in space. Watching oneself in a mirror is this sort of displacement, except that a mirror image is a right-left reversal of a televised image taken "outfront."

PRIOR OBSERVATIONS ON NONSYSTEMATIC VISUAL DISPLACEMENTS

We have summarized in Chapter 6 most of the prior reports that have been made of nonsystematic visual displacements, from Stratton's[297] original mirror study of displaced locus of vision. In this experiment he observed relatively

rapid and dramatic perceptual orientation in about three days, but only in relation to objects and situations which were made familiar by overt motion during the experiment.

Rotation of the Visual Field

Early observations of rotation of the visual field were those of Brown[32] and Cox,[55] whose reports indicated that subjects encountered considerable difficulty at some angles of rotation if they were required to carry out precise motions in the field. We have also noted that subjects can tolerate considerable rotatory displacement if the only response required of them is one of passive perceptual judgment.

Witkin[331] investigated visual perception of the vertical under conditions in which both the body and the visual field could be displaced from their normal orientation. His apparatus is diagrammed in Figure 10-2. The subject sat in a chair that could be displaced at various angles from its normal upright position, enclosed in a box-like room that could be rotated around him. One of the findings of this research was that when visual and kinesthetic reception were at variance due to tilting the chair and the room, the subject most

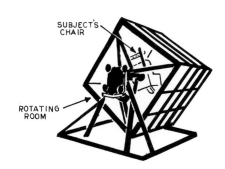

SUBJECT'S
CHAIR

ROTATING
ROOM

Figure 10-2. Witkin's[331] apparatus for the study of perception of the vertical with angular displacement of the visual field and of the body in space. (Based on photograph, courtesy of Dr. H. A. Witkin.)

generally attended to visual cues. For example, if the chair were kept stationary and the room tilted, subjects frequently reported feelings of body movement. But if the chair were tilted while the room remained upright, subjects generally judged the nature of the situation correctly. We know from these and other observations that knowledge of the true relationships of an experimental condition does not preclude persisting perceptual illusions about the relative displacement of the visual environment. A subject may ignore contradictory information in reacting to certain displaced conditions in which ordinary reference directions are absent.

Witkin found marked individual differences among his subjects in depending on visual and kinesthetic cues for direction. Although most depended mainly on visual cues, a few based their perceptions of direction more on kinesthetic sources of information. Women were apt to be more visually "dependent" than men. There were also differences in the degree of displacement of the environment that could be tolerated before detecting the shift. Some subjects reported the change only after rotation of 50 to 75 degrees. In some subjects, tilting the room produced headache, dizziness, sweating and nausea. Tilting the chair alone did not produce these effects.

Displacement of the Line of Sight

Our summary of Wooster's[334] and Kohler's[149] studies of displacements of the line of sight indicated that subjects appeared to adapt completely to small angular displacements, but experienced considerable difficulty with larger angles. After-effects were more persistent after the smaller displacements.

Relevant here are observations on the capacity of the eyes to maintain binocular fusion when the line of sight of one or both eyes is displaced by means of

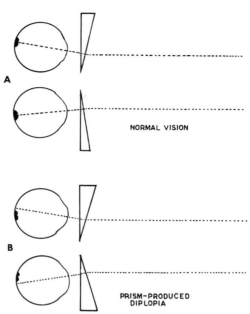

Figure 10-3. Testing binocular fusion power. A. Binocular angular displacement within normal range, fused for single vision. B. Breakdown angle of binocular displacement, with prism-produced diplopia.

prisms. Figure 10-3 illustrates how this ability to fuse the two retinal images is tested. The top diagram represents the condition of normal binocular fusion with single vision, while the bottom diagram represents prism-produced diplopia, brought about by displacing the line of sight toward the temporal side of each eye. A pair of Risley prisms are placed base out before the eyes and gradually moved inward. As the prism power is gradually increased, the subject must converge his eyes more and more in order to maintain fusion of a fixated object, until a point is reached beyond which the eyes no longer converge. At this point, the eyes will move back to their "phoria" position, the stimuli will become widely separated on the retinae, and the subject will report double vision (diplopia). The total amount of convergence which the subject will exert to maintain single vision constitutes a measure of binocular fusion, and represents the capacity of the neuromotor system to compensate for increasing amounts of displaced visual feedback by regulating eye movements.

If, after a fusional break has occurred, the prism power is gradually decreased, the stimuli come nearer the corresponding parts of the two retinae. Eventually, the eyes will make a convergence movement sufficient to bring the two stimuli back to their ordinary positions on the two foveae and thus will recover a condition of fusion. Inasmuch as this fusion recovery movement may be of several degrees in magnitude, the stimuli producing the movement may be widely separated across the two midlines of the retinae. Thus the visual system reacts dynamically to compensate for conditions of displaced vision by such compensatory ocular reactions.

If prisms are used base-in in tests of this sort, the eyes must diverge in order to maintain or to recover fusion. The power of the visual system to correct for angularly displaced vision by divergence movements is less than can be achieved by convergence movements. A normal individual will converge approximately 11 degrees to maintain fusion and 6 degrees to recover fusion, but will diverge only about 5 degrees before fusion is lost and about 3 degrees to recover fusion.

Bridgman and Smith[31] reported on the effects on binocular fusional breakdown and recovery of cutting the main commissures of the cerebral hemispheres in man. The neurosurgical operations had been carried out in relation to epilepsy control.[307] The results showed that, among some 10 patients tested, fusional breakdown and recovery angles were in the normal range. Three of these cases were presumed to have the main commissural connections between the two cerebral hemispheres completely sectioned. Among three patients tested both preoperatively and postoperatively, only one showed any reduction in the angular values for fusional breakdown and recovery.

The normal capacity of the visual system to adapt to angular displacement of the retinal image is well known in the correction of strabismus by ocular training methods. Accordingly, Kohler's[149] observations of perceptual adaptation to monocular angular displacement of the line of sight, as well as the persisting visual after-effects of such displacement reported by him, are scarcely surprising in view of the fact that many of his experimental displacement angles were not much greater than the normal compensatory convergence angles of 10 to 15 degrees.

Concept of Normal and Breakdown Angles of Displacement

Our own analysis of the problems of nonsystematic displacement has been based on these prior objective observations, as well as our theoretical formulation of the nature of sensori-neuromotor control of motion. All indications are that visual regulation of perception and motion is very flexible in the human individual. Thus the term "visual displacement" is a relative one. There is no absolute condition of visual alignment, either with the perceptual field or the performance field, but a range within which perceptual-motor integration can be considered normal. This interpretation leads directly to the concept of normal, breakdown, and recovery angles of neurogeometric control, which we have already described with respect to binocular fusion and diplopia. We believe all space-structured motions, including the many different types of lateral, convergence, divergence, fixation, and pursuit movements of the eyes, are defined by the system's tolerance for angular displacement.

The diagrams in Figure 10-4 illustrate

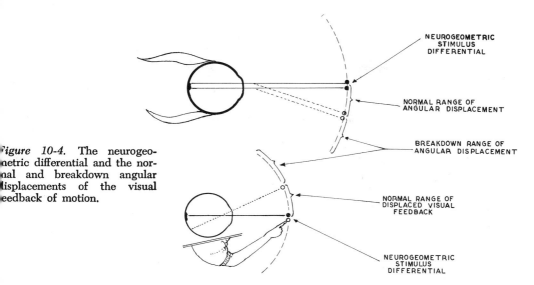

NEUROGEOMETRIC
STIMULUS
DIFFERENTIAL

NORMAL RANGE OF
ANGULAR DISPLACEMENT

BREAKDOWN RANGE OF
ANGULAR DISPLACEMENT

NORMAL RANGE OF
DISPLACED VISUAL
FEEDBACK

NEUROGEOMETRIC
STIMULUS
DIFFERENTIAL

Figure 10-4. The neurogeometric differential and the normal and breakdown angular displacements of the visual feedback of motion.

three hypotheses of geometric regulation of motion derived from neurogeometric theory. The first hypothesis proposes that the maintenance and regulation of motion and perception are based on stimulus differentials — the spatial separations of two sources of intrareceptor or interreceptor stimulation. The second is that there is a normal range of angular displacement within which the motor system, by compensatory action, can maintain normal organized patterns of perception and motion. The third hypothesis is that there is a breakdown range of relative displacement of a motion and its stimulus feedback within which the neuromotor system can accommodate only in part to the spatial discrepancy.

These ideas of neurogeometric control can be applied to the coordination of eye movements and to visual control of hand movements. One eye is controlled relative to the other in the performance of at least eight different patterns of lateral, convergence, divergence, vertical, fixation, saccadic, pursuit, and rotatory movements. Further, the pattern of hand motion can be controlled relative to any one of these patterns of eye movement. We assume that a small stimulus differential is basic to all control of continuous, visually guided hand movements. We assume further that there is a normal range of displacement of the visual stimulus pattern within which the neurogeometric coordination of hand and eye will not be disturbed, because the central system can compensate for it by various kinds of ocular, head, or body movements. Beyond this normal range of angular displacement, breakdown angles will be found, beyond which the individual can adapt in varying degrees depending on the magnitude of the geometric displacement and the type of performance required.

The experiments described in this chapter have been designed to test some of these neurogeometric concepts, as applied to visuomotor coordination. We are interested in determining whether there are in fact "normal displacement angles" and "breakdown displacement angles" of control, and whether the degree of motor disturbance and degree of adaptation to breakdown displacement is a function of the magnitude of such displacement.

TELEVISION INSTRUMENTATION

Our own experiments on nonsystematic displacement have involved varying the locus of vision in relation to the body, to which television techniques are particularly adaptable. The television camera can be used as a substitute "eye" and located at any desired point to observe performance. This experimental achievement was speculated about by Stratton, who wrote in 1899, "If we were always to see our bodies a hundred yards away, we would probably also feel them there."[297] With the development of television systems, one can now view his own body in motion a hundred yards away, and, moreover, from any angle within the physical field surrounding it. Figure 10-5 shows how the television camera is used as a displaced substitute eye, much as if the individual's eyes were detached from the head and placed, still functional, at some other point in space. Each of the cameras in this drawing represents establishing the locus of vision at some point other than in the head. As the monitor picture suggests, a second variable that can be controlled with television is the amount of visual information provided for the feedback regulation of motion. Optical and electronic variations in the camera and its lens system can be used in combination with camera displacement to displace or distort the visual feedback in various other ways.

Using such television methods, we have carried out several types of experiments to test our theoretical assumptions. Angular displacements, both horizontal and vertical, some involving inversion or reversal of the field of vision, have been tested as to their effects on assembly motions, target tapping, drawing and writing. Comparisons have been made between displacements effected by moving the camera with respect to the performance situation, and by moving the performance situation with respect to the camera. Long-term adaptation, using both direct and compensatory types of reaction to angularly displaced vision, has been analyzed. Finally, we have studied systematically the degree of movement disturbance and adaptation as a function of the magnitude of angular displacement of visual feedback.

EXPERIMENTS ON NORMAL AND BREAKDOWN ANGLES OF DISPLACEMENT

Our original observations on the use of television in motion research dealt with the effects of angularly displaced visual feedback on handwriting movements.[274] No disturbance of motion resulted from limited change in the position of the camera from the normal line of sight, but with 90-degree displacements, marked disturbances occurred in writing familiar letters and words and in drawing common forms, such as triangles and circles. Additional experiments have shown that relatively specific "normal" and "breakdown" angles of visual displacement can be determined for various types of motions.

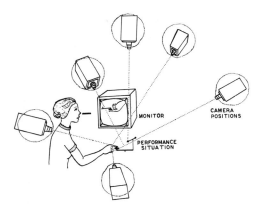

Figure 10-5. The closed-circuit television camera used as a substitute eye to effect geometric displacement of the locus of vision.

Displacements in the Horizontal Plane

In a series of studies, the television camera viewing the performance area was tilted at a vertical angle equivalent to the normal line of sight, and then displaced horizontally various degrees from the normal. For these horizontal displacements, the camera was not moved in the vertical dimension, and the tilt of the camera was not varied.

EFFECTS OF ANGULAR DISPLACEMENTS ON AN ASSEMBLY TASK. The diagram in Figure 10-6 shows the arrangement of the subject, the performance area, the television monitor, and the camera for a study of assembly operations. Three experimental positions of the camera were used, as shown, 7, 90, and 225 degrees from the mesial plane. The task consisted of inserting a wooden dowel (¼ in. in diameter and 1¼ in. long) into a hole, placing a washer (¾ in. outside diameter) on the dowel, a metal sleeve (⁵⁄₁₆ in. outside diameter and ½ in. long) on the washer, and then another washer on the sleeve. The number of assemblies completed in each one-minute trial period was recorded.

Two groups of subjects were used, an experimental group of 24 and a control group of 10. The 10 control subjects were given 5 practice trials and then 15 test trials with normal untelevised viewing. The 24 experimental subjects performed under four conditions: one blindfold condition, when no vision was allowed, and three television conditions, when their direct vision of performance was blocked by blinders mounted in aviator goggles and they guided performance by watching the television monitor. The three television conditions involved the horizontal camera displacements of 7, 90, and 225 degrees. Each experimental subject performed under all four conditions, but the order of presentation was varied systematically by subject. On the first day, each of these subjects was given 5 practice trials for each viewing condition, and then 15 test trials for each of two of these viewing conditions. The test trials for the other two viewing conditions − 15 for each − were given within 72 hours on a subsequent day.

The learning curves in Figure 10-7 represent the mean number of assemblies for the four experimental viewing conditions and for the normal viewing condition of the control group, plotted in terms of successive blocks of five trials. The curves show that performance with 90-degree and 225-degree displacements was essentially equivalent to blind performance. Performance with televised viewing displaced 7 degrees was markedly poorer than that of the control group with normal vision, but this effect was undoubtedly due in part to the difference between televised and direct viewing of the performance field. Analyses of variance and appropriate tests of significance confirmed these relationships − that performance with 7-degree displacement was significantly

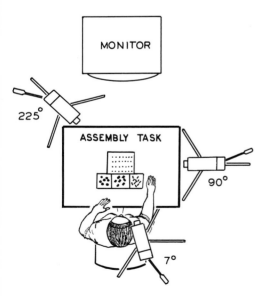

Figure 10-6. The performance situation and television camera placements for studying the relative effects of different horizontal displacements on assembly performance.

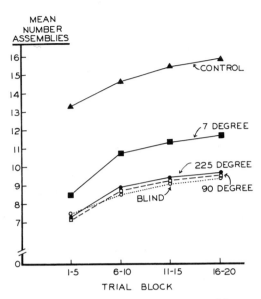

Figure 10-7. Learning curves of assembly performance with normal viewing, with different horizontal displacements of televised visual feedback, and with no vision.

better than with 90-degree or 225-degree displacements or blindfold, and that performances in these latter three conditions were not significantly different.

DIFFERENTIAL EFFECTS ON COMPONENT MOVEMENTS. A detailed analysis was made of the differential effects of horizontal displacements on the component movements of an assembly task — grasp, loaded travel, assemble, and non-loaded travel. The assumption was that the movements that were most highly organized visually, in particular the loaded travel and assemble components, would be affected more severely by angular displacements than other less precise components.

The experimental set-up is diagrammed in Figure 10-8. The subject's direct vision of the assembly bin and plate was blocked by a screen located at chest level. Five standard viewing conditions were used in this experiment. The first four involved camera place-

ments at 0 degrees, 60 degrees, 120 degrees, and 180 degrees horizontal displacement to the left from the mesial plane. At 0 degrees, the subject's view of his right hand in the performance field was normal, with the wrist toward the bottom and the thumb at the left. At 60 and 120 degrees, the thumb was more in the forefront, while the wrist was at the right of the visual field. At 180 degrees, the wrist was toward the top of the subject's visual field and the thumb toward the right, as he watched himself performing "head-on." Thus, at 180 degrees, there was a right-left reversal of motion, when movements made toward the right were seen as movements to the left. There was also a front-back reversal with this viewing condition, so that the horizontal movements used in this task were, in effect, both reversed and inverted in the visual field. (Movements in the vertical dimension, however, would not appear inverted.) For the fifth viewing condition, an inverting prism was mounted over the camera lens when the camera was displaced at 180 degrees. This produced a normal-looking hand, with the wrist

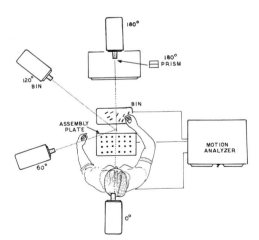

Figure 10-8. The experimental set-up used to analyze the effects of horizontal displacements on different component movements of an assembly task.

toward the bottom of the visual field, and canceled out the front-to-back "inversion" of horizontal movements, although there was still a right-left reversal of the visual field. It must be remembered, however, that with the locus of vision displaced, the subject has an entirely different view of the performance field than he has in our so-called systematic conditions of inversion and reversal.

The subject's task was to take metal pins (¼ in. in diameter but tapered, and 1 in. long) from a supply bin and insert them into holes (¼ in. in diameter) in an assembly plate. There were 24 holes in the plate, 1 inch apart, and one trial consisted of filling all the holes. The four component movements of the assembly cycle — grasp, loaded travel, assemble, and nonloaded travel — were timed separately by a four-channel motion analyzer.

Forty right-handed subjects were divided into five groups of eight subjects each. Each group performed with a different displacement condition: 0, 60, 120, and 180 degrees, and 180 degrees with prism. Each subject performed three trials per day for five successive days. The median duration of the three obtained for each component movement in a daily session was used as the subject's time score for that component on that day.

The learning curves in Figure 10-9 represent the mean total performance times for the assembly task on the five successive days. Performance with 120-degree displacement of the locus of vision was consistently the slowest on all five days of the study. Next slowest performance was obtained with the 180-degree displacement (appearing inverted and reversed), followed by the 180-degree displacement with prism (reversed); the differences between these two conditions were slight. Performance with 60-degree displacement started fairly slowly, but after four days had

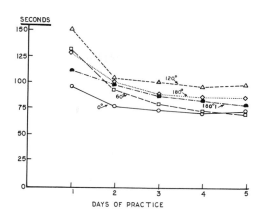

Figure 10-9. Learning curves of assembly performance over five days with horizontal displacements of 0, 60, 120 and 180 degrees, and 180 degrees with inverting prism.

reached the level obtained with 0-degree displacement. Although a 60-degree displacement was initially within the breakdown range for this particular motion pattern, the subjects were able to adapt to it within a few days, whereas the more extreme angular displacements appeared to disturb motion organization more or less permanently. The fact that motion was disturbed somewhat less with 180-degree displacements confirms our general assumption that displacements that conform to the axes of the body are less disturbing than extreme nonsystematic angular displacements.

The differential effects of the displacement conditions on the various component movements are indicated in Figure 10-10, which shows the relative durations of each component on the fifth day of the experiment as a function of displacement conditions. The values plotted are ratio scores, computed relative to the durations recorded with 0-degree displacement. It can be seen that the various movement components were not always affected in the same way by visual displacement as the complete motion pattern. Although the grasp, assemble, and empty transport

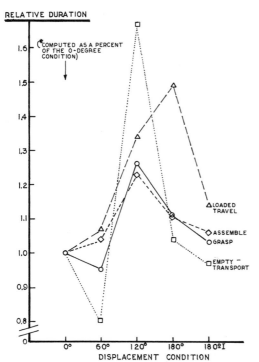

RELATIVE DURATION

*COMPUTED AS A PERCENT OF THE 0-DEGREE CONDITION)

△ LOADED TRAVEL
◇ ASSEMBLE
○ GRASP
□ EMPTY TRANSPORT

0°   60°   120°   180°   180°I
DISPLACEMENT CONDITION

Figure 10-10. Relative durations of component movements of an assembly task on last day of practice as a function of displacement conditions, when durations at zero degrees are made equal to 1.

movements showed the greatest disturbance with 120-degree displacement, the loaded travel component was slowest with the 180-degree displacement. Overall, the variation in travel movements was greater than for manipulative movements. Statistical analyses indicated that variations in manipulative components were not significant. For the loaded travel component, the mean at 0-degrees differed significantly from all but the 60-degree condition, and the mean at 180 degrees differed significantly from all other conditions. For the nonloaded travel component, the mean at 120 degrees differed significantly from all other conditions.

The results of this experiment confirmed our expectations only in part. As

expected, different conditions of visual displacement affected the various movement components differentially, i.e., the degree of disturbance depended not only on the displacement conditions but on the nature of the movement under consideration. We also confirmed our assumption that there exists a range of displacement within which the system can compensate, so that relatively complete adaptation can occur. In the situation studied here, this range turned out to be fairly large; recovery appeared to be complete with a displacement of the locus of vision of 60 degrees, but at 120 degrees the disturbing effect could not be entirely overcome. A third result that conformed to our expectations was that, in general, disturbance was less severe with systematic displacements, which conform to bodily axes, than with extreme nonsystematic displacements. Also, when the motion pattern appeared both inverted and reversed, the effects were somewhat greater than when it appeared reversed, although the differences were not generally significant.

The effects of displacement on the different component movements were not entirely as expected. We had predicted that the movements which were most highly organized visually — loaded travel and assemble — would suffer the most severe effects. Actually the results seemed to show a differential effect between manipulative and travel movements, with the travel components showing the most severe disturbances. It is possible that control of the manipulations in this assembly task was taken over to some extent by touch and kinesthesis, so that the greatest effects of the distorted visual cues were seen on the travel movements.

VISUAL DISPLACEMENT VERSUS PERFORMANCE DISPLACEMENT. An experiment was designed to compare the effects of two types of displacement of the visual feedback of target tapping motions: first, changing the locus of the television camera, and second, changing the orientation of the performance field with respect to the body and the television eye. In Figure 10-11, the diagram to the left shows the task and camera arrangement, while the diagram to the right indicates the details of the target panel and monitor. The target panel was a 24-inch square glass plate within which 36 round metal targets, ¼ inch in diameter, were embedded, 3 inches apart in six rows of six. A black cardboard was mounted behind the glass panel so that the targets appeared on the television monitor as white spots. The size of the monitor picture was approximately one-half the actual size of the target panel. The task was to touch each target with a stylus, starting at the upper right and proceeding toward the left across each row in order until the lower left target was touched. The subjects were told to strike the targets cleanly, and to work as fast as possible. One trial consisted of striking all the targets in order once. A two-channel electronic motion analyzer recorded separately the durations of contact and travel movements.

Fifty right-handed subjects were divided randomly into five groups of ten subjects each. The first group performed with 0 degrees displacement of the television camera and 0 degrees displacement of the work panel. That is, the camera viewed performance from a position equivalent to the normal locus of vision, and the target panel was oriented perpendicularly to this line of sight, and to the orientation of the subject. The second and third experimental groups performed with the television camera at 0 degrees, but with the target panel displaced angularly 30 and 45 degrees respectively. The fourth and fifth experimental groups performed with the target panel at 0 degrees, but with the television camera displaced angularly to the right 30 and 60 degrees respectively. These displacements of panel and

camera are shown in Figure 10-12. Each subject performed five trials per day for five successive days. On the fifth day, the first, second, and third groups were given five additional trials with each of the other two positions of the work panel, to test for transfer effects.

The camera displacements and work panel displacements used in this study produced monitor images that were very similar. The two 30-degree displacements looked much the same on television, and the 45-degree displacement of the work panel produced an image not too far different from the 60-degree displacement of the camera. However, the motion patterns for the two types of

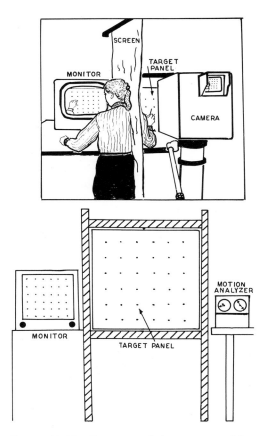

Figure 10-11. Diagrams of the set-up used in target-tapping experiment.

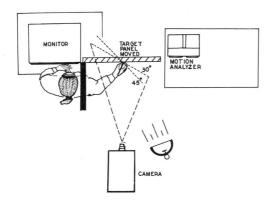

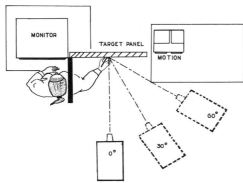

Figure 10-12. Displacements of the performance field and of the television camera used in the target-tapping study.

displacements were very different. When the work panel was displaced, the movements of the subject had to be reorganized to conform to the diagonal orientation of the performance field, but when the camera was displaced, the movement pattern remained the same and only the pattern of visual feedback changed. Our assumption was that displacements of the work panel would thus disturb motion more than displacements of the camera.

In analyzing the data, the median contact and travel times for each subject's five daily trials were taken as that subject's scores for that day. Learning

curves for contact times for the five groups are summarized in Figure 10-13. The most disturbing condition for contact movements was the 45-degree displacement of the work panel (45° P). This effect was statistically significant for all days taken together and for the last day alone. Although the fastest contact movements on the last day were made with the 60-degree camera displacement (60° C), this performance was not significantly different from that with 0-degree displacement. Nor did the contact means for the 30-degree displacement differ significantly from those for 0-degrees. Similar curves for travel movement times are shown in Figure 10-14. It should be observed that the time scale for this graph is different from

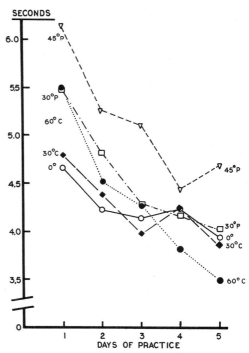

Figure 10-13. Learning curves of contact time under the different conditions of camera-produced (C) and panel-produced (P) displacement of the visual feedback of target-tapping motions.

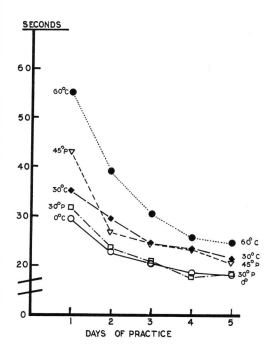

SECONDS

Figure 10-14. Learning curves of travel time under the different conditions of camera-produced (C) and panel-produced (P) displacement of the visual feedback of target-tapping motions.

near the breakdown angle for effective performance. With the 60-degree displacement in this experiment, contact movements recovered to normal speed after five days, but travel movements did not entirely recover. We can conclude that the range of normal angles of displacement and the size of breakdown angles vary with the type of motion pattern, and the nature of the movement component.

IMPROVED ACCURACY IN DRAWING OVER FOUR DAYS. In the studies described so far, movement duration scores were used as the performance criterion. A further study was carried out with horizontal displacements to determine whether motions improved in accuracy with practice under extreme displacement conditions. Twelve subjects were asked to reproduce four geometric figures — circle, square, triangle, and star — while watching their drawing performance on the television monitor. The figures were approximately the size of a two-inch square. All four figures were drawn with horizontal displacements of 0, 120, and 180 degrees on each of four days.

In this experiment, we were interested primarily in the nature of movement control at the 120-degree displacement angle, inasmuch as performance time scores had shown but limited improvement with this viewing condition. Figure 10-15 reproduces the drawings of three representative subjects at this displacement angle over the four days of the experiment. Progress of a single subject can be followed by observing the blocks of four figures in a column from top to bottom. It can be seen by looking at the topmost drawings that the initial effects of the angular displacement were very severe. Complete blocking of motion was frequent, and repetitive motions, comparable to stuttering in speech, sometimes occurred. Repeated movements in the wrong direction were characteristic of many subjects. Tremor-

the contact movement scale, for travel movements in this task were roughly ten times the duration of contact movements. The slowest travel times occurred with the 60-degree camera displacement, an effect that was statistically significant. The 45-degree panel displacement and the 30-degree camera displacement produced travel curves that were much the same, while the 30-degree panel displacement produced a travel curve similar to 0 degrees.

These results indicated that the displacement of the performance field used in this experiment did not hamper performance significantly, except for an increase in contact time with the larger displacement. The data on displacing the locus of vision are in keeping with other comparable observations. A displacement of 60 degrees appears to be

DAYS   SUBJECTS

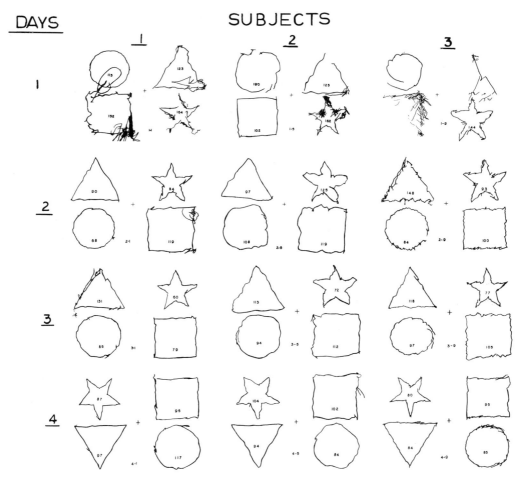

Figure 10-15. Improved accuracy in drawing geometric figures over four days with 120-degree horizontal displacement of visual feedback.

like movements can be seen in some drawings as irregularities superimposed on movements made in the correct general direction.

Practice materially improved the performance of all subjects. Complete blocks in motion disappeared for the most part, and the general appearance of the drawings showed marked improvement. However, none of the subjects achieved highly accurate control in the four days. About half of them still showed on the last day of practice persisting incoordinations of motion, quite frequently marked by tremor-like loss of control. For some subjects, the attempt to draw was a painful effort, almost as bad on the fourth day as on the first. Performance times (shown in seconds by the number inside each drawing) were reduced generally but not consistently over the four days.

The results of this experiment are consistent with those described above. At extreme angles of nonsystematic visual displacement, patterned motion is seriously disturbed both in accuracy of control and time of performance. With practice, some improvement occurs, but there is no indication that recovery is complete.

Displacements in the Mesial Plane

An experiment on handwriting was carried out with camera displacements in the mesial plane, from back toward the front overhead, as shown in Figure 10-16. Our assumption was that these displacements would disturb motion very little, because of the normal anatomical relationships between eyes and hands, and the range of normal eye-hand displacement angles in ordinary behavior. The direction of gaze in observing one's own manual motions can change remarkably along the mesial plane, due to variations in posture and the positions of the hands, without disturbing the visual control of motion. In contrast, normal variations in horizontal displacement of locus of vision are much more limited.

Three camera positions were used in this experiment, at mesial displacement angles of 55, 90, and 125 degrees from the horizontal plane of the performance field. The 55-degree displacement was well within the ordinary range defined

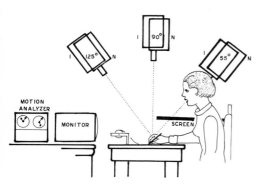

Figure 10-16. Experimental set-up used to study handwriting performance with mesial displacements of the locus of vision.

by direction of gaze and performance field. The 90-degree position was directly over the field, while the 125-degree position was farther toward the front. In addition to these three viewing conditions, an inverting lens was used on the camera at each position to invert the visual field. Thus there were six viewing conditions in all – upright and inverted at the three angular displacements. Thirty-six subjects were divided into six groups of six, with each group performing under a different viewing condition. They wrote rows of dots, k's, and triangles, three rows of each character per day for nine days, while contact and travel times were recorded by means of a handwriting analyzer.

The learning data from this experiment are summarized in Figure 10-17. Means are plotted for each of three writing tasks – making dots, writing k's, and drawing triangles – at all viewing conditions. Contact movement means are plotted on the graph to the left, and travel movement means to the right. Open circles represent performance in inverted visual fields, and closed circles represent performance in upright visual fields. It can be seen that there is no overlap in means between upright and inverted conditions, except for the fact that the contact times for making dots in inverted fields fall within the range of means for noninverted fields. The noninverted displacements at the three angles used caused little or no disturbance of either contact or travel movements in any of the tasks, and differences related to the different angles were not significant. When these displaced fields were inverted, however, all movements were seriously impaired except the contact movements in the dotting task. With practice, performance in the inverted fields improved, but it never reached the level of performance in noninverted fields.

Although the three mesial displacements used did not result in significant

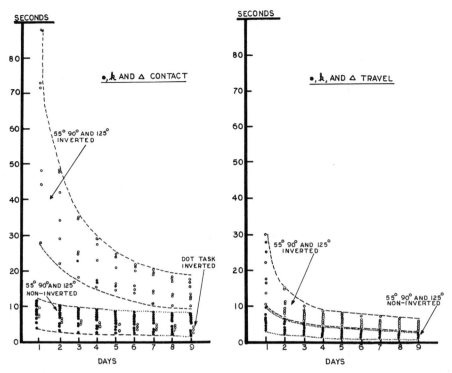

Figure 10-17. Graphical distributions of the means for contact and travel movements of hand-writing with three mesial displacements (55, 90, and 125 degrees) when the feedback image was upright and inverted. The upright condition is indicated by closed circles, and the inverted condition, by open circles.

differences in performance with upright viewing, differential effects related to the magnitude of the angle of displacement were observed when the visual feedback was inverted. The graph in Figure 10-18 plots mean contact times of the three different tasks on the last day of practice as performed with inverted feedback, as a function of the displacement angle. It can be seen that movement times increased with the magnitude of displacement. Statistical tests of the data showed that performance at 125-degree displacement, with inversion, differed significantly from performance at the other two angles, also with inversion.

The results of this experiment have some interesting implications for our concept of normal and breakdown

angles of displacement. As predicted, the mesial displacements, within the range used, caused very little disturbance of motion; the differences related to the different angles were not statistically significant. However, when the mesially displaced feedback was also inverted, performance with the different displacement angles was no longer equivalent, but varied according to the magnitude of the angle. This means that different breakdown functions can be determined for mesially displaced feedback, for non-inverted and for inverted feedback. Results such as these confirm our interpretation that so-called visual displacement is not an absolute condition, but is defined by a number of feedback variables.

When the results of this experiment

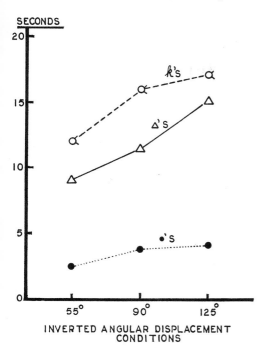

SECONDS

Figure 10-18. Durations of different handwriting tasks as a function of mesial displacements, when the visual fields are also inverted.

obtained with noninverted feedback are compared with the experiments on horizontal displacements, we see that the normal range of displacement in the mesial plane is much larger than in the horizontal plane. This can be confirmed easily by casual observations of eye-hand relationships in different types of skilled performances. The direction of gaze can vary easily between 20 and 90 degrees in the mesial plane with no apparent effect on performance.

DIRECT VERSUS COMPENSATORY ADAPTATION TO ANGULAR DISPLACEMENT

A major experiment was designed to compare the relative efficiency of using direct and compensatory reactions to angularly displaced visual feedback. The tasks used were making dots, writing k's, and drawing triangles. Direct and compensatory reactions were compared with three different conditions of angular displacement, over a relatively long adaptation period of nine days.

Procedures

The set-up and camera placements used in this experiment are shown in Figure 10-19. Forty-eight right-handed subjects were divided randomly into eight groups of six subjects each, and each group was assigned a different condition of viewing or performance. The first group wrote normally, with a normal direct view of the writing area. The second group wrote with televised viewing, with a 0-degree displacement of the camera. The third, fourth, and fifth groups were assigned three extreme angular displacement conditions: 90 degrees to the subject's left, 180 degrees, and 270 degrees (equivalent to 90 degrees to the right). Because the 180-degrees camera displacement produces a reversal and inversion of the motion pattern of a task performed with horizontal movements, as explained in the last section, we shall speak of this condition as inversion-reversal (IR). It should be remembered that this inverted-reversed motion pattern caused by shifting the locus of vision is not the same feedback condition as that produced by inverting and reversing the visual field without shifting the locus of vision. These three experimental groups performed in their respective displaced fields with direct reactions — that is, they wrote characters in their normal upright orientation. The sixth, seventh, and eighth groups were given the same 90-degree, 180-degree, and 270-degree displacements, but used compensatory reactions that looked normal in the displaced fields.

The experimental task was to write rows of nine dots, nine k's, and nine

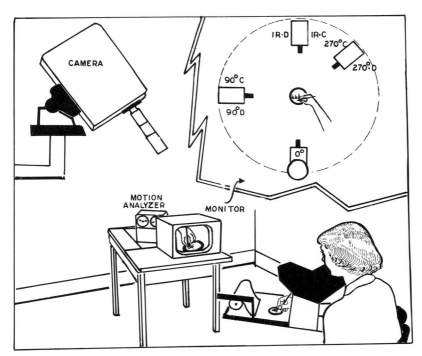

Figure 10-19. Set-up used to compare direct and compensatory handwriting performance with horizontally displaced feedback.

triangles with the base down, each row constituting a single trial while contact and travel movement times were recorded separately. Each subject wrote three rows of each character each day, and the median scores for the day, for each different character, were used for data analysis. All groups performed with their assigned viewing and performance conditions for nine days. On the tenth day, those subjects who had been using direct reactions shifted to compensatory, and vice versa.

Learning Effects

The learning curves in Figure 10-20 represent the mean total time for all writing tasks plotted separately for each condition as a function of days of practice. The letter N refers to normal direct viewing, IR refers to inverted-reversed, or 180-degree displacement, and D and C refer to direct and compensatory reactions. It can be seen that all groups showed some learning effects, and that the curves leveled off more rapidly for the easier conditions. Very little learning occurred with either the normal direct viewing condition, or the television viewing with 0-degree displacement. These curves are essentially parallel throughout, although the television viewing shows the characteristic increment in performance time over direct viewing. The curves showing slowest performance are those for compensatory reactions to 90-degree and 180-degree displacements. These two conditions produced by far the slowest performance initially, and after nine days of practice were still slower than any other condition. Direct reactions to 90-, 180-, and 270-degree displacements, and compensatory reactions to 270-degree displacement showed remarkably similar learning curves. At the end of nine days, they were all very close in performance time, and all somewhat slower than performance with the 0-degree displacement.

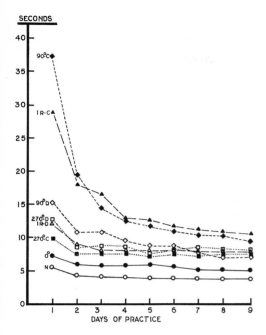

Figure 10-20. Learning curves of mean total durations of direct and compensatory handwriting performance with different displacements.

Differential Effects According to Writing Tasks and Movement Components

The specific effects of the different conditions of viewing and performance can be seen more clearly when movement times are plotted separately for each movement component and for each writing task used. To make these comparisons, we show mean performance times for the different groups on the first day of practice, in Figure 10-21, and on the last day, in Figure 10-22. These bar graphs show data only for the six groups that used direct and compensatory reactions to extreme angular displacements. The performance time of the group that used television viewing with 0-degree displacement is indicated by a vertical line through each set of bars.

Figure 10-21 shows that, on the first

day of practice, the effects of using compensatory reactions to displacements of 90 and 180 degrees (IR) were very severe, often causing near breakdown of movement control. The writing task showing the most severe disturbance was the most complex task spatially — that of writing *k*'s — and the task showing the least disturbance was the dotting task. Even in the dotting task, however, travel movements were markedly increased in duration by the 90-degree displacement.

On the ninth day of practice, as shown in Figure 10-22, the differential effects

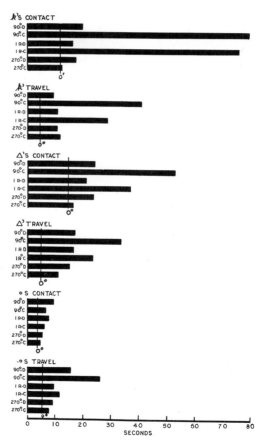

Figure 10-21. Mean first-day durations of contact and travel movements with the six feedback conditions.

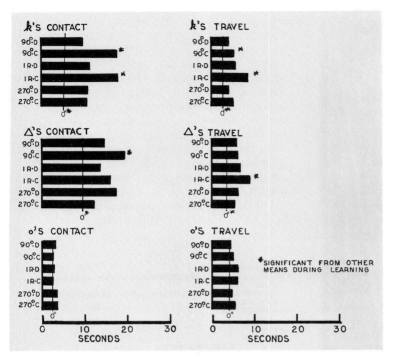

Figure 10-22. Mean last-day durations of contact and travel movements with the six feedback conditions.

of the 90-degree and 180-degree displacements were still evident, although proportionally the effects were not as severe as on the first day. All groups performing with extreme angular displacements were slower than the groups with 0 degrees, except for the contact time in making dots. The conditions in Figure 10-22 marked with asterisks represent means that were significantly different from almost all other conditions during the nine days of practice. The ones so marked are the 0-degrees displacement (vertical line) and the 90-degree and 180-degree (IR) displacements with compensatory reactions.

Transfer Effects between Direct and Compensatory Movements

On the tenth day of this experiment, the groups that had trained with direct reactions to displacement were transferred to compensatory reactions, and the groups that had trained with compensatory reactions were transferred to

direct. To determine what effects the intermediate nine days of training had on performance on the tenth day, we compare tenth day transfer scores under a particular experimental condition with first day scores made by the paired group under the same condition. For example, the group that trained with direct reactions to 90-degree displacement transferred on the tenth day to compensatory reactions. Their mean transfer score can be compared with the mean first-day score made by the group that trained with compensatory reactions to 90-degree displacement.

These comparisons between transfer scores and first-day scores are presented in Table 10-1, as per cent reductions in mean total performance times shown by the transfer group from the original performance times of the training group. The most marked reductions due to transfer effects were shown by groups that trained with direct reactions at 90-degree and 180-degree displacements, and then transferred to compensatory

Table 10-1. Per cent Reduction in Performance Times Due to Transfer Effects

DEGREES OF DISPLACEMENT	TRANSFER FROM DIRECT TO COMPENSATORY	TRANSFER FROM COMPENSATORY TO DIRECT
90	30 per cent	68 per cent
180	−15 per cent	42 per cent
270	35 per cent	−3 per cent

reactions on the tenth day. However, the results are not clear-cut. Two negative effects are shown, indicating that two of the transfer groups did more poorly on their tenth day tests than the groups that had been started on the same conditions on the first day. In most cases, however, training in writing performance with angularly displaced visual feedback, using either direct or compensatory movements, showed positive transfer effects to the other type of movement.

Theoretical Implications

The results of this experiment were fairly consistent from day to day and in general confirmed other experimental findings. The learning data show clearly that, although performance with extreme angular displacements of visual feedback improves with practice, it does not usually recover completely to normal levels. The curves for total performance time leveled off after a few days, but continued to be elevated above performance with 0 degrees displacement. This generalization does not necessarily hold true for some movement components of very simple tasks. For example, contact times for the dotting tasks recovered to normal levels. Recovery was poorest for tasks with a high degree of spatial complexity, requiring almost continual visual guidance.

The use of compensatory reaction in displaced visual fields resulted in slower performance initially than direct reactions. In some cases, compensatory performance continued to be slower throughout the experiment.

Confirming our expectations, the 90-degree displacement proved to be very difficult. However, we did not expect that the 180-degree displacement would be almost as difficult or that the 270-degree displacement would cause so little disturbance. Here we have a writing task that shows marked disturbance when the television camera is displaced 90 degrees to the left, but much less disturbance when the camera is moved 90 degrees to the right (the 270-degree condition). Using compensatory movements at 270 degrees seemed to be particularly easy for the subjects. We have no ready explanation for these results, unless it has something to do with ordinary patterns of writing of most right-handed persons. Many people habitually turn their writing paper to the right at quite an angle and, therefore, write diagonally away from themselves. Writing with compensatory movements at the 270-degree displacement would not be too different from this ordinary diagonal pattern.

QUANTITATIVE FUNCTIONS OF ANGULAR DISPLACEMENT OF VISION

An experiment was designed to establish quantitative angular displacement functions for visually guided motion. Subjects were trained in two tasks, drawing circles and maze tracing, at four different angles of horizontal displacement of the locus of vision, 0, 20, 40, and 60 degrees, and then tested for accuracy of performance of eight different displacement angles: 0, 10, 20, 30, 40, 50, 60, and 70 degrees. The use of accuracy measures was a departure from most of the other experiments described in this chapter, where time measures were used. The television arrangement is shown in Figure 10-23.

Twenty-four undergraduate students were used as subjects, with each subject performing both tasks under all conditions. The first nine days of the experiment were given over to training trials. On each of these days, each subject first drew three circles under each of the four training displacement conditions, and then traced one maze under the same four conditions. The order of presentation of conditions was varied systematically by subject. On the tenth day, all subjects performed both tasks under each of the eight test conditions of displacement. The order of presentation of conditions was randomized as far as possible, so that each subject followed a different order.

Drawing Circles

In drawing circles, the subjects were instructed to try to draw as perfect a circle as possible, regardless of the appearance of the form in the television monitor. Obviously a perfect circle would appear distorted at all angular displacements except 0 degrees. The ratio of the vertical axis/horizontal axis of a circle was used as a quantitative measure of accuracy in this task. Of the three circles drawn by each subject in a given condition, the median score was used in data analysis.

The accuracy of performance in circle drawing on the tenth day is summarized in Figure 10-24, where mean ratios for all subjects are plotted against the different displacement angles used in the final day tests. A perfect circle is represented by a ratio of 1.00. It can be seen that the function represented here is essentially linear, with progressive distortion as the angle of displacement increased. The subjects were compensating in their motion patterns for the distorted appearance of the visual field,

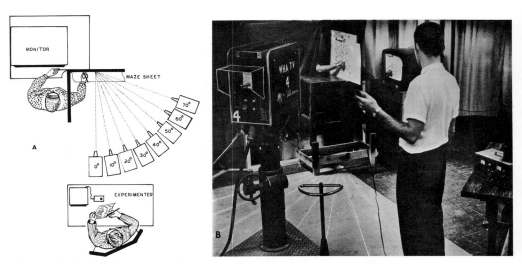

Figure 10-23.   A. Experimental set-up used to determine quantitative breakdown functions for horizontal angular visual displacement. B. Photograph of maze-tracing experiment.

Table 10-2. Summary of Significant Differences between Circle Ratio Means at Different Angles of Displacement

Angle	70°	60°	50°	40°	30°	20°	10°	0°
Mean°	81.0	86.0	89.1	90.6	95.5	96.3	97.8	100.8

° Any two means not underlined by a common line are significantly different at the 1 per cent level of significance.

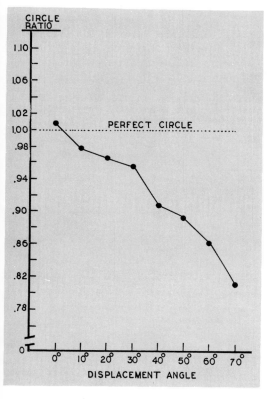

Figure 10-24. Accuracy in circle drawing as a function of magnitude of horizontal visual displacement.

were obtained. Any means not underlined by the same line were significantly different at the 1 per cent level. While only the mean at 70 degrees differed significantly from all other means, all of the means differed significantly from at least three other means.

Maze Tracing

The maze pattern used in this experiment is shown in Figure 10-25. The subject was required to trace a marked path through a series of short passageways, as can be seen in the figure. Although the image of the maze on the television monitor appeared very distorted at the larger angles of displacement, it never appeared to offer an impossible task. That is, the subject could always see the openings clearly

and did so from the smallest to the largest displacement angles.

These data were subjected to analyses of variance, and Duncan range tests were applied to determine the significance of differences between means. Table 10-2 lists the mean circle ratios, in order of increasing magnitude, under the displacement angles at which they

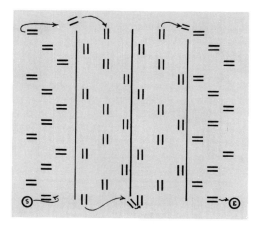

Figure 10-25. The maze pattern used in determining breakdown function of horizontal visual displacement.

through which he had to trace. An error was recorded in this task whenever the subject's traced pathway came into contact with one of the walls of a passageway. Only one error per passageway was counted.

The mean error scores for the tenth (test) day are plotted in Figure 10-26 as a function of displacement angles. The graph shows clearly that throughout a range of 40 degrees of displacement there was no significant variation in the accuracy of performance. Beyond 40 degrees, increasing magnitudes of horizontal displacement of the locus of vision caused decreasing accuracy of maze tracing, until a nearly complete breakdown of motor control was shown at 70 degrees. Statistical analyses confirmed these relationships. The mean error scores obtained at displacement angles from 0 through 40 degrees were not significantly different from each other, but the means at 50 degrees, 60 degrees, and 70 degrees differed significantly from all other means at the 1 per cent level of significance.

Concept of Normal and Breakdown Angles Confirmed

The difference between the displacement functions for circle drawing and maze tracing undoubtedly was due to the nature of the tasks. In circle drawing, there were no guideposts in the visual field by means of which the subjects could judge the precision of their performance. Consequently, they tended to compensate for the visual displacement by drawing ellipses which looked like circles. These compensatory reactions were used at every displacement angle, from 10 degrees on. Thus there was no marked break in the curve throughout the displacement range used for testing, but a progressively poorer performance when judged by the experimenter's criterion. From the subjects' point of view, their performance was about as effective at the larger angles as at the smaller.

In contrast, the curve of accuracy in maze tracing showed a sharp break. From 0 to 40 degrees displacement, performance was statistically equivalent, thus defining the normal range of horizontal displacement for this motion pattern. From 50 degrees on, accuracy decreased as the displacement angle increased. In a sense, the quantitative function shown in Figure 10-26 summarizes the main point of this chapter. It confirms our belief that the normal angular displacement range of neurogeometric control of motion is a perceptual-motor fact of life, and indicates that the phenomenon of movement breakdown with magnitudes of displacement beyond the normal range is a

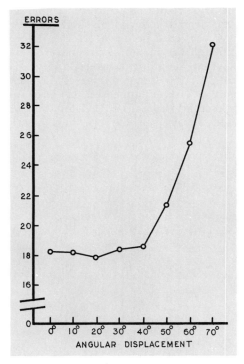

Figure 10-26. Accuracy of maze tracing as a function of magnitude of horizontal visual displacement. Breakdown range is indicated by the rising part of the curve.

function of the magnitude of the displacement angle within the breakdown range.

It has long been our belief that a true understanding of human skill patterns — how they are acquired, why they are so specifically organized, what are their limiting conditions — depends on more basic knowledge of the mechanisms of perceptual-motor integration, including particularly the functional anatomy of the visuomotor system. In this connection, it is significant that the course of mammalian and primate evolution has led to the positioning of the eyes in a progressively more frontal position. From this vantage point, human eyes survey readily not only the physical environment, but also most of the body, and the motions made by the body in relation to the environment. Our theoretical assumption is that this evolutionary process has been defined by selective geometric factors of organization at both the neural and muscular levels, which have had the result of bringing ocular and manual behavior into more efficient and refined spatial correspondence in the manipulation of objects.

According to neurogeometric theory, the anatomical correspondence of eye and hand (or paw) in primates is a significant aspect of motion organization. We see in it a genetically defined mechanism of dynamic regulation of posture, transport, and manipulative movements. The eye-hand function depends on detection of displaced visual feedback of motion at all levels of movement organization, and the neurons acting as detectors for such displacement must have been elaborated through the selective processes of evolution. In man, the relationship of eye and hand is perfected to such a point that a major part of visual perception consists in observing oneself in motion, particularly the movements of the hands or their effects in the manipulation of objects. Other animals use their eyes to guide body motion in space, but human vision is more concerned with guiding the movements of the hands in relation to the body and to the manipulative world.

One of the most critical features of these visually guided manipulations is their geometric flexibility, for the angular relationships between line of sight and manipulative planes vary widely in ordinary behavior without disturbing motion efficiency. We have confirmed this fact of visuomotor behavior by the experiments described in this chapter, and we have shown further that there are definite limits to the flexibility and adaptability of the motion system — limits to the angular displacement between eye and hand within which normal motion can occur.

The limits of feedback displacement are defined by many variables, some of which we have investigated. Specifically, we have shown that normal and breakdown ranges of visual displacement depend on the plane of displacement, on its relation to the axes of the body, on the movement component, on the type and complexity of motion pattern, on the criterion of performance, and on whether compensatory movements are used. Further, we have found that relative effects are often unpredictable, due to the multidimensional nature of motions and their several channels of feedback control. When we attempt to study the visual control of motion, we cannot cancel out cutaneous and kinesthetic control, or specify precisely their roles in a particular situation.

SUMMARY

1. This chapter takes up experiments on nonsystematic visual displacement, as contrasted to systematic displacements corresponding to body axes. The studies reported here are of angular displace-

ments of the locus of vision, effected by moving the television camera to different positions with relation to the performance field.

2. Prior experimental observations and our own theoretical analyses have led to formulation of the concept of normal and breakdown angles of feedback displacement. The assumption is that there is a range of displacement within which normal perceptual-motor activity can be carried out, and that beyond this range, breakdown of motion control occurs. The size of breakdown angles of displacement varies with both stimulus and performance variables.

3. In a series of studies, the effects of various visual displacements in the horizontal plane were determined. In an assembly task, displacements of 90 and 225 degrees slowed down performance as much as blindfolding the subjects, but a 7-degree displacement permitted effective performance.

4. In another assembly task, a 60-degree displacement caused initial slowdown, but could be adapted to; 180-degree displacements caused somewhat more disturbance; and a 120-degree displacement caused the most severe disturbance. Displacements affected component movements differentially, as predicted, but at 120 degrees, travel movements were more disturbed than manipulative movements, contrary to our expectations.

5. Target tapping was compared with displacements of the locus of vision and displacements of the orientation of the performance field. Contact movements were disturbed initially by 30 and 60 degree displacements of the camera, and 30 degree displacement of the tapping panel, but in all three cases recovered to normal level within a few days. With displacement of the tapping panel of 45 degrees, contact movements were slowed down more and did not recover within five days. Travel movements were affected differently, with the greatest

disturbance with 60 degree camera displacement, somewhat less with 30 degree camera displacement and 45 degree panel displacement, and no significant disturbance with 30 degree panel displacement.

6. When accuracy of drawing figures was tested with extreme displacement angles (120 and 180 degrees), it was found that performance improved somewhat over four days, but did not recover to normal.

7. Displacements in the mesial plane, at 55, 90, and 125 degrees from the horizontal, did not affect handwriting significantly, but when the performance field also was inverted, these mesial displacements affected performance differentially, with degree of disturbance increasing with the magnitude of the angle.

8. Direct and compensatory handwriting reactions with horizontal visual displacements of 0, 90, 180, and 270 degrees were compared over a period of nine days. Overall, the 90 degree (to the left) condition was most difficult and the 270 degree condition (90 degrees to the right) was relatively easy. Compensatory reactions at 90 and 180 degrees were slower throughout than direct, but not at 270 degrees. More complex motions (making k's) were slowed down far more than simpler motions. There was generally some positive transfer between direct and compensatory learning with displaced feedback, but the effects were not consistent.

9. Quantitative functions of motion control were determined for circle drawing and maze tracing at horizontal displacement angles of 0, 10, 20, 30, 40, 50, 60, and 70 degrees. Subjects compensated in drawing circles for the displacement, to make their circles look round, so that their accuracy ratios dropped off gradually in a roughly linear function as the displacement angles increased. In contrast, accuracy in maze tracing remained at normal level through 40 de-

grees displacement, and then decreased sharply as the angle was increased from 50 through 70 degrees. This function is a quantitative expression of the concept of normal and breakdown ranges of visual feedback displacement.

10. In general, motion is disturbed more by extreme nonsystematic displace-ments than by displacements in the di-mensions of the body axes. Normal and breakdown angles vary with the plane of displacement, with movement com-ponents, with type and complexity of motion, with the criterion of perform-ance, and according to whether com-pensatory movements are used.

CHAPTER 11

SIZE-DISTORTED VISUAL FEEDBACK

A perennial problem of the study of perception as well as of armchair science is to understand the determinants of perceived size. Perceptual judgment of size corresponds neither with actual size of stimulus objects nor with the relative size of the sensory area stimulated. Generally speaking, the perceived size of an object remains relatively constant, but this constancy is not absolute. Variations in perceived size do occur, as a result of both external and internal factors.

The facts of so-called size constancy are so commonplace as to escape ordinary attention. A person seen across the room does not change in apparent size as he walks toward the observer, al-

though the size of the retinal image is changing remarkably. For the most part, we live in a world of constant objects, but under some conditions, constancy gives way to variability. The person whose size remains the same at ordinary distances appears tiny if seen from the top of a high building. Radical changes in the perceptual field of an object also can lead to perceived size variation. The moon illusion — the apparent decrease in the size of the moon as it moves from horizon to zenith — has been a subject of speculation since the time of Ptolemy. Some early British psychologists tried to account for this illusion as resulting from sensory information from specific ocular muscles, but no entirely satisfactory explanation has ever been given, either of this illusion or of other perceptual discriminations of size.

Interpretations of size variation or size constancy in perception have varied among psychologists according to their general interests and points of view. Gestalt psychologists,[33, 148, 305] searching for experimental foundations for a science of perception, cited the events of size constancy as evidence for a theory of neural equivalence and dynamic cortical organization of perceptual experience. More recently, social psychologists have made much of facts of interaction of perceived size and distance in support of the general argument that attitudes influence perception.[138] Learning theorists find in the events of size variation or size constancy, as the occasion demands, evidence for the point of view that what we perceive changes with learning or can be made constant with learning.[147] There also have been claims among those interested in personality that the apparent sizes of objects in the surrounding world can be related to emotional and conflict variables.

The events of size constancy and size variation in behavior are of particular interest to us here in relation to the assumptions of neurogeometric theory. The theory assumes that geometric properties of objects and space-structured movements are recorded by differential neurons of the brain, and that perception and motion are organized in terms of relative space differences. Visual perception of size is determined by the relative differences that exist in the whole visual field, and the reactions made to these differences. Accordingly, size constancy obtains when the differential pattern of stimulation remains *relatively* constant, leading to "behavioral constancy" of response. Optimal size constancy is found in well-organized visual fields, at moderate distances within which binocular differences are clearly defined, and when the observer maintains his normal geometric orientation with respect to the field. Any disturbance of the spatial organization or elimination of differential cues to which the observer can respond breaks down the size constancy effect to some extent. An object viewed within an absolutely homogeneous field is not as constant in size as if viewed within a well-articulated visual surrounding. Also, postural changes of the observer can influence size perception, e.g., an observer who

stoops over to view the full moon between his legs generally loses the moon illusion.

Monocular and Binocular Factors in Size Constancy

The primary factors determining visual size constancy are those related to retinal stimulation. In monocular vision, apparent size is relative to the overall pattern of stimulation, and size constancy can be demonstrated to some extent within an organized field of reference. With binocular vision, apparent size is more stable because of the additional cues provided by binocular parallax. The disparate images, the movements related to them, and the various feedback relationships — visual and kinesthetic — provide the important cues for depth perception. Apparent size is very closely dependent on perceived depth; an object moving away from the observer remains fairly constant in apparent size as long as the cues for depth perception are effective. With restricted visual conditions, variation in size of the retinal image can be reacted to either as variations in object size or as variations in distance.

Under normal conditions, the individual adjusts his movements accurately to the spatial properties of his visual world within a wide range of stimulus variations. This is possible because reactions are organized according to relative differences in stimulus patterns — not absolute differences. Furthermore, it is possible to adjust rather easily to visual worlds of distorted size, as long as the proportionate relationships hold true. For example, a technician can adjust visually to the magnified world seen under a microscope, and also can adapt his manual movements to this world in moving or manipulating magnified objects. Once this adaptation has been made, he can shift without difficulty from performance in the ordinary visual world to the magnified one. Overall size distortion does not lead to disturbance and breakdown in motion patterns such as that brought on by displacement of the visual field.

One study that points up some basic differences between binocular and monocular factors in perception of size was carried out by Burian[36] on the effects of prolonged wearing of an aniseikonic lens. Three subjects wore such a lens in front of one eye for periods varying from eight to fifteen days. The effect of wearing the lens was to cause the size difference in the two retinal images. The magnitude of this induced image size difference, as measured by an eikonometer, varied from 1.5 per cent to 6 per cent for the different subjects. Extensive objective tests were made of localization and other aspects of visual perception, and many subjective reports were obtained.

The initial effects of the induced retinal size difference were very apparent to the subjects, who reported spatial disorientations, such as tilting of surfaces, and so forth. These effects gradually disappeared during the course of the experiment, as long as the subjects' visual environment was unrestricted, and was rich in monocular cues for size and depth. However, when the subjects' visual information was limited to binocular disparity factors, the distorting effect of the lens was still clearly apparent. In other words, the subjects adapted very well to the interocular size distortion, but only when they could view a highly articulated visual environment defined by factors of perspective; relative position of objects; textural, color, and brightness effects; relative movement, and so forth. These monocular cues for distance permitted an effective adaptation to the size distortion. But when the monocular cues were eliminated, the binocular size disparity persisted.

One interesting effect reported in this study was a very slight change in measured image size during the period when the lens was worn. That is, the image size difference measured at the end of the experiment had decreased slightly in comparison to the measured difference at the beginning. Burian referred to this effect as "psychologic adaptation or physiologic compensation," but the basis for it is not entirely clear.

This experiment is of particular interest to us not only because it is one of the few studies of adaptation to visual size distortion, but also because it differentiates between adaptive and nonadaptive perceptual-motor effects under the conditions of interocular distortion. When many differential cues were present, the subjects were able to adapt to the distortion and achieve a behavioral size constancy more or less equivalent to their pre-experimental mode of reaction. But the basic discrepancy between the retinal images was apparent when other cues were eliminated. The subjects could not compensate to any significant degree to disturbances in the highly precise intrinsic mechanisms of interocular control.

These results indicate to us that there are neurogeometric detectors of the visual centers related to corresponding retinal points which are highly specialized to achieve the precise convergence, divergence, and coordinate movements of the eyes necessary for accurate binocular vision. When distortion is introduced into these interocular mechanisms, very little adjustment occurs. But there are other neurogeometric mechanisms relating visual stimulation to the movement systems of the body which are much more flexible, and permit the individual to adapt to various kinds of distortion.

Our experiments on size distortion of the visual feedback of motion to be described in this chapter deal with general binocular effects, either increase or decrease in the size of the image feedback. In such a situation, we would not expect the persisting effects of inter-ocular distortion as observed by Burian, but only limited effects on precise spatial localization, which would be reduced by adaptation.

ANALYSIS OF MOTION IN SIZE-DISTORTED VISUAL FIELDS

Closed-circuit television provides a method for both magnifying and reducing the visual field of performance. By using a television camera equipped with lenses of various sizes, and by shifting its position, we can more than double the apparent size of objects viewed in the television monitor, and reduce their apparent size by one-half. By televising a person's hand performing manipulative tasks, we can explore the effects of magnification and reduction of the visual performance field on various aspects of motion.

Using these television techniques, we have carried out a number of experiments on motion in size-distorted visual fields, ranging from studies of simple tapping movements to studies of the drawing performance of professional artists. We have also observed some of the interacting effects of size distortion and reversal of the visual field. According to the hypotheses of neurogeometric theory, we anticipated that size variation of the visual field would have much less effect on performance than various types of visual displacement. The results of our experiments in general confirmed this expectation.

Target Tapping

A simple tapping task was used to assess the effects of size variation of the visual field on the timing and accuracy of motion. A clock and counter system was used to record and time contacts made on a 2.5 inch square tapping board. Four small tapping plates, 0.25 inch square, were arranged in the form of a square 1.6 inches on each side in the center of the tapping board. Measures were obtained of total number of contacts per trial and total time on target.

The subject sat before a television monitor, with the screen 23 inches directly in front of him. The tapping board was located to the right, screened from his eyes by a black curtain. His hand was thrust through a slit in the curtain. An RCA miniaturized vidicon camera, trained on the performance field, was mounted at such an angle that the line from lens to tapping board paralleled the subject's line of sight to the television monitor. Variation in size of the televised image was obtained by shifting the television camera to different distances, keeping the angle of elevation with respect to the tapping board constant. Three positions were used, to produce an image size approximating that of normal vision, an image magnified by a factor of two, and one reduced by one-half.

Two groups of right-handed student subjects were used, a control group of six and an experimental group of twelve. An experimental trial consisted of tapping counterclockwise around the four tapping plates for a period of 30 seconds. Subjects were instructed to tap as rapidly as possible but to make clean stylus contacts, i.e., not to slide across the contact plates. Fifteen trials were given for a daily experimental session, five for practice and ten for test. Between the third and fourth test trials, a five minute rest period was given. In the experimental group, pairs of subjects were assigned at random to each of six possible orders of the three television viewing conditions. Each subject then performed the series of fifteen trials for each condition on three different days. The control group performed one series

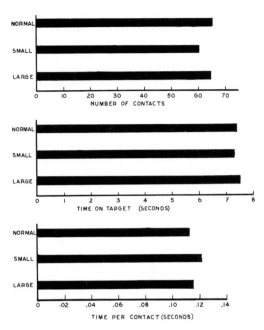

Figure 11-1. Three measures of performance in a target-tapping task when the visual feedback was normal, reduced, and magnified in size.

of trials with direct vision of the tapping board.

The main quantitative results are summarized in the bar graphs in Figure 11-1. For each experimental trial, the total number of contacts and total time on target had been recorded, and from these values we computed a third measure, the mean time per contact, for each trial. Mean values for the ten test trials of the 12 experimental subjects were then computed for each of these three measures, for the three conditions of television viewing separately. In general, performance with an image of normal size was very similar to performance with a large image, while the rate of tapping decreased somewhat with a small image size. Although the differences in total contacts and total time were not statistically significant, the mean time per contact was significantly greater for performance with a small

image than that with either a large or normal image. This difference between mean contact times for reduced and normal images was significant at the 1 per cent level, and for reduced and magnified images, at the five per cent level.

The performance measures obtained from the control group, which carried out the task with direct vision of the tapping board, were compared with the data obtained from the experimental group with a television image of normal size. The tapping rate was significantly higher with direct vision, with about one-fourth more contacts per trial and about one-third less time per contact. These differences between normal and televised performance can be ascribed to the distortion and blurring of the television image, and to the displacement of the hand from its normal position in relation to the body during televised performance.

The main experimental results show that size distortion of the visual field had a relatively minor effect on performance. Although reduction of the size of the performance field caused some disturbance and slowdown of motion, magnifi-

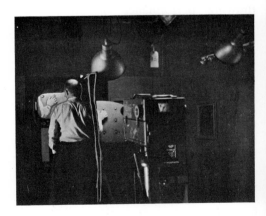

Figure 11-2. Set-up used to study the effects of size distortion of televised visual feedback of panel-control motions. The motion analyzer clocks can be seen beneath the image-orthicon camera.

cation had no appreciable effect. Thus, we observe a sort of behavioral size constancy, in spite of variation in the size of the retinal images.

Panel-Control Task

A second experiment testing the effects of size reduction of the visual field on performance measured separately the durations of manipulative and travel motions in a panel-control task requiring the turning of a series of switches. Figure 11-2 shows the arrangement of the panel-control board, the television camera, the cloth screen hiding the panel from the subject's direct view, and the monitor screen. The televised view of the subject's hand that can be seen in the monitor is larger than the sizes actually used in the experiment. A small-size image of the performance panel can be seen in the range-finder on the back of the camera. For this experiment, the camera was located 36 inches behind the panel board, and different lenses were used to vary the size of the visual image. A 4-inch lens gave a picture about two-thirds the actual size of the performance situation, and a 2-inch lens, about one-third the actual size.

The task was to turn in order a series of nine switches arranged in three rows of three. The switches were six inches apart, extended one inch from the surface of the panel, and turned through a 45-degree arc. An electronic motion analyzer measured separately the durations of the manipulative turning movements and the travel movements between switches.

Eighteen undergraduate subjects were assigned at random to three groups of six. The two experimental groups performed under two television viewing conditions involving reduction in apparent size of the performance field. Each day for five days, they were given eight trials with one television lens and then eight trials with the other. Group I performed with the 4-inch lens for the first eight trials, and then with the 2-inch lens, while Group II performed with the 2-inch lens first, and then with the 4-inch lens. The control group, Group III, were given eight trials each day for five days with direct vision of the panel board. On the sixth day, the control subjects were tested for transfer from direct vision training to television performance, by being given four trials with each lens.

To summarize the results, the median durations of travel and manipulative movements were determined for each series of eight trials performed by a subject on the five training days, and each series of four trials made by the subjects of Group III on the sixth day. These median scores were then averaged to get mean scores representing the performance of one group on one day with one viewing condition.

During the five-day training period, durations of travel and manipulative (contact) movements decreased for all groups. The learning curves showing the duration of manipulative movements are given in Figure 11-3, and those for travel movements in Figure 11-4. The fastest performance was that of the control group (open squares), who used direct vision. Two curves (closed circles and closed triangles) show performance with the 4-inch lens, and two (open circles and open triangles), performance with the 2-inch lens. Performance with the two different lenses was almost identical. The curves show that where differences did occur, they were related to the order in which the lenses were used rather than the size of the lens. That is, each experimental group showed some slight tendency toward faster performance during the second half of the series of trials, no matter which lens was used then. Statistical analyses showed that the differences between performance with direct viewing and

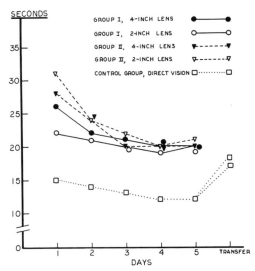

Figure 11-3. Learning curves for contact time in a panel-control operation under different conditions of size-distorted visual feedback. Transfer data are given for the control group on the sixth day.

effects of visual size distortion on handwriting. Subjects wrote series of *a*'s, *k*'s, triangles, and the combination *ak*. A setup similar to that illustrated in Figure 11-2 was used, with a vertical writing surface located to the right of the subject, screened from view by a curtain. Three different lenses were used on the television camera at two different distances to obtain six different sizes of visual image on the monitor screen. The ratios of image size to actual size of the moving hand were approximately 6:1, 3:1, 2:1, 1.5:1, 1:1, and 0.75:1. That is, with the 6:1 ratio, an actual movement of one inch appeared on the monitor as six inches in extent, and so on.

Twenty-four students served as subjects for two consecutive days. One day's task was to write groups of three horizontally aligned *a*'s, *k*'s, triangles, and *ak*'s, spaced at one inch intervals, three times with each of the six image sizes. Although the order of writing the sym-

television viewing were significant, but that the differences related to the two different image sizes were not significant.

Figures 11-3 and 11-4 also show the performance of the control group when they were transferred from direct viewing to television viewing on the sixth day. The motion times for both travel and manipulative movements were very similar to the level of performance reached by the experimental groups on the fifth day. Here again there was no significant difference in performance related to the size of the visual image. The results of this experiment generally confirm those of the study on tapping. With a task involving limited visual guidance, change in the size of the visual image of performance within experimental limits produced very little effect on the speed of patterned motion.

Handwriting

Six different image sizes were used in a further experiment analyzing the

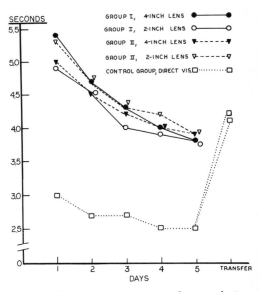

Figure 11-4. Learning curves for travel time in a panel-control operation under different conditions of size-distorted visual feedback. Transfer data are given for the control group on the sixth day.

bols was not varied, each subject was presented with the six image sizes in different order. These orders were not completely at random because of the physical difficulty of shifting the camera from one distance to another. This shift was made only once for each subject per day. Thus, a subject performed first with the camera at far distance, where the three lenses gave ratios of 6, 2, and 1.5 to 1, and then at the near distance, with ratios of 3, 1, and 0.75 to 1, or vice versa. The presentation of distances and lenses at each distance was randomized. An electronic handwriting analyzer was used to record contact and travel times separately.

In this experiment, as in the panel-control experiment, a subject's median travel and contact times for each of the four writing tasks were determined for each day separately. These median scores for all subjects were averaged to get mean scores for each task, at each image size, on each of the two days. The means for the second day are summarized graphically in Figure 11-5, where durations are plotted against image size ratios.

Statistical analyses revealed significant

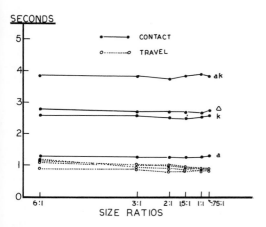

Figure 11-5. Mean contact and travel times on the second day in writing *a, k,* and *ak* and drawing triangles under different conditions of size-distorted visual feedback.

change in mean contact and travel times for all six image sizes between the first and second days, indicating that learning did occur. All of these changes were significant at the 1 per cent level. However, there were few differences related to image size that were found to be statistically significant. The travel durations in writing *a* and *k* with the largest image size (6:1) were significantly different at the 5 per cent level from travel durations with all other image sizes. Also, travel duration in writing *a* with the smallest image size (0.75:1) was significantly different from the durations with the three largest images. Thus, most of the differential effect related to image size was due primarily to longer mean travel times for the largest image. Actually, with this greatly magnified image, the subject's televised view of the performance field was not complete. The outer "stop" ring on the handwriting analyzer, the terminus of the final travel movement, was outside his field of vision. The necessity of making this final movement "blind" could well account for the greater total travel time required under this condition. Because this effect was observed only for *a* and *k,* the first two writing tasks performed, the subjects apparently learned the motion pattern necessary to hit the ring and showed no further effect of the large image size on performance. One can only conclude that changing the size of the retinal image of performance within the range used in this experiment has no appreciable effect on the speed of handwriting movements.

Target Tapping with Combined Size Distortion and Visual Reversal

The experiments just described indicate that the speed of manual performance of tasks involving limited visual control remains almost constant with wide variation in the size of the visual image. Televised images were magnified to six times normal and reduced to one-third of normal, but in general the rate of motion varied insignificantly. We have limited data from another experiment, however, which suggest that reduced image size may reduce the speed of motion if the performance is otherwise stressed.

The results to which we refer were obtained in an experiment in which the televised image was reversed and varied in size as well. The reversal was accomplished by directing the television camera toward the opposite side of a plate glass performance panel, as shown in Figure 11-6. The subject performed a target-tapping task on the panel while observing the "mirror image" of his movements in the television monitor. A white screen was mounted behind the subject's hand to sharpen the image. Thirty-six brass tapping plates, 0.25 inch in diameter, were mounted three inches

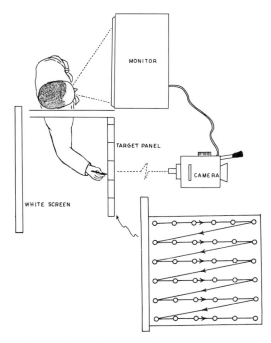

Figure 11-6. Set-up used to study size distortion and front-back reversal of the visual feedback of target-tapping motions.

apart on the glass panel in six rows of six. The task involved tapping the plates in order, from left to right, top row first, and so on. The subject was instructed to tap the plates cleanly and not to slide his stylus across them. The duration and number of contact and travel movements were measured separately.

Two different lenses were used in the television camera. A 4-inch lens gave an image of performance on the monitor about two-thirds normal size, while a 2-inch lens gave an image about one-third normal. Twenty undergraduate subjects were divided into two groups of ten, each of which performed under one of the viewing conditions. Each subject performed five trials per day for five days, and on the sixth day transferred to the other viewing condition, performing five trials with the other lens. The data analyses are based on the median score obtained by each subject on each day of the experiment.

The results are summarized graphically in Figures 11-7 and 11-8, which show respectively the mean contact and travel times for each group for each day of the experiment. The solid circles represent performance with the 4-inch lens, and the open circles, performance with the 2-inch lens. Transfer on the sixth day is indicated by dotted lines. The curves show that performance with the two lenses was very similar at first, but, as training progressed, motion was somewhat faster with the larger visual image. The difference between the two groups was significant at the 5 per cent level for travel movements, but was not significant for contact movements. When the groups were transferred on the sixth day, travel movements became somewhat slower for both groups; in the case of contact movements, this change in image size resulted in reversal of the groups in their relative speed of performance.

Although these data are limited, they suggest two conclusions. First, they con-

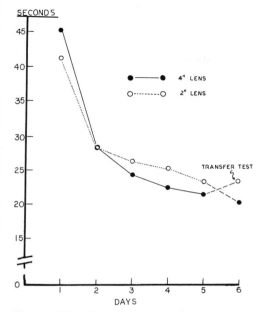

Figure 11-7. Learning curves of contact time in target tapping with reversed and size-distorted visual feedback.

firm our belief that, in general, size variation of the visual image has but minor effects on performance. In this experiment, subjects trained with one size of televised image transferred with little or no deterioration in performance to the other size. The second conclusion is a tentative one: that performance may be affected more by size distortion when it is otherwise stressed.

PERFORMANCE OF ARTISTS IN SIZE-DISTORTED VISUAL FIELDS

Our interest in perceptual-motor organization has led us to a consideration of the motion patterns used by artists in structuring uniquely expressive objects and forms. Very early in the work with television, we thought that this method of displacing the visual field might be of some use in training graphic artists in distinctive techniques of visual-

ization, but this interest was quickly displaced by the realization that the skilled artist himself is of central interest in the study of motion with displaced and distorted vision. In executing forms and patterns without prior practice in the particular work created, artists display a form of motor control which goes beyond specific learning. How, then, are the organized patterns of artistic motion regulated?

Our theory of perceptual-motor integration has some direct implications for artistic behavior. It puts the study of artistic activity on a broad behavioral rather than a strictly perceptual basis, and raises a question about the perceptual-intellectual approaches to understanding artistic performance. We feel that artistic motions are no different from any other perceptual-motor skills in the nature of their integration, and are distinctive only insofar as they involve expression of the behavior organization of the individual artist. The

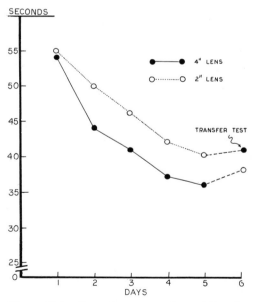

Figure 11-8. Learning curves of travel time in target tapping with reversed and size-distorted visual feedback.

graphic production is an example of highly precise, highly complex neuro-geometric integration of component movements in space-structured motion, i.e., the reproduction of environmental patterns by means of differential neural recording of motion-produced patterns of stimulation.

One of our first efforts in the study of artistic motion was to investigate the drawing behavior of professional artists in televised visual fields of different size. It is sometimes believed, even among artists themselves, that artists learn to control their motions in painting and drawing by other than visual means. We wished to determine if this belief is true to the extent that professional artists can control the size of their drawings in spite of variation in the size of the visual image of their performance, or whether they are dependent on vision in regulating the size of their movements. Television methods provide an interesting new experimental approach to the study of artistic technique and the artist's perceptual control of motion.

Procedures

The set-up seen in Figure 11-9 was used throughout the study. The subject stood facing the television monitor, with an easel located to his right. A black curtain hid the surface of the easel from direct view, so that the hand executing the drawings could not be seen. The objects to be drawn, a pot 10 inches high and a box 5 inches square, were located to the left, approximately 52 inches from the subject's eyes. They were observed with direct vision. An image orthicon television camera, placed 52 inches directly behind the easel, provided a clear image of the details of the subject's drawing on the 21-inch monitor screen. As shown in the photograph, the subject saw his hand in the monitor much as he would view it normally in relation to the easel.

Three different lenses were used on the camera to give three different sizes of visual image. With the 4-inch lens, image size on the monitor was reduced to approximately four-fifths of normal. This image size was doubled with the 8-inch lens, and reduced by about one-half with the 2-inch lens. The photograph in Figure 11-9 shows a subject drawing in the televised visual field with a 4-inch lens.

The cooperation of six professional artists and six amateur painters or

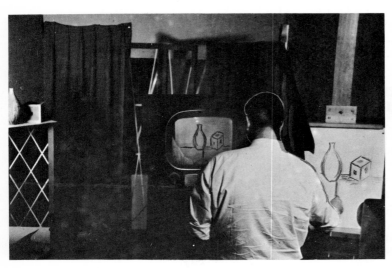

Figure 11-9. Subject's performance situation in television study of artistic drawing with size-distorted visual feedback. The pot and box models viewed with direct vision can be seen at left.

graphic artists was secured for a series of experimental observations. Six professional psychologists also served as subjects. Subjects were observed in three different experimental sessions, at about one-week intervals. They were asked to draw the pot and box to their true size, while observing their own performance in the television monitor. In each session, all three lenses were used, but the order of presentation was varied randomly by subject, and also varied by session for any one subject. At the end of the third session, most subjects were asked to draw the pot and box blind, without the aid of vision, and then to draw them normally while observing the easel directly. The subjects were not shown their television drawings directly until after the three experimental sessions.

Qualitative Results

The drawings in Figure 11-10 are those made by a highly accomplished artist in his third session of drawing with size-distorted televised visual fields. The drawings made with the 2-inch, 4-inch, and 8-inch lenses are shown, as well as a "blind" drawing and a normal drawing with direct vision. It is at once apparent that this artist was able to execute competent drawings with only a televised image of his performance. The sketches made with both the 4-inch and the 2-inch lenses compare favorably with the one drawn with normal vision. The blind drawing shows that he had good kinesthetic control of his movements when no visual control was allowed.

The most interesting thing about this artist's performance was his mode of reacting to visual size distortion. His drawing with normal vision was oversize (he made a pot 13 inches high instead of the true 10 inches), and his blind drawing was almost the same. In the televised visual fields, he reacted to

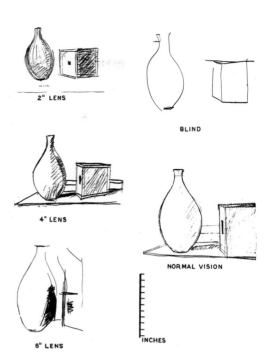

Figure 11-10. Artist's drawings under three different conditions of televised size-distorted visual feedback compared with drawings made with no vision and with normal direct vision.

size distortion by overcompensating for the distortion. In the slightly reduced field given by the 4-inch lens, he produced an accurately sized drawing (the pot is 10 inches high), but with the 2-inch lens, he made a drawing which was actually undersize (8 inches), and appeared very, very small (about 3.2 inches) on the television monitor. In other words, he overestimated the amount of size distortion and in trying to compensate made his drawing even smaller than normal. In drawing with the 8-inch lens, he again overestimated the distortion effect of the lens, in this case magnification, and drew a pot one and a half times its true size. Only part of this drawing could be viewed on the screen.

This overcompensation is only one of the patterns of individual adjustment of artists to change in the size of the visual image of performance. Other artists consistently underestimated the magnification and reduction effects of the camera lenses and produced very small drawings with the 8-inch lens and very large drawings with the 2-inch lens. This was essentially a matter of following visual cues of size. Still other artists reacted in different ways to the size-distorted visual fields.

The verbal comments of the artists disclosed some of the characteristics of control involved in the two-dimensional view of the televised performance field, indicating that professional artists rely heavily on vision. Both professional and amateur artists almost invariably expressed feelings of uncertainty and disturbances in control in drawing with the various lenses. One commented that it was hard to get the pencil to do what you wanted it to do; another, that a line you wouldn't think of normally became a difficult and inexplicable kind of action. They often expressed a preference for one size of lens over another, but there was no consistency in these choices from one individual to another, and often one person would change his preference from one session to another. Some preferred the small lens because "the lines are more definite," or because "you can see more of yourself." Others liked the large lens because they thought they had better control with it, or could make easier comparisons with hand size. One amateur artist disliked the small lens in the first session, liked it best in the second session, disliked it again in the third. Another found the small lens difficult during the first session because, "You can't see what you've done," but by the last session thought the small lens more fun because, "You can see what you have done."

One of the most interesting comments, which seemed to indicate the interdependence of perception and motion, was made by a professional artist. He observed in both the second and third sessions that he noticed more detail in the actual objects he was drawing — the pot and the box — when he drew with the large lens. Another stated when he was drawing with the small lens that his arm "feels a good deal larger than it is."

The general uncertainty and variability of reaction to the different lenses undoubtedly was related to the fact that the artists made no effective adaptation to the situation. In trying to draw to correct size in size-distorted fields, they apparently were unable to judge the accuracy of their performance with any degree of assurance, and showed no improvement in this respect in successive sessions. In fact, one professional artist remarked that the more she drew, the less sure she was of what she drew. A number of them made specific comments to the effect that they could not really judge the accuracy of their own performance.

The comments of the psychologist subjects reflected the same sort of indecision and vacillation in dealing with the experimental situation. In addition, they made more technical observations about the psychological aspects of the problem. One stated that the task was about as hard as mirror drawing; also, that there was a definite conflict between visual and kinesthetic cues. One said it was too hard to judge distances, and another, that he had lost his sense of depth.

Some of the difficulties encountered by the subjects were due to the televised viewing conditions, including the two-dimensional characteristics and the slight distortion of the monitor image. Also, when the large lens was used, the performance field was not completely within the camera's range, so that a larger image meant a restricted field. However, the major source of difficulty for the subjects was the size distortion of the visual field.

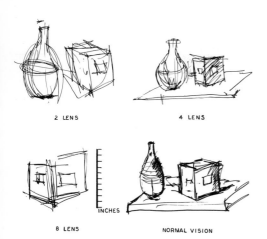

2 LENS   4 LENS

8 LENS   NORMAL VISION

Figure 11-11. Indecisive drawings made by a highly skilled artist under three conditions of televised, size-distorted visual feedback compared with drawing made with normal vision.

Figure 11-11 shows the efforts of an accomplished painter and print maker to draw in the three size-distorted visual fields, compared with his quickly executed normal drawing with direct vision. With the 8-inch lens, the artist in this attempt drew only the box, and overestimated its size by at least three inches. His drawing with the 2-inch lens was also about 2.5 inches too large. With the 4-inch lens, both pot and box were a little undersized. His normal drawing of the pot was exactly ten inches. The drawings done in the televised fields show marked indecision in both size and lines. With both the 2-inch and 4-inch lenses, the artist executed forms of several sizes before completing the contour of the pot. In contrast, the drawing done with direct vision, which was done in about 30 seconds, shows both accuracy and quick decision.

Quantitative Results

The requirements of drawing to true size in a size-distorted visual field created a visual-kinesthetic conflict from which the artist could not escape. The only constant cues for true size as the television lenses were changed were the kinesthetic feedback signals from the drawing movements themselves. Conflicting with the kinesthetic cues were the visual cues from the monitor, which the artist quickly noticed were unusual. He saw that his pencil and his hand did not appear normal size, but that they gave him his only visual frame of reference for true size. As he drew, he discovered quickly that visually perceived magnitudes and directions did not correspond with what he "intended" his pencil to do or "felt" that it was doing.

To see how successfully the subjects resolved the conflict inherent in the experimental situation, we have measured the drawings of the pot made by each subject in the third session. These data are given in Table 11-1. If a subject had been able to follow instructions exactly, each pot which he drew would measure ten inches in height. Table 11-1 shows a considerable range of error in drawing in the three size-distorted visual fields. In general, the professional artists judged size no more accurately than did the amateur artists or the psychologists. The performance of the amateur artists was most variable. The means for all subjects show that drawings with the 4-inch lens were slightly more accurate than those made with either the large or the small lens, and performance with the 4-inch lens was least variable.

As we have said, there were several patterns of adjustment to the size-distorted visual fields. Some subjects (e.g., Ss 2 and 12 in Table 11-1) depended almost entirely on visual cues of the picture size as seen in the monitor. They drew pots which looked similar in height. To achieve this, they made very large pots with the small lens and very small ones with the large lens. Others (Ss 1, 10, 11) overcompensated for the distortion by making very small drawings in the reduced visual field and very large drawings in the magnified

Table 11-1. Heights of Pots Drawn in Third Session (in inches)

SUBJECTS		2-INCH LENS	4-INCH LENS	8-INCH LENS
Professional Artists	1	7.5	10.0	14.0
	2	15.7	10.7	4.8
	3	9.5	11.0	7.5
	4	12.5	8.7	12.5
	5	9.0	7.0	5.5
	6	10.0	12.0	7.0
	Mean ± σ	10.7 ± 2.7	9.9 ± 1.6	8.6 ± 3.5
Amateur Artists	7	11.0	14.2	10.0
	8	8.3	9.2	6.0
	9	17.5	15.5	11.5
	10	6.5	6.8	15.0
	11	7.2	11.5	16.0
	12	16.0	8.0	6.0
	Mean ± σ	11.1 ± 4.3	10.9 ± 3.3	10.8 ± 3.9
Psychologists	13	8.3	9.5	7.0
	14	7.7	8.0	6.2
	15	13.0	11.5	9.5
	16	8.5	6.5	12.0
	17	11.0	9.2	13.0
	18	12.0	6.7	7.5
	Mean ± σ	10.1 ± 2.0	8.6 ± 1.7	9.2 ± 2.6
All Subjects	Mean ± σ	10.6 ± 3.2	9.8 ± 2.5	9.5 ± 3.5

field, such as the ones in Figure 11-10. Some subjects (3, 4, 6, 7, 8, 13, 14, 16, 17, 18) succeeded in producing two or three drawings not too far different in size. These people were able to overcome the visual size distortion to some extent, and to judge size by kinesthetic cues and the televised image of their hand and pencil. Finally, there were several subjects (Ss 5, 9, 15) who effected a sort of compromise between visual and kinesthetic size constancy, achieving something about midway in between.

The inaccuracies of drawing in televised visual fields were not due to the inability of the subjects to judge size in drawing normally. The measurements of the drawings made blind and with direct vision at the end of the third sessions are given in Table 11-2. It can be seen

Table 11-2. Heights of Pots Drawn Blind and with Direct Vision (in inches)

SUBJECTS	NORMAL	BLIND
Professional Artists	13.0	12.0
	10.0	9.2
	10.5	7.0
	10.0	8.0
	10.2	10.0
	11.8	11.0
Amateur Artists	12.0	10.0
	10.5	8.5
	15.5	16.2
	11.0	10.0
Psychologists	9.0	9.0
	10.0	7.5
All Subjects, Mean ± σ	11.1 ± 1.7	9.9 ± 2.4

that only one professional artist and one amateur were noticeably inaccurate in judging size in drawing normally. The blind drawings showed more error, with the major tendency toward drawing the objects too small.

Temporal Changes in Performance

Both artists and nonartists showed changes in drawing performance during the course of the experiment. Among the artists, there was a noticeable loss in interest and motivation to reproduce detail in the drawings as the experimental sessions were repeated. These changes can be seen particularly in the drawings reproduced in Figure 11-12.

The artist who produced these started out with very careful shading and illustration of detail of the support as well as the objects. In the second session, he used less shading, and in the last session the detail of the drawings was almost completely absent. The relative sizes and idiosyncrasies of executing outline were very similar for each of the different viewing conditions in successive experimental sessions. When this man was asked to execute a normal drawing on the last day, he again drew with marked detail and shading. The series of drawings made in size-distorted visual fields showed that little or no learning had occurred. The artist persisted in making most of his drawings too small, and in being influenced by visual cues for size.

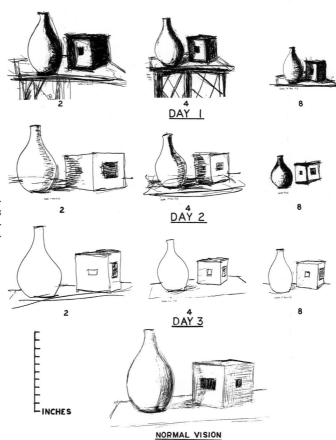

Figure 11-12. Changes in artist's drawings during three days of performance with three conditions of televised size-distorted visual feedback.

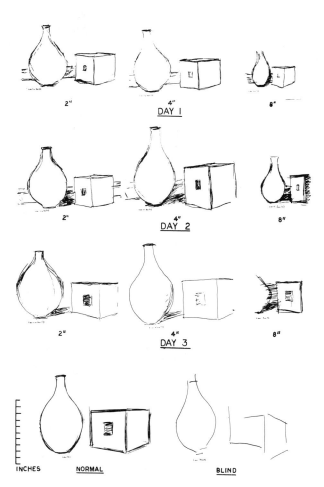

Figure 11-13. Successive daily drawings of a professional artist with size-distorted feedback of performance.

Results somewhat different are seen in the drawings in Figure 11-13. This artist showed little change in the amount of detail drawn, and no overall improvement in judgment of size. At the end of the third session, he made a highly precise drawing with direct vision.

The drawings in Figure 11-14 show characteristic distortions of form that persisted throughout the three practice sessions. At the end of the third session, this artist drew a very inaccurate pot blind, and a very accurate one with normal visual guidance. The perceptual motivation of this artist to complete detail was reduced between the first and

third sessions, but his effort at detail returned when he was asked to make the normal drawing.

The drawings in Figure 11-15,A, again show loss of interest in detail, and also a definite change in size judgments over the three periods. However, the change was toward greater inaccuracy rather than increased accuracy. This artist's drawings on the first day were all undersized, but in his second and third sessions the drawing with the small lens was greatly increased in size and that with the large lens decreased, showing an exaggerated following of visual cues. The artist said that he thought the over-

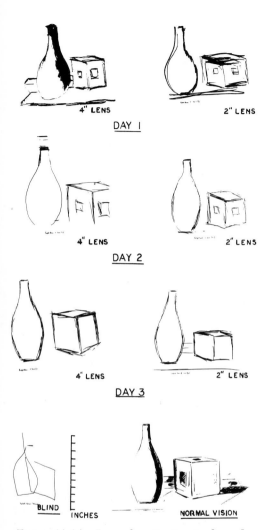

Figure 11-14. Loss of motivation to draw detail over three days of performance by a professional artist under conditions of size-distorted visual feedback.

sized drawings with the small lens were probably "too small." At the end of the third session, he produced a highly accurate normal drawing and a distorted blind drawing. The results of a fourth experimental test of this artist, carried out one month after his third session, are shown in Figure 11-15, B. Even though he had been shown his first

drawings after the third session, he again drew much too large with the 2-inch lens and too small with the 8-inch lens.

In the course of this experiment, time of performance was measured unobtrusively for eleven of the artists. The greatest decrease in time usually occurred between the first and third drawings on the first day. Time decreases between the second and third sessions were not large. At least three of the artists showed little or no change in drawing time between the first and third days. These time changes probably reflect more the change in motivation of the artist than they do change in efficiency in drawing.

Conclusions

A number of significant points can be made concerning the results of this study. In the first place, it seems clear that professional artists as a group are not superior to nonartists in judging true size of their drawings under conditions of visual size distortion. All their years of training and practice in precise perceptual-motor skills did not equip the artists to cope any more effectively than other subjects with the visual-kinesthetic conflict imposed by this experiment. This speaks for the very basic nature of the mechanisms regulating space-structured motions.

Secondly, there were marked individual differences among the members of all subject groups in their manner of adjusting to the demands of the experiment. Some subjects tended to follow the perceived visual size of the performance field, making their drawings large in reduced fields and small in magnified fields, while others overcompensated for the size distortion, making their drawings small in the reduced fields and large in the magnified fields. No subject achieved remarkable accuracy in judging true size while monitoring his drawing with distorted visual cues. The

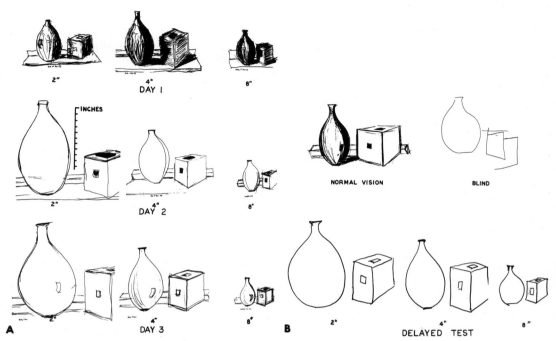

Figure 11-15. A. Loss of motivation in execution and decreased accuracy in artist's drawings over three days performance with size-distorted visual feedback. B. Test drawings one month later.

visual-kinesthetic conflict disrupted the fundamental motion organization of the subjects to such an extent that no easy adjustment could be made. In effect, the experiment destroyed the integrated perceptual or behavioral size constancy of the subjects. They achieved visual size constancy only by losing kinesthetic constancy, and vice versa. We believe that these results relate to the whole problem of size constancy in behavior. Relative constancy and variation in perceived size depend not on some fixed phenomenon of neural equivalence, learning, or attitude, but result from interaction of different space-organized motion systems.

The third point to emphasize is that no real learning occurred during the course of the experiment, but that the motivation of the artists dropped. Loss of interest in drawing repeatedly in the distorted fields was seen in both reduced quality of performance and in loss of detail. These results suggest that a close relationship may exist between the structural and geometric detail of the environment and the maintenance of organized motivated behavior. When the established spatial relationships between the environment and the integrated reactions of the individual were disturbed, the quality of performance deteriorated. Methods such as the ones used here show promise for further exploration into events of perceptual and activity motivation.

One might ask what the relationship is between the results found with the artists and the results found in the experiments on size distortion reported in the first part of the chapter. We said then that variation in size of the visual performance field had but minor effect on performance. Here, with the study of artists, we are speaking of a rather serious disturbance resulting from such size distortion.

Actually there is no real contradiction between the two types of experiments. In the first studies, the subjects were asked to perform organized patterns of motion within a visual frame of reference which they could observe on the monitor screen. Every movement could be checked constantly by visual as well as kinesthetic cues. In this situation, subjects adjusted to variation in visual size quickly and efficiently, and their performance did not deteriorate significantly. In the artists' experiment, the subjects were asked to duplicate "true size" of objects. No visual cues of this true size were present in their visual field of performance, as seen on the monitor. Although they were able to perform creditably in reproducing the overall pattern and detail of the objects, the requirement of true size could not be met. The observed deterioration in drawing performance seemed to result more from loss of interest and motivation than from the size distortion.

The inability to reproduce accurate size in the absence of cues against which performance can be checked and corrected indicates to us that "true size" is almost meaningless for visually structured patterned motion. The individual is organized to respond to constantly varying visual patterns, with the accuracy of his responses checked by the differential recorders of his motion systems. Both compensatory and correlated movements regulate the size of the motion pattern and of the visual feedback of that pattern. The different

motion systems can and do interact to define the resulting differences in neural patterns that determine what is called perceived size and magnitude of motion.

The research reported here is an effort to analyze the phenomena of size constancy and response to variation in size of the visual field in behavioral terms, as contrasted to introspective and subjective estimates of the size of perceived objects. We believe that such an objective approach to size perception is essential in resolving the basic theoretical problems in this field. The studies carried out generally confirm our view that the multidimensional space-organized motion patterns defining size perception and related motion patterns are not controlled in the introspective approach. Motion analysis of the events of size perception support the main tenets of neurogeometric theory in indicating that: a) size perception and behavioral size constancy are based on correlated and compensatory interactions defining different levels and patterns of space-organized motions; and b) the events of size are not defined fundamentally by learning phenomena but by more basic neurogeometric integration of motion.

SUMMARY

1. Constancy and variability in perceived size depend on space-organized reactions to the entire stimulus field, and are affected by many interacting factors of perception and motion.

2. Individuals adapt to many visual size variations, including experimentally induced variations in size of the two retinal images. However, these retinal discrepancies persist under restricted visual conditions.

3. In magnified and reduced televised visual fields, subjects performed target tapping approximately as fast as in a televised field of normal size.

4. In televised fields reduced to two-thirds and one-third of normal size, subjects performed a panel-control task with no significant decrease in speed.

5. Handwriting tasks were performed in televised fields of six different degrees of magnification and reduction, ranging from six times larger than normal to three-fourths of normal. There were significant increases in rate due to learning, but very little variation due to image size, except for minor rate increases with the largest size, which may have been due to restriction of the visible field.

6. When the visual field was reversed as well as distorted in size, the size variation was related to differences in performance, indicating that performance may be affected more by size distortion when it is otherwise stressed.

7. Artists and nonartists who were asked to draw objects to true size in size-distorted televised fields showed no basic differences in accuracy or ability to adapt. All subjects were inaccurate and showed no learning effects in three sessions.

8. There were individual differences in mode of reaction to the problem, but none solved the visual-kinesthetic conflict. There was marked loss of interest and motivation to draw in successive sessions.

9. These results indicate that size perception is regulated by basic regulatory systems of motion which interact to produce effects of size constancy and variation. When these established relationships were disturbed, performance deteriorated and there was loss of motivation.

CHAPTER 12

DISPLACED VISION AND THEORY OF TOOL USING

An understanding of the mechanisms of human motion must include an account of tool-using functions. There are two general fields of interest that have contributed information concerning the nature and significance of human tool-using behavior. The first is concerned with the evolution of prehistoric and modern man as a tool user and a tool maker, and with the development of the human brain as a regulatory mechanism of tool-using motions. The second body of information is derived from the advancing fields of human engineering and cybernetics, which pro-

ceed from the basic fact that operational aspects of motion are critical in all features of machine design and use.

Notwithstanding wide interest today in the evolution of man as a tool user, and in the operational and systems problems of machine design and control, we have no systematic theory of tool-using behavior. The nearest approaches to such theory are the ideas of instrumental conditioning,[122] operant learning,[248] and insight learning in animals.[153] However, such learning theory is limited in accounting for tool-using behavior inasmuch as no animals below man use tools systematically, and in none except man does the mode of natural adaptation involve sustained use of even the most primitive stick or stone tools. Thus, any theory of tool-using behavior must propose a set of principles dealing exclusively with the distinctive organization of human motion. We are attempting here to define a theoretical-experimental approach to the problems of tool-using motion in terms of our concepts about displaced vision and the geometry of motion. We believe that the central problem of operational behavior, as studied in the evolution of man as a tool user and in human engineering, is to understand how motion is organized geometrically and regulated according to movement-produced space differences in stimulation.

In this chapter, we report three types of experiments that were designed to deal with basic tool-using functions. The first deals with the question of whether there is any difference in the neural regulation of unaided motion and similar aided, or tool-using, motion. In accordance with our theoretical assumption that brain neurons detect space differences in movement, we would expect no fundamental difference in the control of unaided and tooled motions as long as the space patterns in the two types of motion are much the same. The internuncial systems of the brain can detect space displacements in the operational motions of tools guided by the hand as well as displacement of the hand itself.

We have explored a second problem of tool-using behavior in relation to directional properties of motion. It is widely recognized that all kinds of skilled motions, including tool-using motions, are highly specific in nature, i.e., they neither correlate highly with one another nor does learning transfer to any great extent from one to another. Does this specificity of motions in tool using depend on learning or upon the intrinsic geometric and directional organization of motion? We have investigated this problem by measuring the quantitative characteristics of movements made in different directions in displaced visual fields of different orientations. Our view is that the specificity of motion stems from its basic spatial organization, which may have been established in evolution through the use of tools, but which persists now as a genetic and neurophysiological feature of the human system.

A third type of experiment concerns the effect on motion organization and learning of general perceptual organiza-tion of the behavioral field. To what extent does the orientation of the entire visual field affect motion within a more restricted field? Does a subject actually recognize his own manual motions in tool-using activity? Is such perceptual identification necessary for learning to adapt to a specialized task involving delayed visual feedback?

In these experiments on displaced vision and tool-using, we have been interested more in identifying some of the perceptual-motor events that are critical in tooled activities than in ana-lyzing particular examples of the actual use of tools. Thus, the experiments to be described deal with events that are not confined exclusively to the use of tools. Nevertheless, these events — the relative significance of behavioral and mechanized visual feedback of motion, the geometric determinants of movement specificity, and the effects of general perceptual organization on performance — have for us a special theoretical sig-nificance relative to tool-using behavior. These phenomena can be considered as the crux of the relation or interaction between the tool or device and the living body in motion. Our view is that if we can resolve some of these ques-tions of the perceptual-motor status of instrumental types of manual behavior, in time we can identify the neural and behavioral factors which are crucial to the evolution of man as a distinctive tool user.

TOOL-USING MOTIONS WITH VARYING DEGREES OF VISUAL FEEDBACK

Few, if any, objective studies have been made of the basic characteristics of perceptual-motor integration involved in the use of tools. Technological con-cepts about instruments and machines suggest that tool using requires far dif-

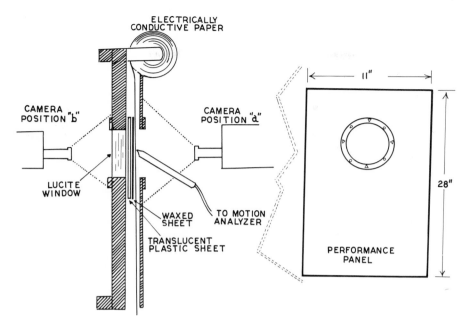

Figure 12-1. Set-up used to study pencil-drawing performance with varying degrees of visual feedback. With the camera in position "b," feedback of motion trace can be given.

ferent motor coordinations from those used in unaided behavior. On the other hand, current learning theory makes no distinctions between instrumental activity and unaided behavior, inasmuch as both are considered to be organized as response sequences through the effects of reinforcement.

Our geometric conception of perception and motion attempts to define the similarities and differences in aided and unaided behavior in specific terms. We expect no differences between tool-using activity and unaided motion as long as the geometric relationships in the two types of motion remain much the same. In the experiment reported here, we proposed testing this point by comparing the organization of motions when the movements and performance output of the tooled hand could be seen, when only the manual movements could be seen, and when only the output pattern of performance could be seen.

Procedures

Subjects performed pencil-drawing tasks on a drawing board constructed to permit various types of visual feedback. A closed-circuit television chain was used to supply the feedback image on a monitor, and an electronic motion analyzer measured movement durations for the different tasks.

The construction of the writing board is shown in Figure 12-1. It presented the subject with an 11 by 28 inch vertically oriented surface, with a circular hole 5 inches in diameter centered 10 inches from the top of the board. Writing paper was fed past this hole from a roll at the top. Index points, delineating the various tasks, were marked on a metal ring surrounding the task area. The apparatus was devised to allow three feedback conditions: (a) tool-trace feedback, in which the subject was able to see both his hand operating the tool and the results or trace of his work, as in normal working situations; (b) tool-only feedback, in which the subject could see his hand operating the tool but not the results of his performance; and (c) trace-only feedback, in which the subject saw only the visible trace of his work and not the movements of his hand. For tool-trace and tool-only feedback, the television camera was placed in position "a," as shown in Figure 12-1, where it viewed both the hand operating the tool and the writing surface. For tool-only feedback, the lead was removed from the subject's pencil to deprive him of trace or results information. To obtain trace-only feedback, a special procedure was used. The writing board backing, as can be seen in Figure 12-1, was constructed on the principle of a child's magic slate. Pressure of a pencil on the writing surface caused a wax-coated sheet of black paper to adhere to a piece of translucent plastic. This adhesion destroyed the reflective interface at the points of pressure, and was visible as black marks through the translucent film. The television camera was moved to position "b," where it viewed the back surface of the plastic film through a plexiglass window framed to appear identical to the writing area on the other side of the board. The right-left reversal of movements which would normally occur when seen from this position was corrected electronically in the television system.

The relationships of the entire experimental set-up are shown in Figure 12-2. The camera, which was located 14 inches from the writing surface in position "a," and the same distance from the plastic film in position "b," was equipped with circuits that allowed the experimenter to present a normally oriented image, a vertically inverted image, a horizontally reversed image, or one that was both inverted and reversed. An electronic motion analyzer was used to measure the performance

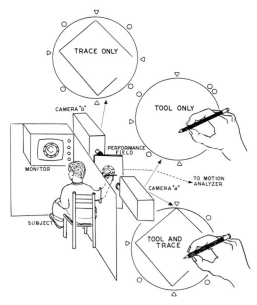

Figure 12-2. Subject's performance set-up and the three types of perceptual feedback of tool-using motions.

durations for the various tasks. The specific tasks, shown in Figure 12-3, were chosen to allow comparison of the effects of various feedback conditions on axially and diagonally oriented movements. Diamond patterns consisted entirely of diagonal movements, and square patterns, of axial movements. Both patterns were performed clockwise and counterclockwise. An experimental session consisted of performing all four tasks, each with a different orientation of the visual field, but all with the same condition of visual feedback (tool-trace, tool-only, or trace-only).

Twenty-four undergraduate subjects were assigned randomly to three groups of eight, each of which performed under one of the feedback conditions. Each subject served for one 35-minute session. During the first five minutes, standardized instructions explaining the general nature of the experiment were read. Twenty minutes were used for intensive

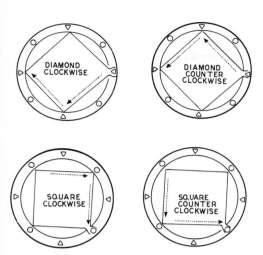

Figure 12-3. The patterns of motion used to compare the effects of different degrees of visual feedback on tool-using performance.

practice of all tasks under all conditions of orientation of the visual field, and ten minutes were used for the recorded trials. The order in which the tasks and orientations were presented to the different subjects was determined by a standard experimental design. Each task was performed three times, and the median time value was taken as representative of performance for that trial and used in the statistical analyses.

Results

Mean performance times for the different tasks, orientations of the visual field, and conditions of visual feedback are shown in Table 12-1. Statistical analyses disclosed that there were significant differences in performance time related to the tasks performed and to the various orientations of the visual field. The diamond-shaped drawing tasks were of significantly longer duration than square-shaped tasks; that is, diagonal movements took longer than axial movements to perform. Also, performance with normal orientation of the visual field was significantly faster than with any other orientation, and performance in a reversed field was not significantly different from performance in an inverted-reversed field. These results are consistent with similar findings described in earlier chapters.

With respect to mean performance times for the different feedback conditions, statistical tests showed that the differences between means were not significant. Subjects were not significantly slowed down by depriving them of trace feedback, and showing them just their hand and pencil, or by depriving them of the sight of their hand and pencil, and showing them just the trace of their performance. This finding indicates that simple perceptual-motor integrations, such as those involved in this task, are not significantly different in unaided and tool-using motions. Whether such a conclusion applies to the highly complex tool manipulations of ordinary work is conjectural without further experimental data.

Table 12-1. Mean Performance Durations for Tasks, Orientations of the Visual Field, and Feedback Conditions (in seconds).

TASK	MEAN	ORIENTATION	MEAN	FEEDBACK	MEAN
Diamond C	13.35	Normal	8.67	Tool-Trace	11.79
Diamond CC	13.35	Reversed	12.24	Tool-Only	12.44
Square C	10.96	Inverted	14.83	Trace-Only	12.10
Square CC	10.78	Inv.-Rev.	12.67		

SPECIFICITY OF TOOL-USING MOTIONS WITH DISPLACED VISION

Skilled human motions are not only almost infinitely diverse in their organization, but they are also noted for their specificity, or independence. This is a fact of some importance in training programs, for the learning of one motion pattern shows little transfer to others. We are convinced that such specificity cannot be explained in terms of general concepts of learning and perception, but must derive from the basic physiological organization of the human system. We believe that the relative independence of motions, and the nearly permanent retention of learned skills depend on the neurogeometric organization of movement in terms of the relative spatial displacements between perception and motion.

We have discussed the general idea of motion specificity in several earlier chapters, pointing out that adaptation to displaced vision is specific to the situation, that different displacement conditions have different effects on motion, and that different movements are affected differently by the same displacement condition. Because an understanding of the basis of motion specificity is so important to theoretical and practical problems of tool using and machine operations, we have planned the following experiments as studies of some of the characteristics of operational motions in displaced visual fields.

Analysis of Tool-Using Motions in an Inverted Visual Field

The effects of prism-produced visual inversion on different types of operational tooled movements were analyzed in the experimental set-up shown in Figure 12-4. The subject sat behind a screen in which an inverting prism was mounted, observing his performance

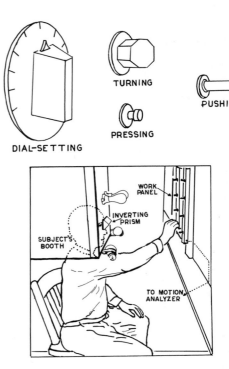

Figure 12-4. Set-up used to study the effects of visual inversion on different types of tool-using manipulative motions. The four devices used on the work panel are shown at the top.

field through the prism. He was required to perform four types of manipulative motions (pushing, pressing, turning, and dial setting) on the four devices shown at the top of the figure. Four pairs of work panels were prepared with these devices, one pair for each type of device. A work panel contained four units of the same device, so that when a pair was mounted in the subject's manipulation board, he was faced with two vertical rows of identical devices, eight in all. The work panels could be changed quickly between trials to shift from one task to another. For a given trial, the subject was required to operate first the device at the upper left, move across to the upper right, back to the second left, and so on back and forth across the board to finish at the lower right. The eight manipulation movements and seven travel movements were timed separately by an electronic motion analyzer.

Forty-eight subjects were divided randomly into two groups of 24. Each subject performed three trials each day with each type of device, with the order of presentation varied by subject. On the first day, all subjects performed with direct vision. For the next seven days, the experimental group worked in the inverted visual field provided by the prism, while the control group continued to work with direct vision. On the ninth and tenth days, the experimental group shifted back to direct vision, and the control group transferred to inverted vision.

The mean durations of manipulation and travel movements for the four different types of task are shown in Figure 12-5. The graphs plotted with broken lines show the slightly falling learning curves of the control group. The solid lines show performance of the experimental group, which reacted to the inversion of their visual field by marked slowing down in performance. By the end of seven days of practice, their performance curves were leveling off at noticeably higher levels than those achieved by the control group. When each group transferred to the other viewing condition on the ninth day, their performance was similar to that of the other group early in the practice series. Practice under one viewing condition had very little effect on performance when the condition was changed.

We were primarily interested in this study in determining whether displaced vision affected different manipulations differentially. In Figure 12-5, the curves for manipulation time for the control group show consistent, although slight, differences in time for pressing, pushing, and turning, with considerably longer performance time for dial setting. Inversion of the visual field, on the

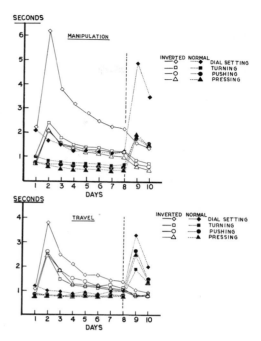

Figure 12-5. Learning curves of contact and travel time of different tasks with normal and inverted visual feedback. The first day of performance was with normal vision for all subjects. Transfer tests were given on the last two days.

second day for the experimental group and the ninth day for the control group, caused a much greater increase in dial setting than in the other three. To see whether these increases were proportional to the normal time required, we have plotted the durations in Figure 12-6 as relative values, computed in terms of the performance of the control group on the eighth day for each task. Here we see the complete curves for the experimental group and the transfer data for the control group expressed as relative durations, with normal performance time for each task equal to 1. These curves show that the relative time increases were not equal; visual inversion affected the different manipulation times to a variable degree.

The curves for travel times show the differential effect of inversion less clearly

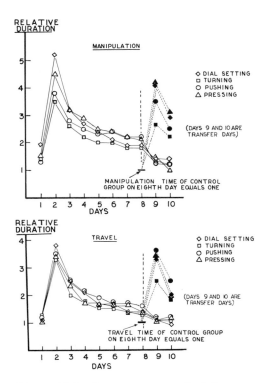

Figure 12-6. Learning curves of relative contact and travel time of different tasks with inverted visual feedback.

We conclude from these data that even simple manipulative tasks are affected differentially by a changed orientation of the visual field. Even after days of practice, the differential effect of the visual inversion on manipulation time persisted. The specificity of the performance was defined not only by the nature of the task, but by the conditions of visual displacement as well.

A word should be said about the perceptual orientation of the subjects in this experiment. Although the optical arrangements seemed obvious to the experimenter, many subjects of the experimental group did not know even at the end of the experiment that they had been performing in an inverted visual field. Some recognized that there was some kind of perceptual distortion, but not over five were sure of the nature of the distortion. However, recognition of the type of visual displacement apparently did not influence performance time or the rate of learning.

Interaction of Movement Direction and Visual Orientation

Among the variables that determine motion specificity are the direction of movement and the relative orientation of the visual field. In an experiment already reported in Chapter 9, we determined that these two factors also interact to affect the patterning of motion. That is, we found that the relative speed or efficiency of a movement in a certain direction is determined in part by the orientation of the visual field.

This experiment involved testing performance in tracing a four-pointed star in televised visual fields, as shown by the diagram in Figure 12-7. A photograph of this apparatus can be seen in Figure 8-4, and the pattern of the star and the eight different directions of movement required are shown in Figure 9-15. It will be recalled that four groups of sub-

than the manipulation curves. One might expect that travel times would be equal for all tasks, because the travel movement covers the same distance in all cases. However, in Figure 12-5, the travel times of the control group were almost identical for three tasks, but were noticeably longer for dial setting, showing that the more complicated manipulation influenced even the duration of the travel movements. The effect of visual inversion was to spread out these travel curves throughout the seven-day practice period for the experimental group, and on the ninth and tenth days for the control group. When these values were plotted in Figure 12-6 as relative increases over normal travel time for each task, the variability was less apparent.

jects performed respectively in normal, reversed, inverted, and inverted-reversed visual fields.

The data from this experiment showing movement times for the different directions, which were summarized in Figures 9-17 and 9-18, showed distinctive patterns of directional time values for the different conditions of visual orientation. Directional variations were not marked for normal or reversed viewing, but marked variations occurred in both time values and the patterns of time values for the other two conditions. With the normal and reversed conditions, vertical movements were slowest, and the horizontal movements were fastest. With an inverted visual field, all diagonal movements slowed down considerably, and vertical movements were fastest. Combined inversions and reversal also increased greatly the time

of all the diagonal movements, but vertical movements were just about as slow as the diagonals, and horizontal movements were again the fastest.

Analyses of variance showed that time differences relative to movement direction were significant at the 1 per cent level or beyond for all four visual orientations. Duncan multiple range tests were then applied to determine which movement directions differed significantly from each other. With eight different directions involved, a total of 28 comparisons could be made for the means for each experimental viewing condition. When the means for the last day only were tested, 17 significant differences (out of 28) were found for the normal viewing condition, 22 for reversed condition, and 24 each for the inverted and the inverted-reversed conditions.

The results of this experiment indicate that the temporal patterning of movements varies significantly not only with their direction, but with their direction in relation to the orientation of perceptual fields. Thirty-two systematic variations in perceptual-motor displacement, among a near infinite number that could be sampled, were found to produce many quite different and persisting performance patterns. When we consider all the possible variations in relative directions of perceptual displacement and motion (as produced by different degrees of nonsystematic angular rotation of the visual field, dislocation of the line of sight, dislocation of the origin of vision, and so on), the number of potential specific movements appears to be astronomical. We believe these variations in relative geometric displacement of perception and motion account for much of the specificity of motions, and thus contribute to the operational differentiation of human tool-using activities.

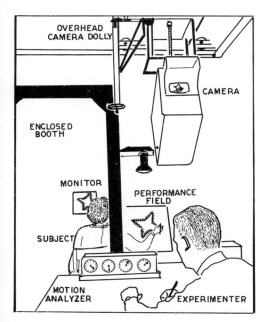

Figure 12-7. Set-up used to study the effects of different conditions of inversion and reversal on movements in different directions.

EFFECTS OF GENERAL PERCEPTUAL ORGANIZATION ON MOTION

The main thesis of this chapter is that the instrumental process, i.e., tool-using motion, is a function of specific conditions of perceptual-motor displacement and the feedback conditions defined thereby. The objective studies we have described to support this view are admittedly tentative, and do little more than delineate the areas that we consider worthy of further exploration. In this last section, we wish to call attention to still another area related to instrumental motion that needs clarification.

We refer to some of the general ideas that have emerged from the gestalt point of view, and their relation to an overall theory of motion. In general, gestalt psychology has been concerned primarily with describing the organization of perception in terms of the dynamism of the perceptual field. The events of motion are secondary, although they are assumed to be structured in terms of the primary perceptual pattern. Within this theoretical framework, the behavior of an individual in work would be influenced by the entire perceptual field, and his own position within it.

Ideas such as these have had considerable impact on psychological thinking, although they have not always been subjected to rigorous experimental evaluation. For this reason, and because of the general significance of gestalt principles, we have been interested in designing experiments that would analyze some of the effects of general perceptual organization on motion.

Adaptation to Displaced Vision within an Inverted Visual Surround

One gestalt precept is that the visual surround affects the patterning of response. According to Kohler,[153] the visual surround or background contributes not only to perceptual organization of the field, but also to the organization of behavior, or motion. In gestalt theory, the interaction betwen the behavioral field and surround defines which movements occur in the situation, and the extent to which insight learning can take place.

In the experiment to be reported here, we have tried to determine whether the inversion of the surround of the critical visual field of motion has any effect on performance with different orientations of that motion field. The television set-up diagrammed in Figure 12-7 was used, but for this experiment, the face of the television monitor was surrounded with a large white cardboard, 36 inches by 42 inches, upon which a number of drawings of common objects and photographs of familiar events were located. This cardboard surround could be placed upright or inverted around the television performance field. It hid all of the monitor but the glass screen, and was the only articulated surround in the work area. The subject traced a paper maze with a pencil while watching his movements in the monitor.

The plan of the experiment was to test performance under the four conditions described in Figure 12-8. In the first condition, both the visual performance field and the surround were upright. In the second, the field of performance was upright, but the visual surround was inverted. In the third condition, the performance field was inverted and the surround upright, and in the fourth, both performance field and surround were inverted. Twenty-four student subjects traced the maze for one-half hour each day for four days, under the four different experimental conditions. The order of presentation was randomized by subject, that is, each subject was assigned one of the 24 possible orders of presenting the four conditions, and performed the tasks in this

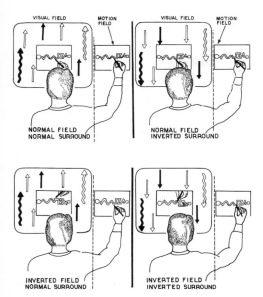

Figure 12-8. Set-up used to test the effects of inversion of the visual surround on performance in tracing with upright and inverted visual feedback.

order throughout the study. Both tracing time and errors in staying within the path were recorded.

The critical test in this experiment was whether there were significant differences in performance related to the two surround conditions, normal and inverted. As expected, there were significant differences attributable to the orientation of the performance field; performance was poorer when the televised field was inverted. However, the results indicated that the orientation of the surround had no effect whatsoever on the speed or accuracy of the performance.

Perceptual Identification of Motion

In our television studies of displaced vision, we have been struck by the fact that under some circumstances a person viewing his own motions in the monitor is in doubt as to whether the movements are his own. We have wondered to what

extent self-recognition is an important or essential factor in the organization and learning of perceptual-motor skills.

In an experiment on simulated delayed visual feedback of motion we have investigated some aspects of perceptual recognition of one's own movements. A tandem, two-camera, closed-circuit television system was set up as diagrammed in Figure 12-9. As in our other television studies, the subject was prevented from seeing his own motions directly, and guided his movements by watching the monitor image before him. In this study, however, the image seen by the subject was not of his own hand, but was of the hand of a trained observer in the next room. The procedure followed was to transmit a televised image of the subject's manual performance to the observer's monitor. The observer watched closely the subject's movements in tracing a maze path, and after a predeter-

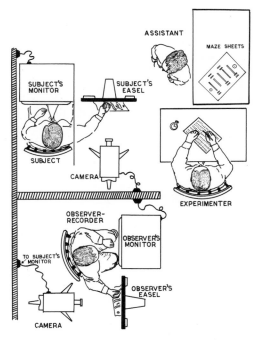

Figure 12-9. Set-up used to simulate televised feedback of maze tracing.

mined delay reproduced these movements on a maze of his own. The second camera located behind his tracing panel then transmitted an image of the observer's movements to the subject's monitor. The subject was told simply that the televised image of his performance was being delayed electronically in transmission. To aid the deception, both observer and subject wore white cotton gloves and black arm covers; the subject was told to wear them to "improve the television image." Precautions were taken so that the subject never saw the observer's hand moving in and out of the televised field.

Twelve subjects traced the maze path shown in Figure 12-10 five times per day on three different experimental days. The experiment was conducted as a study of delayed visual feedback, with three different delay periods. These periods were defined not in terms of invariable time measurements, but rather were set to correspond to phases of the maze-tracing task. The shortest delay period lasted only until the subject reached the first turn of the maze. The half-task delay represented the time needed to trace half the maze, and the longest delay lasted until the subject had finished the entire maze. Four of the subjects performed with the short delay; that is, they saw a hand repro-

ducing their movement after approximately 1 to 2 seconds, the time necessary to complete the first leg of the maze. Another four subjects saw nothing in their monitor until they were half way through the maze, when the televised hand started reproducing their performance from the beginning. The third group of four subjects were given no image until they had completed the task, when they saw their performance reproduced. In general, the observer's reproduction of the subject's performance was faithful and convincing. He tried to reproduce all errors made by the subjects as well as their movement idiosyncrasies. Comparison of the errors made by subjects and by the observer in following the maze path showed no significant differences between the two.

The only aspect of this experiment that concerns us here is whether the subjects recognized the fact that a substitute visual feedback was being used instead of the actual image of their own movements. Only one subject — a male in the short-delay group — commented spontaneously about the substitution. Some of the subjects acted disappointed about their performance and expressed regrets that they could do no better. If others knew or suspected that a substitute visual feedback was being used, they did not mention it. In general, it appeared to the experimenter that decisive perceptual identification of the moving hand had very little to do with the subjects' patterns of motion.

The limited results of this study are not conclusive, but suggest to us that the organization and motivation of patterned motion does not depend on the perception of one's body image. In this experiment, the subjects persisted in trying to adjust to a difficult task without too much concern about the identity of the moving hand. Given a visual feedback, they were motivated to use the information in patterning their motions. We feel that these results emphasize the

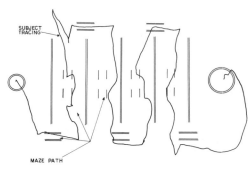

SUBJECT TRACING

MAZE PATH

Figure 12-10. The maze pattern used in the study of simulated delayed feedback.

looseness of the perceptual connection between the performer and his own movements, especially in the initial phases of adaptation to a difficult learning situation. In learning to use tools, the performer does not identify what the hand is already doing and then decide where it shall go next. Rather, the hand in motion is perceived immediately in terms of visual and kinesthetic feedback, and its continuing movements are adjusted according to this differential spatial information. In other words, the motivation to perform and to learn tool-using skills or other patterned motions derives not from perceptions of "self" and decisions concerning what the self should do,. but from the spatial determinants of the motion situation.

CONCLUSIONS

The series of studies reported in this chapter on the relations between displaced vision and tool-using functions, while only touching on the broad biological issues involved in such behavior, suggest an important relationship that bears further investigation. That is the physiological tie that relates the genetic nature of man as a distinct tool-using species to his characteristic tool-using behavior in modern society. The specialized operational and design problems of modern man in using tools and machines demand a fuller understanding of how human motion is organized and regulated. The characteristics of tool using and other perceptual-motor skills depend on the high degree of spatial organization of the internuncial systems of the brain.

The television studies on perceptual organization and motion described in this chapter represent an attempt to evaluate experimentally some of the widely held gestalt concepts of perception as a basis of behavioral integration.

In our experimental comparison of motion patterns within upright and inverted surrounds, we found no evidence that the figure-ground relations had any influence on perceptual-motor integration, either with normal conditions of visual feedback or with inverted visual feedback. Moreover, no evidence was found that perception of self or recognition of object-person interactions were essential for performance, for adaptation to inverted and reversed vision, or for motivation of psychomotor learning with delayed visual feedback.

The main positive finding of this series of studies is the experimental demonstration that the rich variety of movements and the high degree of movement specificity in man may be traced to the relative geometric relationships of the spatial feedback of motion. It may very well be that every directional orientation of an afferent receptor system in space defines the specific quantitative properties of movements made in different directions under that condition of afferent orientation. Thus, movement specificity in the use of tools as well as in expressive motion is based on a fundamental geometric interaction in the neural system, i.e., the spatial perceptual feedback of movements made in particular directions. We believe the specificity and distinctiveness of all tool-using motions and of all human skills arise from this basic neurogeometric interaction.

SUMMARY

1. Theory of tool using must embody a set of principles which apply to this distinctively human type of behavior. Some exploratory experiments were designed to define tool using in neurogeometric terms.

2. Subjects performed pencil-drawing tasks under three conditions: with visual

feedback of their hand, pencil, and the pencil trace (tool-trace); with feedback of their hand and pencil only (tool-only); and with feedback of the pencil drawing only (trace-only). Speed of performance did not vary significantly under the three conditions.

3. Subjects practiced four different manipulative tasks in a prism-inverted visual field, and then transferred to direct vision, while a control group practiced with direct vision and transferred to inverted vision. Inversion increased manipulation time of the tasks to different degrees, showing specificity of effects.

4. Star-tracing movements in eight directions showed significantly different time patterns in four different orienta-tions of the visual field. Variation in relative geometric displacements of perception and motion may account for the specificity of learned and unlearned motions.

5. Gestalt principles that the organization of the entire perceptual field defines the patterning of behavior were not confirmed in a study of maze tracing in upright and inverted fields, with upright and inverted surrounds. The orientation of the surround had no effect on performance.

6. Subjects perform in televised visual fields just as efficiently when they do not identify themselves with the moving hand as when they do. Self-recognition appears not to be important to organization of the perceptual-motor skill.

CHAPTER 13

DELAYED
SENSORY
FEEDBACK

An objective understanding of perceptual-motor behavior must deal not only with its spatial patterning, but its temporal patterning as well. We have said that motion is organized primarily on a spatial basis, because of the differential functioning of the central nervous system in reacting to stimulus differences at specific spatial points. However, these differential stimulus patterns are not static, but change continually, thus defining the on-going, dynamic characteristics of motion. The regulatory systems involved in this temporal patterning of behavior are the sensory feedback mechanisms, which provide a constant barrage of sensory signals — visual, auditory, somesthetic, vestibular — concerning the nature and precision of the motion in progress.

The experiments described so far have been concerned with varying the spatial relationships — or spatial displacement — of perception and motion, an experimental procedure more than a half century old. A natural extension of these studies is experimental temporal displacement of the critical stimulus variables in motion. This general procedure appeared in behavior science only recently, in studies of delayed sensory feedback in which a time lag or delay is introduced between the execution of a motion and the self-stimulation or feedback produced by that motion. Although the phenomena of delayed feedback are relatively new and limited in scope, we believe that they will have far-reaching significance in behavior theory.

The first experimental application of the idea of temporal displacement of movement-produced stimulation was made in connection with speech and its auditory control. The experimental delay of an individual's speech signal to his own ear was first discussed as a "delayed side tone"[24-26, 160-162] to differ-

247

entiate the delayed airborne signal from the immediate bone-conducted signal of the sounds of speech. A number of studies of delayed auditory feedback and its relation to the coordinations of speech and other performance have been made in the last decade.

Delayed visual feedback received its first recognition as a practical problem related to the use of electromechanically controlled indicators in tracking devices, when it became apparent that accuracy of tracking with these devices is affected by the time lag inherent in the controls. Some incidental observations and a few systematic studies of this important problem have appeared since the years of World War II. In this case, however, the delay between movement of the operator and the visual indication of that movement is not a clear-cut example of delayed sensory feedback, for the effect is secondary, mediated by the machine system. The tracker can see his own movement without delay, but cannot see immediately the effect his movement has had on the pointer. A more clearly defined visual feedback delay has been described in two studies of delayed graphic feedback of handwriting performance.[21, 145]

Systematic study of the effects of delaying true pictorial feedback of motion has awaited techniques by means of which the visual stimulus pattern could be controlled temporally. In our original article on application of television to study of displaced vision, we wrote, "We hope, when television tape-recording methods become available, to investigate . . . the spatial and temporal dimensions of the physical environment of vision in the regulation of perceptual organization, motion, and other aspects of behavior. It may be that the television screen will make possible, for the first time, the relative operational control of the factors of space and time in the scientific analysis of the genesis and maintenance of behavior organization and perception."[274]

The hope that videotape recorders eventually would make possible analysis of time displacement or delay of visual feedback of motion has been realized, for we have carried out the first studies of delayed televised visual feedback and its effects on performance. The flexibility of this technique permits investigation of many kinds of behavior, and opens an exciting new field of research (Figure 13-1). In this chapter we shall be concerned with studies of delay of both auditory and visual feedback of motion, and their theoretical implications.

THEORETICAL PREDICTIONS

In studying temporally displaced stimulation, as in studies of spatial displace-

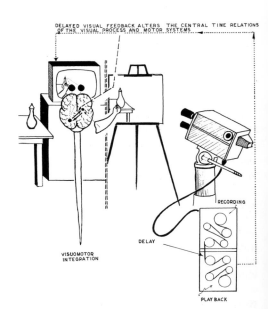

Figure 13-1. Experimental delay of the visual feedback of motion. Such delay separates in time the neural processes of vision and movement, on the basis of which neurogeometric detection occurs, and affects all levels of movement integration, particularly manipulative and transport control.

ment, our ultimate concern is in testing the validity of the major theories of the neurophysiological basis of perceptual-motor organization — the integrated processes of perception and motion. In the introductory chapter, we described several general theories of psychomotor activity that have been advanced in behavior science. These are the belief in conscious, voluntary control of motion; the theory of organized perceptual control of behavior (gestalt theory); different concepts of conditioning, association, and reinforcement as used to describe psychomotor activity in terms of learning; and, finally, neurogeometric theory. In the novel problems to be described here dealing with feedback delay, a valid theory of perceptual-motor organization should provide one with some useful ideas of experimental design as well as some very direct expectations about the results.

We shall not go into the implications of the notion of volitional control of motion, or of the gestalt type of theory, except to point out that such ideas apparently would predict no great disturbance of movement under conditions of delayed sensory feedback. In particular, perceptual organization theory should predict no disturbance of motion organization with delayed feedback if this delay were less than perception time, or the time needed to report the occurrence of perception of stimulus patterns.

Implications of Reinforcement Theory

The concepts of reward reinforcement,[136, 303, 304] stimulus reinforcement,[247] and information reinforcement[86] of learning have definite implications concerning the effects of delayed sensory feedback. In all of these theories, the self-stimulation effect of a given movement (as the observed accuracy of tracking, or the reward, stimulus, or information value of any discrete movement) is interpreted most naturally as a form of reinforcement or information feedback which strengthens the primary movement. The general model is that of progressive growth of the strength or probability of occurrence of such a reinforced response, in which the reinforcement effect is conceived of as having quantifiable properties. That is, the effects of successive reinforcements add up to produce certain increments in learning to perform a given motion. Most learning theorists assume that all skilled motions are specifically learned, and that the processes of conditioning or reinforcement can be used to "mold" or pattern the motion of an animal or individual in any way desired.

If sensory feedback is to be conceptualized as a form of reinforcement, reinforcement theories necessarily would predict the effects of delayed sensory feedback in terms of the known time relations between the response to be learned (reinforced response) and the goal reaction or reinforcing response. It is generally agreed in learning psychology that some temporal flexibility is permissible between the various critical factors in a learning situation without seriously jeopardizing the learning process. The optimal interval between conditioned and unconditioned stimuli has been determined to be about one-half second, but a plus or minus variation of a tenth of a second or so makes little difference. In instrumental learning, it is agreed that the reinforcing stimulus should follow the instrumental act "immediately," but a delay of a few tenths of a second is not seriously detrimental to the efficiency of learning. Thus, if sensory feedback functions as reinforcement to promote effective learning of psychomotor skills, its effectiveness would fall off when it is delayed, but some learning would still occur even after delays of some seconds or even minutes.[136] The form of the learning curve should be approximately the same with all intervals, inasmuch as the same drive conditions obtain in all delay conditions.

Neurogeometric Predictions

Our own theory of motion organization has a number of direct implications about the effects of delayed feedback. On this basis, we have formulated specific hypotheses about certain quantitative and qualitative effects of delay, and have designed our television experiments to test these ideas.

Neurogeometric theory conceives of sensory feedback as an intrinsic regulatory process in organized motion, necessary to the smooth patterning of behavior. Any imposed delay is interpreted as an interruption of precisely timed stimulus-response relationships. Thus, any feedback delay beyond the normal transmission time of sensory signals would be assumed to have deleterious effects, the severity of which would depend on the type of movement and the spatial requirements of the motion patterns. Complex motions and motions which must conform precisely to stimulus patterns require greater spatial precision than less complex or less precise motions, and consequently their temporal requirements are more precise. That is, as the spatial precision of a motion increases, its time requirements are also refined; as the spatial precision of the motion is reduced, its time requirements are correspondingly less precise. Thus, we predict that the magnitude of disturbance caused by a given delay interval would vary with the complexity and precision of the motion pattern. At a given delay interval, a more precise motion would be disturbed more than a less precise motion. This would probably mean that some precisely organized movements would be affected by delay intervals shorter than standard reaction time, or perception time.

Further predictions are made concern-ing differential effects of delayed feedback on continuously controlled and discrete motions. We assume that continuously controlled motions are regulated by adjacent or proximally located Type I neurogeometric detectors, whereas discrete movements, i.e., unitary movements which proceed from one point to another with no intervening regulation, are regulated by dispersed or distantly located Type I (intrareceptor), Type II (interreceptor), or Type III (efferent-afferent) detectors. Discrete motions necessarily are localizing movements which must be made in step-wise fashion. Their essential characteristic is that their manipulative or contact components are functionally separated in time from transport movement components. In continuously controlled motions, however, the transport movements overlap in time the positioning or manipulative movements. In such a constantly monitored motion pattern, we predict that the effects of delayed sensory feedback would be more severe than in discrete motions, which are performed with intermittent control. Also, we expect that continuously controlled motions of relatively high velocity would be disturbed by shorter feedback delays than slower motions.

Neurogeometric theory also predicts certain qualitative changes in movement organization that would be likely to occur under conditions of temporal displacement of feedback signals. First, we would expect persisting variability in motions when either spatial or temporal disturbances are introduced into the neurogeometric control system. No smooth learning curve would be predicted for subjects trying to adapt to the distorted conditions. Second, we would expect integrative changes in motion patterns, such as a shift from continuously controlled motion to a pattern of discrete, jerky movements. This shift would occur because of the greater effect of feedback delay on continuous movements than on discrete movements. We see such shifts in performances such as tracking when the source of stimulus guidance is interrupted. Other integrative changes that might be expected with delayed feedback are changes in the temporal pattern of interacting component movements, or the adoption of different types of movements which would reduce the effects of the delay on perceptual-motor integration or compensate for the particular delay. Finally, we would predict that with one mode of sensory feedback delay, e.g., visual, the control would shift to some other afferent channel. It seems very likely that, under some conditions of delayed visual feedback, the control of movement would shift back and forth from visual to somesthetic channels to reduce the disturbing effects of the visual delay while maintaining general orientation by means of the visual signals.

These predictions of neurogeometric theory are at variance with the logical implications of reinforcement theories concerning the effects of feedback delay on learning and performance of motions. Reinforcement theory would have nothing to say about the differential effects of feedback delay on different kinds of motions. Further, reinforcement theory would predict no permanent disturbance of organized behavior from feedback delay — if feedback is considered equivalent to reinforcement — but would simply predict a falling off in the effectiveness of such delayed feedback in promoting the learning (or relearning) of the motion under consideration.

DELAYED AUDITORY FEEDBACK

The general method of delaying the auditory feedback of the sounds of speech is to record speech sounds on tape, and then hold these sounds for the required delay period by means of a tape loop. The tape travels through the loop before reaching the playback head, which then transmits the recorded speech to the subject's ear by means of earphones (Figure 13-2). The intensity of the reproduced speech is raised above normal so as to mask the immediate bone-conducted sound.

Qualitative Effects

In his original studies of delayed auditory feedback, Lee[160-162] reported that such delay caused a slowing down of speech, increased intensity and higher pitch, and serious articulatory disturbances, which he called "artificial stutter." Fairbanks and Guttman[80] analyzed the nature of errors of articulation, and observed that there were three main types of error — additions, omissions, and substitutions of words or syllables — in addition to miscellaneous errors such as slighting and shifted juncture. Additive errors could be either repetitious or nonrepetitious insertions, but were almost always double articulations.

Quantitative Effects

The most generally observed effect of delayed auditory feedback, a slowing

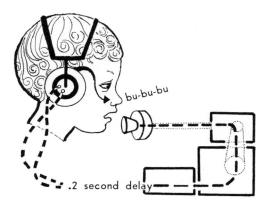

Figure 13-2. The technique of delaying auditory feedback of speech.

down of speech, was observed by Lee[160–162] and Black[24, 25] with delays from 0.03 to 0.18 second. Rawnsley and Harris[215] used sound spectrograms for observation and measurement of speech sounds, and reported that phrases spoken with delayed auditory feedback were almost invariably spoken more slowly than under normal conditions. In a comparative study of children of different ages, it was reported that the slow-down effect was more pronounced in children seven to nine years of age than in children four to six years of age.[46]

Fairbanks[79] found that the delay interval producing the greatest decrease in reading rate was about 0.2 second. Another systematic study of the effects of different delay periods on reading rate was carried out by Chase, Sutton, Rapin, Standfast, and Harvey.[47] The summary of their results in Figure 13-3 shows the Correct Word Rate in words per second for synchronized feedback and five different magnitudes of feedback delay, ranging from 0.138 to 0.394 second. The most marked reduction in reading rate was found at 0.244 second, a value similar to that reported by Fairbanks. Fairbanks also reported a peaking effect at about 0.2 second delay for the number of articulatory errors. Curves showing increases in intensity and pitch level of speech apparently also reached a maximum at about 0.2 second, but fell off only slightly.

Interesting to us from a theoretical point of view are studies of acceleration of auditory feedback to the ear. Normal air-conducted feedback requires an interval of about 0.001 second. By using electronic transmission and earphones, feedback time to the ear can be speeded up faster than this normal interval. Peters[207] found that such acceleration caused subjects to read faster than their normal rate, even though they had been instructed to read in a natural way.

Increased repetition rate of speech units has been reported by Chase[43]

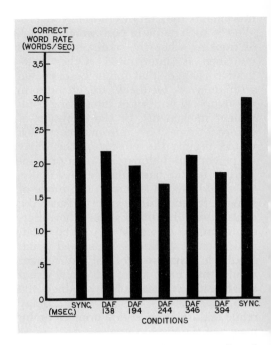

Figure 13-3. Correct words per second with different magnitudes of delayed auditory feedback. (From Chase, Sutton, Rapin, Standfast, and Harvey.[47])

under certain conditions of feedback delay. He reported that with an auditory delay of 0.216 second, his subjects uttered the single sound "b" more frequently than under normal or slightly accelerated feedback conditions. Chase stated that he had observed repetitions of "speech units smaller than the syllable" to be three times as frequent as syllables. According to the best available analysis of speech movements, however, the syllable should be recognized as the basic unit of speech.[291] In this light, Chase's statement is somewhat ambiguous. The syllables to which he refers probably contained both an initial and a final consonant (such as "bet"), while his "smaller speech units" were simple consonant-vowel combinations, such as the letter "b" ("be"). The accelerated repetitions of such a speech syllable must have been very like a stutter, and perhaps equivalent to the speech errors observed by other investigators with delayed feedback. The repetition rate may have increased with feedback delay if the subjects unknowingly, i.e., in the absence of normal auditory monitoring, shifted to an easier speech pattern, such as "buh, buh, buh," instead of "be, be, be."

Adaptation to Delayed Feedback

Only a few observations are available on adaptation to delayed auditory feedback. Atkinson[9] found no adaptation to delayed feedback in terms of measured reading rate over a single five-minute period of exposure. Tiffany and Hanley[306] studied adaptation over a series of 24 readings during two weeks. Their subjects showed no increase in reading rate, but in general learned to make fewer errors. Winchester, Gibbons, and Krebs[328] found a slight increase in reading rate during successive exposure periods that was significant after the first two periods.

Black[26] reported that the increased speaking time induced by auditory delay persisted after the delay had been discontinued. His statistical analyses indicated that this persistence effect lasted at least two and a half minutes after the auditory feedback to the ear was again presented at the normal interval.

While these observations on adaptation are too few to support general conclusions, it seems apparent that only the most limited adaptation occurs with continued or repeated exposure to delayed auditory feedback.

Effects of Delayed Auditory Feedback on Motions other than Speech

In his first observations of delayed auditory feedback, Lee[160] tested the ability of a skilled wireless operator to tap signals and of a tympanist to perform on his instruments when the sounds of their movements were delayed. Both of them performed erratically and made many errors.

Kalmus, Denes, and Fry[144] appear to have carried out the first systematic studies on the effects of delayed auditory feedback on performance other than speech. They studied the effects of a 0.25 second delay on whistling, playing musical instruments, and handclapping. Deterioration of performance comparable to that described for speech was found.

More recently, Chase, Harvey, Standfast, Rapin, and Sutton[44, 45] have studied delayed auditory feedback of manual tapping movements, and have described effects equivalent to disturbances in speech with delayed feedback. In this experiment, records were secured from 14 subjects when they repeated the sound "b" in groups of three and when they tapped a key three times in succession. In both situations, the subject wore earphones, and the sounds of his performance were recorded on a magnetic tape loop and presented to his ear after a 0.244 second delay. Oscillograms of the speech sounds were obtained, and the patterns of the tapping were recorded by amplifying the signal of a strain gauge. As shown in Figure 13-4, both speech and tapping movements increased in intensity, in duration, and in time between movements.

Interpretations

The first effort to interpret theoretically the effects of delayed auditory feedback on speech and other performance was made by Lee,[162] who speculated that delayed hearing affects a specific level of speech control in the central nervous system. He described the speech mechanism as consisting of four types of neural loops, of different levels and transmission lengths — articulation loops, voice loops, word loops,

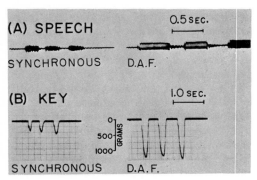

Figure 13-4. Changes in intensity and rate of speech and tapping motions with delayed auditory feedback. (From Chase, Harvey, Standfast, Rapin, and Sutton.[44])

and thought loops. He thought that feedback delay interrupted the aural monitoring of the voice loop, thus inducing artificial stutter.

Fairbanks[78] proposed an analogy between the aural-vocal system and a servosystem to account for the effects of feedback delay. As shown in the diagram in Figure 13-5, A, a servomotor activates an output motion that must be controlled or directed according to some prescribed rate or signal such as the direction of a target. The input of the system senses the differences between the output action of the system and the time, rate, or direction that is used to control the system. This sensing is done by comparing the output feedback of the system and the true rate, or direction. Thus, the system is self-regulating in relation to the external signals to which its action is directed.

The analogy of the aural-vocal system with a servosystem is diagrammed in Figure 13-5, B. In this case, the output of the system (speech musculature) is adjusted to produce sounds according to a definite time and sound pattern. The sound pattern of the output is fed back to the ear in two ways — as a bone-conducted sound pattern and as an air-conducted sound pattern — and is used by the ear to control brain integration

(neural amplification) which in turn controls the speech musculature. When a delay is put in the air-conducted feedback, the action of the system is distorted.

Chase repeated the analogy between the aural-vocal system and a servosystem in discussing the effects of delayed auditory feedback on speech. In addition, he described some of the changes that may occur as a result of the delay. He noted that the delay may produce variations in the physical quality of the speech sounds, in the nature of the syllable as a unit of speech, and in the acoustic environment, due to interaction of bone-conducted sound and the delayed airborne sound.

Drawing an analogy between the action of a behavior mechanism and a self-regulating motor system[327] in reality adds little to our understanding of the actual physiology of the mechanism. Although pointing up the importance of the element of self-regulation in the control of speech patterns, such analogies fall short of providing an account of how such self-regulation is carried out by the living system. These theoret-

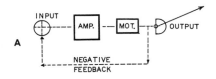

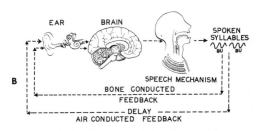

Figure 13-5. The speech-hearing mechanism as a self-regulating motor system. A. General diagram of a servosystem. B. Servosystem analogy of speech and hearing.

ical accounts do not indicate how many output feedback controls may be involved in speech. For example, they say nothing of whether or not there are critical kinesthetic controls in speech, or whether air pressure in the lungs and trachea produces critical feedback signals in speech production. In general, the servosystem models, while rightly emphasizing the importance of objectivity and a quantitative point of view, tend to oversimplify the relationships of the speech mechanisms.

At present, there is no theoretical account of the speech control mechanism that specifies clearly why delayed auditory feedback has such disruptive effects on the control of speech. The problem quite clearly goes beyond the particular characteristics of hearing and speech and applies generally to the regulatory mechanisms of patterned behavior. Our account of delayed visual feedback will reveal many effects similar to those that have been described in studies of delayed hearing.

PRIOR STUDIES OF DELAYED VISUAL FEEDBACK

The disturbing effects of delayed visual feedback were a human engineering problem for some years before Lee first studied delayed side-tone in speech. As we have indicated in our brief description of tracking systems in Chapter 3, the introduction of automated rate-control devices (velocity tracking) into such machines as radar trackers or gun-laying systems in World War II greatly reduced the accuracy and efficiency of the human operators. For example, the delay factor inherent in the computing mechanism of the central fire control system of the B-29 bomber rendered it less than adequate as a machine for human use. These automated tracking systems were greatly improved by introducing "aided

tracking" controls to speed up at least in part the visual feedback to the operator of the effects of his movements. Although it is recognized generally that delay in perceptual information is detrimental to performance, few systematic studies have been carried out to analyze quantitatively the effects of the visual tracking delay.

Introduction of the auditory feedback delay problem stimulated interest in devising a technique for delaying the direct visual feedback of motion. Prior to our own use of television and videotape techniques, two studies were carried out on delayed graphic feedback of handwriting, using a telewriter and a telescriber.

Delayed Visual Feedback in Tracking Performance

Velocity tracking devices were introduced in World War II because it was felt that partial automation of the tracking task would increase the efficiency of the operator. In such tracking, a movement of the operator generates a rate of movement of the cursor by means of an intervening motor control, but the operator's movement does not position the cursor directly. Hence, there is a delay or lag between the action of the operator and the response of the cursor. When it was found that these systems were highly inaccurate, the visual lags were eliminated partially by introducing aided tracking controls. In these systems, a movement of the operator positions the cursor directly, without delay, but also generates a rate of movement of the cursor by means of the motor system. Thus, in aided tracking, the visual information of the rate that the operator has initiated is delayed, even though there is immediate feedback of the initial position that the cursor has assumed.

Velocity tracking and aided tracking are just two examples of controlling devices with delayed visual feedback. Power-driven steering in automobiles usually involves a lag between the driver's movements and visual knowledge of his performance, unless special designs are used to eliminate the delay in information feedback. Systematic comparisons of the accuracy of velocity and aided tracking with direct pursuit tracking have shown that, while aided tracking is far superior to velocity tracking, it is still somewhat inferior to direct pursuit tracking.[48, 168] The obvious inference is that even a partial feedback delay reduces the accuracy of tracking performance.

Specific studies of the effects of introducing transmission lags into the perceptual display given a tracker have shown invariably that the visual delay reduces accuracy and that in general accuracy decreases progressively as the delay magnitude is increased. Systematic studies of these relationships have been carried out by Warrick,[315] Levine,[165] and Conklin,[52, 53] who used partial or complete transmission delays up to 16 seconds. The central question posed in such experiments is how the magnitude of tracking error varies with the magnitude of the delay. Warrick found a progressive decrease in tracking accuracy with delays up to 0.32 second, but the form of the curve was not well defined. Levine reported that with feedback delays less than 0.15 second, the relationship between the delay value and magnitude of error was exponential in nature, although with delays from 0.15 to 2.7 seconds, the relationship was found to be linear. Conklin also found a linear relationship with time lags varying from 0.2 to 1.0 second.

Theoretical interpretation of tracking performance under conditions of delayed visual feedback depends on one's general theory of tracking behavior. We can differentiate at least three general theoretical positions in this field: (a) the technological view that the regulation of tracking can be described as analogous to the workings of a servosystem, and that a general mathematical formulation of the tracking function can be obtained; (b) the view that tracking can be described in terms of some generalized psychological function, such as learning, in which case perceptual information feedback is interpreted as a form of reinforcement; and (c) our own point of view that tracking motions are made up of interacting space-organized movements of positioning (manipulation) and rate control (transport) that are differentially affected by time and space factors in both direct and aided tracking. This is not the place to go into a lengthy evaluation of these different points of view either in general or as they apply to the problem of delayed feedback. One point can be made, however. The first two theories seem to lack certain advantages possessed by the differential movement theory in accounting for the effects of many variables on tracking. Using this theory, we can distinguish among various forms of tracking behavior in terms of concrete concepts of perceptual-motor integration, and specify the relative accuracy of different kinds of tracking under the various feedback conditions. This theory also has the great advantage of being able to specify which way the human operator will move or steer his cursor initially when the target moves in a given direction, without invoking concepts of mental decision and past learning to explain this elementary fact. That is to say, the tracking behavior of animals, including man, can be interpreted in neurogeometric terms.

Delayed Graphic Feedback of Handwriting

Delayed visual feedback of handwriting motions has been studied by van Bergeijk and David[21] using a telewriter, an instrument which transmits and reproduces on an electronic tube the pattern of handwriting formed by a stylus point on a separate surface. The instrument accomplishes this electrical reproduction by generating voltages corresponding to X and Y coordinates of the stylus movement. These voltage values were frequency modulated and passed through a delay network in order to introduce a delay between the movements of writing and the visual feedback of those movements. The components of the apparatus are diagrammed in Figure 13-6. Subjects were not permitted to view their hand directly, but watched the reproduction of the handwriting pattern on the viewing surface of a storage tube called a Memoscope.

Two separate experiments were carried out, comparing delays of 0.0, 0.04, 0.08, 0.15, 0.27, and 0.52 second. Six subjects were used in each experiment. They were required to write pairs of words out of a list of 12, with different words used for each delay condition, and the order of presentation varied by subject. The list was composed of three 2-letter words (me, an, of), three 4-letter words (rose, dare, four), three 8-letter words (graceful, hangover, pleasure), and three 12-letter words (commonplaces, overremember, prepossessed). In the first experiment, the subjects were told to write "the best you can." A duration score of time-per-letter and a legi-

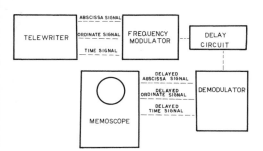

Figure 13-6. Van Bergeijk and David's technique for delaying the graphic feedback of handwriting. (Based on van Bergeijk and David.[21])

bility score, measured by means of a neatness rating, were obtained. In the second experiment, the instructions were: "You will be scored for speed as well as for neatness and errors; you should try to optimize your score." Further measures of performance were obtained by recording errors of omission, duplication, and substitution of letters in the writing tasks.

The neatness ratings were very similar in the two experiments, and in both cases there was marked reduction in neatness as the magnitude of delay was increased. The subjects in the first experiment wrote much more slowly than those in the second and made no errors. The effects of the instructions that emphasized speed as well as neatness and accuracy were to increase the speed very remarkably and to introduce errors, leaving the neatness scores much the same. The authors concluded that speed and errors were interdependent, so that subjects could increase their speed of writing under conditions of feedback delay only by sacrificing accuracy.

The average neatness, error, and time scores for the second experiment are plotted in Figure 13-7 as a function of delay periods. The neatness and error scores appear to follow an exponential curve, with no sign of having reached a maximum. The time-per-letter scores show but a slight increase with increase in the magnitude of delay, and it is not clear whether a maximum has been reached. These results can be contrasted with results on delayed auditory feedback, which have shown that there is maximum interference with speech at delays of about 0.2 second.

A similar method was used by Kalmus, Fry, and Denes[145] to delay the graphic feedback of handwriting, drawing, and tracing performance. They used a telescriber, which transmits electromechanically the movements of a stylus to an ink-writing pen, and used a delay element which could provide feedback

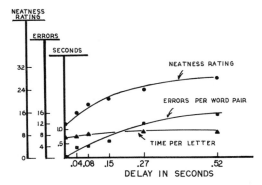

Figure 13-7. Changes in neatness, accuracy and speed of handwriting as a function of different magnitudes of feedback delay. (Based on van Bergeijk and David.[21])

DELAYED TELEVISED FEEDBACK OF PERFORMANCE

The development of videotape recorders provides a new technique for research in many areas of behavior. It is already being adapted for use as a training device. For example, the Ampex videotape recorder has been installed on Navy carriers to give pilots a review of their landing behavior immediately after alighting from their planes.[2]

Our own interest in videotape recording is directed generally toward evaluating the uses of this device in training and the control of motion, and specifically toward using this technique in studies of delayed visual feedback. The television method has several advantages over the other methods that have been used to study delayed sensory feedback. It is more flexible than other methods in providing feedback of many different kinds of behavior. Also it has the marked advantage of providing complete control of the visual signal, in contrast to methods of delaying auditory feedback that control only the airborne sound. The speech studies are complicated by the immediate feedback of bone-conducted sound. The greatest disadvantage of the television method is the high cost of acquiring and maintaining videotape recording units.

We are reporting here three types of experiments on delayed televised performance, using three different techniques. The first was to use a single videotape recorder to study what we call "complete-task delay," or blind performance with consecutive delayed feedback at the completion of a prescribed task. While the subject was moving, a televised picture was recorded on a tape loop, adjusted to run its course in approximately the time taken to perform the task. During this time there was no visual feedback of movement at all, but at completion of the task, the recorded picture was played back to be

delays varying from a few milliseconds to about a second and a half.

When subjects wrote either from memory or dictation, delayed feedback slowed down performance, disturbed the organization, and induced errors of spelling and making letters. Repetitions, omissions, and additions were noted. When subjects attempted to draw familiar symbols, gross distortions of pattern occurred. In general, the magnitude of disturbance increased with increases in the delay interval.

In order to obtain quantitative measures of error, the experimenters presented patterns on the viewing screen and asked subjects to trace them. Performance time and error scores generally increased with increased magnitude of delay, but this correlation was higher for error than for time. In this tracing task, the error scores appeared to increase with the delay independently of time scores. This finding contrasts with van Bergeijk and David's observation concerning the interdependence of speed and errors in handwriting.

Kalmus, Fry, and Denes observed that subjects varied their mode of response in trying to adapt to the delay, but there was no consistent improvement that could be attributed to learning.

viewed by the subject on a television monitor.

Our second technique was to simulate televised feedback of motion, as described in Chapter 12 (see Figure 12-9), in order to provide delayed feedback concurrent with performance. One simulation study was carried out which compared some of the effects of complete-task delay with those resulting from a short delay and a half-task delay. The subject could not see his own hand, but viewed what he thought were his own movements in a television monitor. Actually the televised picture was of the hand of the experimenter, who duplicated the movements of the subject as closely as possible after a specified delay interval.

The third type of experiment was made possible by an unusual opportunity to work for a limited period of time at the RCA Manufacturing Company in Princeton, New Jersey.[273] Two RCA Simplex television recorders were made available to us, so that recording and playback could be carried out concurrently. With this set-up, we explored the effects of a fixed delay of 0.52 second on a series of manual tasks.

Watching one's own performance with delayed visual feedback is extremely disconcerting, and in some cases results in almost complete disorganization of patterned movements. One seems to be divorced from his own motion, and simple movements seem to occur without guidance. Temporal displacement of visual feedback ranks with unusual conditions of spatial displacement as a serious distortion of the normal stimulus-response relationships in visually controlled behavior.

Blind Performance with Consecutive Visual Feedback

The diagram in Figure 13-8 illustrates how the Ampex videotape recorder has been adapted for use in our television

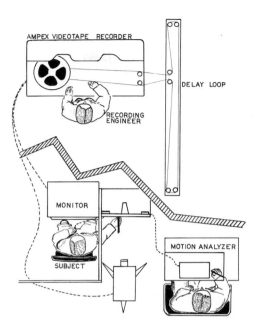

Figure 13-8. Technique of delaying the televised pictorial feedback of performance. The subject performs "blind" and sees the delayed image after he completes the task.

laboratory to provide a delayed visual image of performance on the television monitor. The tape recorder is located in one room and the television camera and monitor in another, with communication between the two achieved by an intercommunication system. As in the studies of displaced vision, the subject cannot observe his own motions directly, but sees only the image in the television monitor. In order to produce a delay of this visual feedback, we constructed a tape loop for the videotape recorder, and put the recorder in the circuit between the camera and the monitor. The tape loop was adjusted in length so that it ran its course in approximately the time taken to perform the task. When the performance had been recorded, a switch was thrown to change from recording to playback. The subject saw nothing while he was performing, but as soon as the task was completed, the recorded visual feedback appeared on the monitor to show him what he had done.

A photograph of the recorder and tape loop is shown in Figure 13-9. The Ampex videotape recorder uses a 2-inch magnetic tape, on which the visual signal is recorded by means of a revolving head that scans the tape crosswise. The tape moves through the recording head at a speed of 15 inches per second. Thus, a tape loop of 35 feet would give a maximal task time of just under 28 seconds. Three different experiments have been carried out with this set-up.

MAZE TRACING. The task performed by three subjects in this experiment was to trace with a pencil a mimeographed maze path, shown by the stippled patterns in Figure 13-10. Three preliminary practice trials with direct vision were given, with instructions to trace the maze accurately as fast as possible, and to remember the pattern in preparation for blind performance. Following the practice trials, the subject's hand was screened, his pencil was positioned on

the starting circle by the experimenter, and he was told to trace the path at the same speed as before. Ten experimental trials were given, which were televised, recorded, and then presented on the subject's television monitor at the completion of the task.

One practice tracing and several experimental tracings from each subject are reproduced in Figure 13-10. Individual trials are numbered at the end of the tracings. These test results show a poor degree of control in blind performance, with some evidence of learning between the first and last trials. Subject 1 showed the learning effect most clearly. His tenth tracing was fairly accurate in size and pattern, although it was displaced to some extent. Subject 2 also showed considerable improvement, but Subject 3 showed little, if any, evidence of learning.

These results emphasize the importance of immediate visual feedback in the control of precisely organized patterns of movements. With complete task delay, the individual had to depend on

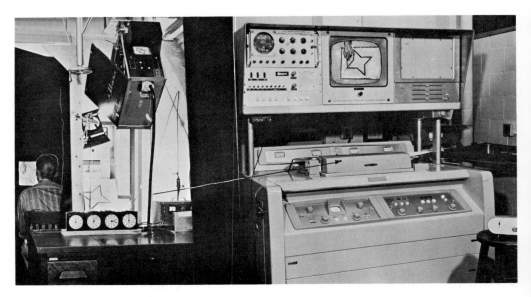

Figure 13-9. Photograph showing the Ampex videotape recorder and tape loop system (right), and the performance room with television camera, monitor and motion analyzer (left).

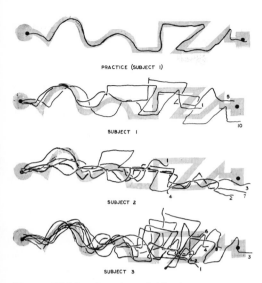

PRACTICE (SUBJECT 1)

SUBJECT 1

SUBJECT 2

SUBJECT 3

Figure 13-10. Samples of blind maze-tracing performance from three subjects with consecutive delayed televised feedback. One practice tracing with nondelayed vision is shown.

cutaneous and kinesthetic signals to guide the activity. Because he was given no visual feedback until his task was complete, his movements did not show the blocking and interference effects typically induced by concurrent delayed feedback; however, the degree of control was poor, and performance in many cases appeared disorganized.

STAR TRACING. In a second study of blind performance, the task was to trace the four-pointed star seen in Figure 13-9. Small notches were cut along the sides of the grooved pathway to trap the subject's stylus if he attempted to slide it along the edge. Thus he could not use cutaneous-kinesthetic feedback for a fast performance, although it did provide an accuracy check. Six experimental subjects were given one practice trial with immediate feedback, and then ten trials per day for two days with feedback after 25 seconds delay. If a subject had not completed the task in 25 seconds, he was stopped by the experimenter so that the recorded televised

image could be presented. Six control subjects performed the task with immediate feedback throughout the two days. Durations of movements in each successive leg of the star were recorded by means of a four-channel motion analyzer. Total number of segments completed per trial were also recorded.

Whereas the control subjects traced the star in a few seconds, the experimental subjects completed it in 25 seconds in only a few instances. The total number of segments completed by all six subjects in each successive trial is shown in Figure 13-11. The highest total for any one trial was 40 out of a possible maximum of 48. As a group, the subjects improved during the first ten trials but showed no further improvement on the second day. The time scores showed a similar leveling effect.

DYNAMIC VERSUS STATIC DELAYED FEEDBACK. In a third experiment we compared the effects on blind performance of presenting delayed televised feedback of motion and delayed feedback of the movement trace, using a dot location task. The first was dynamic feedback — the televised image of performance; the second was a static picture of the marks left by the dotting pen. In addition, both types of feedback were compared with normal orientation

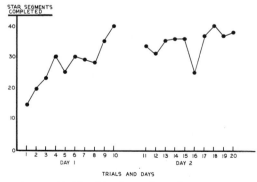

Figure 13-11. Total number of star segments traced blindly by six subjects in successive trials on two days.

and with inverted-reversed orientation of the feedback image.

A diagram of the set-up is shown in Figure 13-12, with an enlargement of the mimeographed dot location task. The subject used a heavy marking pen to dot the 12 small circles in a zig-zag pattern, moving from inner to outer to inner positions, and so on, as shown by the numbers in the circles. The number of dots that were correctly placed in the circles was recorded, as well as component movement times.

Twenty-eight subjects were divided into four groups to perform with dynamic upright feedback, dynamic displaced feedback, static upright feedback, and static displaced feedback. For these groups, the delay interval was kept constant at 30 seconds. An additional six subjects performed with dynamic upright feedback with a 15-second delay. For five days all subjects performed two

practice trials with immediate upright feedback followed by 10 test trials under their assigned conditions. The subjects who were to receive inverted-reversed feedback were so informed.

The mean daily dot location accuracy scores for the first four groups are shown in Figure 13-13. It can be seen that all

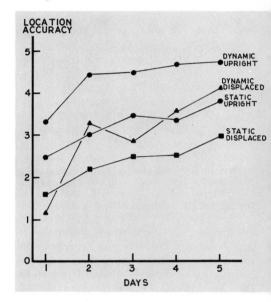

Figure 13-13. Mean dot location accuracy on successive days for groups performing with dynamic upright, dynamic displaced, static upright, and static displaced visual feedback.

groups improved slightly with practice, a change that was statistically significant. Dynamic feedback gave consistently better scores than static, and upright vision gave better scores than displaced. Figure 13-14 compares accuracy means for groups performing with 15-second and 30-second delays. These differences were not statistically significant.

The time data showed fewer clear differences for the first four groups than the accuracy data. Total performance time was faster with upright vision than with inverted, but there were no significant differences in performance time related to dynamic and static feedback.

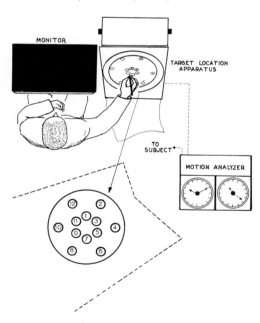

Figure 13-12. Set-up used to study dot location performance with dynamic and static delayed televised feedback. The enlarged pattern shows the arrangement of the task, with correct order of dotting indicated by number.

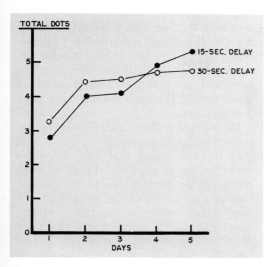

Figure 13-14. Mean dot location accuracy on successive days for groups performing with delay intervals of 15 and 30 seconds.

However, as shown in Figure 13-15, the group performing with a 15-second delay was consistently faster than the group performing with a 30-second delay. These differences in total performance time were significant for all five days combined but not for the fifth day alone.

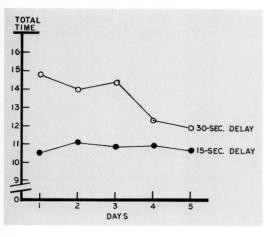

Figure 13-15. Mean total task time on successive days for groups performing with delay intervals of 15 and 30 seconds.

To summarize these results, all groups showed a limited learning effect when judged by accuracy, less clearly so when judged by performance time. As one would expect, upright vision gave consistently better accuracy and time scores than inverted vision. Dynamic feedback was better than static when judged by accuracy, and the 15-second delay gave better time scores than the 30-second delay.

Over all, the studies of blind performance show that delayed consecutive feedback, even after intervals as short as 15 to 30 seconds, is of very little benefit in learning a visually organized skill. Tasks that can be performed with great precision with immediate feedback become grossly inaccurate when the feedback is delayed, and improve very little with practice. The implication for learning or training situations is that knowledge of results delayed even for a fraction of a minute may be of little use. What the individual needs in organizing a perceptual-motor skill is immediate sensory feedback of the precision of his movements.

A Study of Simulated Delayed Feedback

Our interest in concurrent delayed visual feedback led us to devise a technique of studying some of the problems in this area by television techniques, but without using a videotape recorder. Our method of simulating delayed visual feedback of performance has already been described in Chapter 12 (see Figure 12-9). The subject sat before a television monitor tracing with a pencil the pathway of a maze located behind a cloth that screened his hand from view. He wore a black arm cover and white cotton glove, ostensibly to make the televised image of his performance clearer. In his monitor he saw an image of the maze, and after a specified delay period, a black and white arm and hand appeared there, performing the tracing movements that he had just completed. Actually the televised image of the subject's hand appeared on a monitor in another room, where a specially trained observer duplicated the subject's movements on an identical maze, reproducing his errors and observing his movement idiosyncrasies. The image visible on the subject's monitor was that of the observer's hand. Great care was taken to avoid any movements in the image seen by the subject that could not have been his own.

The pattern of the maze with an accurate tracing is shown in Figure 13-16. Three delay periods were used: a short delay, in which the observer's hand started to move as soon as he could react accurately to the subject's movements (1 to 2 sec.); a half-task delay, in which the observer's hand started the task when the subject was half way through it; and a complete-task delay, in which the observer waited for the subject to finish the maze before duplicating his movements. These different delays are indicated in the figure; that is, the observer started his feedback performance when the subject had reached one of the positions indicated.

Four subjects performed under each delay condition. There were three experimental periods for each subject, spaced two days apart, with five tracings

completed in each period. The subject was told that we had a means of delaying the televised image of his performance, and only one of the twelve remarked spontaneously that the hand he saw was not his own. Some of them were definitely disturbed by their poor performance.

QUALITATIVE RESULTS. The superimposed tracings in Figure 13-17, 13-18, and 13-19 compare first and last day's performance of typical subjects at each of the delay periods. In terms of relative accuracy, it can be seen that the short delay resulted in the best performance (Fig. 13-17), and the complete-task delay in the poorest (Fig. 13-19). When first-day performance is compared with last-day performance, it is evident that very little learning took place for any delay period.

Perhaps the most significant difference in peformance with different delay periods lies in the nature of movement organization. The tracings in Figure 13-17 show a jerky movement pattern that was characteristic of all subjects performing with the short-delay feedback. This jumpy progression through the maze usually began in the first trial, and was used throughout. The subject would make a rapid movement and then wait for the televised image to "catch up" before moving ahead. These jerky,

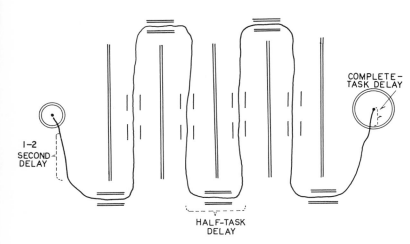

Figure 13-16. Pencil-tracing maze design used in the simulated delayed-feedback study.

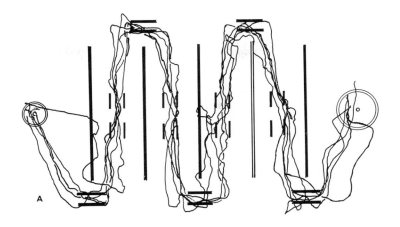

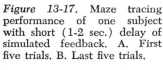

Figure 13-17. Maze tracing performance of one subject with short (1-2 sec.) delay of simulated feedback. A. First five trials. B. Last five trials.

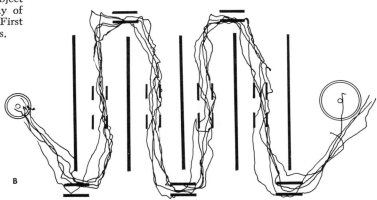

discrete motions were not used with the longer delays. However, with half-task delay (Figure 13-18), there was more irregularity of movement during the second half of the tracing, while the delayed movement image was visible, than during the first half.

QUANTITATIVE RESULTS. The maze path used in this experiment was marked off as shown in Figure 13-20 to provide two measures of accuracy — a measure of "precision tracing," and a measure of "area tracing." One point was given for each block entered by a tracing. The large blocks gave the area-tracing score, up to a maximum of 23, while the small

blocks gave the precision-tracing score, with a maximum of 40.

Using the precision scores, we compared the corresponding tracings made by subject and observer for 55 experimental periods, each consisting of five tracings, to determine how well the observer reproduced the subject's maze path. Nineteen of these periods were preliminary practice runs to train the observer and test his accuracy. Only four of the 55 groups of precision scores showed a significant difference at the 5 per cent level between subjects and observer, and only two, at the 1 per cent level.

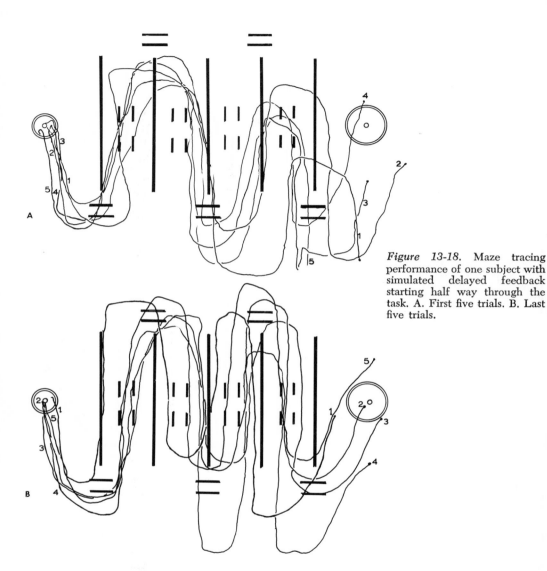

Figure 13-18. Maze tracing performance of one subject with simulated delayed feedback starting half way through the task. A. First five trials. B. Last five trials.

Both precision-tracing and area-tracing scores for each experimental group are plotted according to practice periods in Figure 13-21 and according to length of delay in Figure 13-22. Each point on the graphs represents the mean of four subjects' median scores on a particular day. The curves in Figure 13-21 show a slight increase in accuracy in both precision and area scores throughout the three practice periods, although these differences were not generally significant. The curves in Figure 13-22 show that accuracy varied systematically as a function of the delay periods, which are plotted at their approximate average values of 1, 30, and 60 seconds. In all cases, accuracy dropped with an increase

Figure 13-19. Maze tracing performance of one subject with simulated delayed feedback starting at the completion of the task. A. First five trials. B. Last five trials.

in the magnitude of delay, and these differences were statistically significant.

Although this experiment on simulated feedback sacrificed rigid temporal control of delay intervals for flexible control in terms of task organization, there is no doubt that accuracy of performance decreased with increase in the magnitude of delay. Performance with complete-task delay was poorest in spite of the fact that subjects performing under this condition were not subject to blocking and interference effects caused

by concurrent delayed feedback. It is also obvious that the effects of practice on accuracy in this experiment were very limited.

Concurrent Delayed Visual Feedback

The ideal method of studying delayed visual feedback is to obtain a pictorial record of performance and to feed back this information to the subject after a controlled delay interval, all the while performance continues. In order to carry

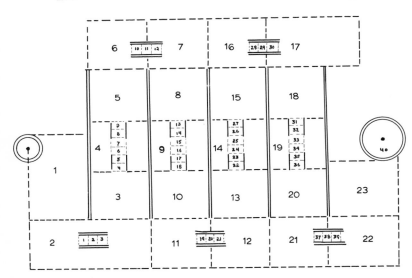

Figure 13-20. Method of scoring visual maze. Number of large blocks entered gives area-tracing score, and number of small blocks entered gives precision-tracing score.

out this type of study, arrangements were made with the RCA Manufacturing Company in Princeton, New Jersey, to carry out a limited series of experimental observations with two RCA Simplex television tape recorders, one for recording and one for playback.[273] These arrangements turned out to be highly successful. It was possible to compare the effects of 0.52 second delay of pictorial feedback on nine different manual tasks involving writing, drawing, or tracing performance. The portable electronic handwriting analyzer shown in Figure 13-23 was used to time separately the contact and travel movements in the different tasks.

The arrangement of the equipment for this experiment is shown in Figure 13-24. The subject sat before a 21-inch monitor screen and carried out the writing and drawing performance on the tilted table surface of the handwriting analyzer. He wore goggles designed to prevent him from seeing his own hand on the table below; he could watch his own performance only by viewing the monitor image. The camera was located so as to give an undistorted picture of the performance area, magnified in size about 1.5 times. The subject could see

in the monitor the writing area, his own hand and pencil, and his lower arm. The televised image was recorded by means of one television recorder and then transmitted to the monitor by means of the playback head of a second recorder. The tape distance between the two recorders (52 inches) determined the magnitude of delay in visual feedback of 0.52 second.

The tasks used in this study are described in Figure 13-25. They were: (1) writing all letters of the alphabet; (2) star tracing; (3) drawing geometric figures; (4) writing 4-letter nonsense syllables; (5) tracing a maze like that described in our simulated feedback experiment; (6) writing 4-letter words; (7) writing 12 words of different length (this was the list of 12 words used by van Bergeijk and David referred to in our chart as the "Bell-Telephone" words); (8) writing 3-letter nonsense syllables; and (9) dotting six small circles of decreasing diameter (⅞ inch to ⅜ inch). The number of trials and repetitions are indicated in the chart.

The nine tasks were arranged randomly for the two subjects, both of whom were professional psychologists. They attempted to work as accurately

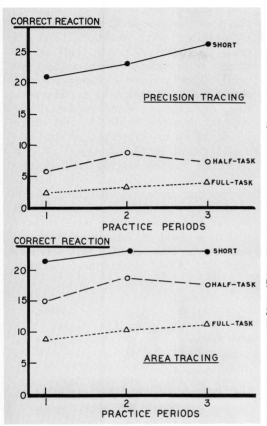

Figure 13-21. Precision-tracing and area-tracing scores as a function of practice for groups performing with different magnitudes of delayed feedback.

feedback made their performance inordinately difficult and frustrating. Even

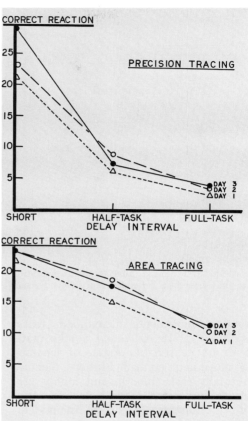

Figure 13-22. Precision-tracing and area-tracing scores as a function of delay magnitude on the different days of practice.

and rapidly as possible. At a later time they repeated the same tasks under normal conditions, when they could observe their movements directly, and with nondelayed televised performance, when they watched their movements in a monitor. It was not possible to make these control observations at the same time and place as the observations of delayed performance, because of the limited time available in the RCA laboratories.

QUALITATIVE EFFECTS. The subjects found that introducing a 0.52 second delay between movement and visual

Figure 13-23. Portable electronic handwriting analyzer.

MONITOR
PLAYBACK
DELAY
VIDEOTAPE RECORDERS
RECORDING
SUBJECT
EXPERIMENTER
HANDWRITING MOTION ANALYZER

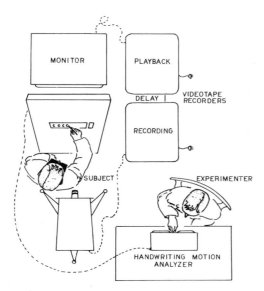

Figure 13-24. Arrangement of television, recording, and motion analysis instrumentation for the experiment on concurrent delayed visual feedback.

simple movements demanded extraordinary effort and could not be made with any reasonable degree of accuracy of movement control. Motions that are normally fast, smooth, and highly precise became erratic and jerky regardless of all attempts to control them. This was particularly true of continuous tracing movements. Handwriting became severely degraded, and, in some cases, completely illegible.

Some of the performance records obtained with delayed feedback are shown in Figure 13-26 along with records of nondelayed televised performance and normal performance. The jerky, oscillatory movements just described are seen clearly in the star tracing and maze tracing. The written verbal material shows some oscillation, and also numerous errors. An analysis of 64 such errors is given in Figure 13-27. The most common, accounting for 40.6 per cent, were letter duplications, examples of which can be seen in Figure 10-26. Van Bergeijk and David also reported the predominance of this type of error. Other errors were insertions (26.6 per cent), omissions (7.8 per cent) and a variety of miscellaneous errors (23.4 per cent). The numerous insertions and duplications are analogous to the repetitive articulatory errors induced by delayed auditory feedback, and might be described as "graphic stuttering."

Evaluation of the accuracy of performance in the tracing and dotting tasks shows more dramatically than in the writing tasks the disturbing effects of delayed vision. Some of the records of star and maze tracing were so poor that they could not be scored. Performance in the circle dotting task was also very poor. About two-thirds of the time,

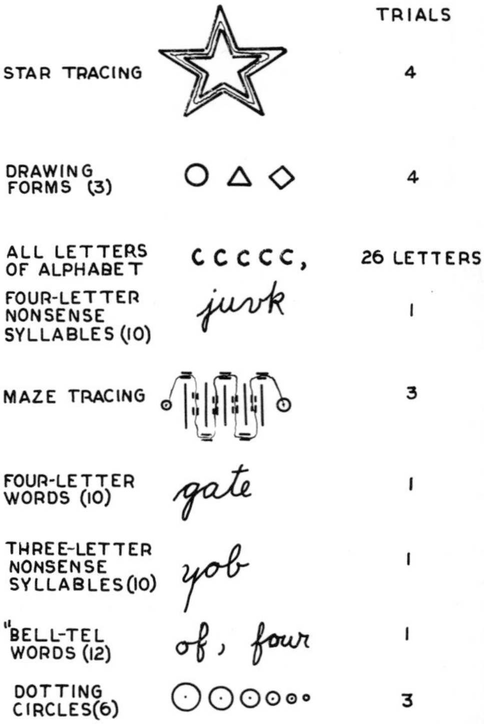

TRIALS
STAR TRACING
4
DRAWING FORMS (3)
4
ALL LETTERS OF ALPHABET
c c c c c,
26 LETTERS
FOUR-LETTER NONSENSE SYLLABLES (10)
juvk
1
MAZE TRACING
3
FOUR-LETTER WORDS (10)
gate
1
THREE-LETTER NONSENSE SYLLABLES (10)
yob
1
"BELL-TEL WORDS (12)
of, four
1
DOTTING CIRCLES (6)
3

Figure 13-25. The tasks and number of trials used in the experiment on concurrent delayed televised feedback.

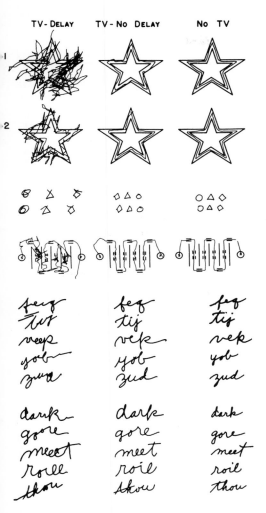

Figure 13-26. Sample records of performance with a 0.52 second delay of visual feedback, with nondelayed television viewing and with direct vision.

dots were placed more than half the radius of the circle away from the center, and in a few cases, dots were located entirely outside the circle.

QUANTITATIVE EFFECTS. The mean contact and travel times per trial for the different tasks under the three viewing conditions are summarized in Table 13-1 for the two subjects separately. As indicated in Figure 13-25, the letter-

writing task was to write a letter five times, the geometric figures task involved drawing three simple figures, and the circle-dotting task required dotting six circles. Time values for writing words represent mean time per word. Travel time for the star-tracing task was the time required to move from the star pattern to the stop plate. No travel times were involved in maze tracing. Some data are missing because of equipment failures or similar reasons.

The data in Table 13-1 show that performance was somewhat slower with nondelayed television viewing than with direct vision, and still slower with delayed televised feedback. The time data for the two subjects were averaged and plotted in Figure 13-28 as relative times for each task under each of the three conditions, when normal time in each case equals 1. (When data were missing for one subject, the other subject's data were used alone.) The bar graphs for contact time show a distinct difference between the group of writing tasks and the tracing and dotting tasks. In writing letters or words, delayed televised performance gave contact times from 2.5 to 3.6 times as long as normal contact

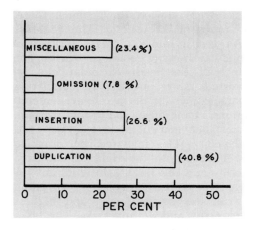

Figure 13-27. Percentage of different types of errors in handwriting with delayed visual feedback.

Table 13-1. Performance Times with Delayed Televised Vision, Nondelayed Televised Vision, and Normal Vision

TASK	SUBJECT	MEAN CONTACT TIME (SEC.)			MEAN TRAVEL TIME (SEC.)		
		TV DELAY	TV NO DELAY	NORMAL	TV DELAY	TV NO DELAY	NORMAL
Letters of Alphabet	A	9.77	3.05	2.77	6.05	1.68	1.30
	B	6.25	3.55	2.62	2.49	1.61	1.41
Star Tracing	A	86.22	13.76	5.86	1.11	0.59	0.54
	B	49.63	16.02	6.28	0.50	0.52	0.54
Geometric Figures	A	6.10	3.47	3.49	2.38	1.31	1.22
	B	5.00	6.43	4.74	1.89	1.57	1.24
4-Letter Nonsense	A	4.08	1.99	1.64	—	0.62	0.54
	B	6.39	2.42	1.90	1.02	0.64	0.46
Maze Tracing	A	102.80	18.00	7.22	—	—	—
	B	107.57	23.92	7.55	—	—	—
4-Letter Words	A	4.30	1.69	1.49	1.48	0.68	0.50
	B	—	2.62	1.59	—	0.65	0.51
Bell-Tel. Words	A	5.88	2.50	2.24	0.74	0.58	0.41
	B	5.54	3.14	2.42	0.75	0.55	0.42
3-Letter Nonsense	A	5.08	1.72	1.42	1.05	0.75	0.52
	B	—	2.22	1.57	—	0.86	0.49
Dotting Circles	A	27.81	2.85	2.49	10.72	3.65	3.77
	B	12.68	4.05	1.69	15.37	5.44	2.27

times, whereas the tracing and drawing tasks were slowed down much more, by ratios of 9.7 to 14.3. The one task with but a minor increase in contact time was drawing geometric figures. The effect of the feedback delay can be assessed more directly by comparing contact times for the two television conditions. In Figure 13-28 the increase ratios between nondelayed (TV) and delayed (DTV) televised performance are indicated to the right of the bars. Here again the ratio is insignificant for geometric figures, very much the same for all the writing tasks, and highest for tracing and dotting tasks. The tasks most disturbed by delayed feedback were those requiring continuous visual control. Less disturbed were writing and drawing tasks which have established kinesthetic patterns. The relative increases in travel time were less marked than for contact time, and show no clearcut differences for the different tasks.

In order to determine whether or not televised performance and delayed feedback altered the relative time spent in travel and manipulation for the various tasks, contact-time/total-time ratios were computed for each subject separately for the different conditions. No consistent trends could be found in these data. In some cases the ratio was significantly higher for delayed televised performance, but in other cases, it was higher for the normal condition. In some tasks the two subjects reacted in opposite ways.

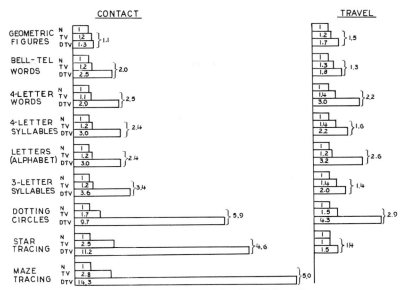

CONTACT   TRAVEL

GEOMETRIC FIGURES — N, TV 1.2, DTV 1.3 } 1.1 · TRAVEL: 1.2, 1.7 } 1.5

BELL-TEL WORDS — N, TV 1.2, DTV 2.5 } 2.0 · TRAVEL: 1.3, 1.8 } 1.3

4-LETTER WORDS — N, TV 1.1, DTV 2.9 } 2.5 · TRAVEL: 1.4, 3.0 } 2.2

4-LETTER SYLLABLES — N, TV 1.2, DTV 3.0 } 2.4 · TRAVEL: 1.4, 2.2 } 1.6

LETTERS (ALPHABET) — N, TV 1.2, DTV 3.0 } 2.4 · TRAVEL: 1.2, 3.2 } 2.6

3-LETTER SYLLABLES — N, TV 1.2, DTV 3.6 } 3.4 · TRAVEL: 1.4, 2.0 } 1.4

DOTTING CIRCLES — N, TV 1.7, DTV 9.7 } 5.9 · TRAVEL: 1.5, 4.3 } 2.9

STAR TRACING — N, TV 2.5, DTV 11.2 } 4.6 · TRAVEL: 1.5 } 14

MAZE TRACING — N, TV 2.8, DTV 14.3 } 5.0

RELATIVE DURATION OF MOVEMENT

Figure 13-28. Relative contact and travel times of the writing, drawing, dotting, and tracing tasks with normal vision (N), nondelayed televised feedback (TV), and delayed televised feedback (DTV). The ratios between measures for delayed and nondelayed televised feedback are indicated at the ends of the bars.

Because only two subjects were used in this experiment, it is of value to compare their performance to established norms where possible. Mean contact times recorded for these two subjects in writing each letter of the alphabet under normal conditions conform reasonably well to normal data published by Smith and Bloom.[261] In Figure 13-29 these earlier data are plotted along with the data from each of the two subjects in this experiment under normal and delayed televised conditions. Here it can be seen that performance with delayed feedback in general exaggerates the variations found in normal handwriting. The letters which normally require long contact times were the ones written most slowly with delayed feedback.

INTERPRETATIONS

The various studies of delayed sensory feedback, both visual and auditory, have produced some strikingly similar results. Delays of even a small fraction of a second cause serious disturbances of behavior organization, often accompanied by emotional effects. All types of motion apparently are affected by feedback delay; observations have been made on speech, singing, musical instrumentation, rhythmic clapping and tapping, tracking, handwriting, drawing, dotting, tracing, object manipulation, panel control operations, and orientation. In these varied motions similar effects are noted, such as general slowing of performance, blocking of activity, increases in intensity and error, occurrence of incoherent or repetitive movements and changes in movement organization. Different types of error — repetition, addition, omission — occur to much the same extent in both delayed speech and delayed handwriting. Most of these effects are most noticeable during concurrent delayed feedback. With consecutive delayed feedback, the interference and emotional effects are much less marked, but accuracy is reduced just as much.

Continuously controlled movements, such as visual tracking and tracing, tend to break down into jerky discrete move-

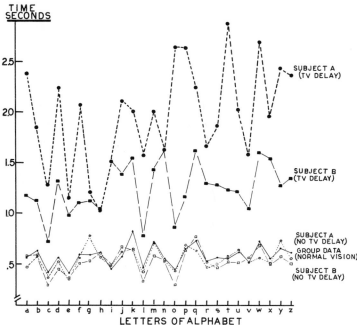

Figure 13-29. Contact times for writing different letters of the alphabet with delayed feedback and normal vision.

ments with delayed feedback. The stuttering effect in speech may be due to loss of control over continuous movements of the chest, diaphragm and abdomen which define the phrasing and breath groups, with consequent degrading of speech into a series of discrete articulations.

In general, the effects of delayed feedback become worse as the magnitude of delay is increased. As an exception, studies of delayed speech have shown that maximum disturbance of speed and accuracy occurs with a delay of about 0.2 second. We assume that this peaking effect may be due to the fact that the maximum interference between auditory and somesthetic control of speech occurs with that delay interval.

The difficulty in defining a quantitative function of the effects of feedback delay is due at least in part to the fact that motion is multidimensional and cannot be described under all conditions by a single measure of efficiency. Further, the pattern of motion becomes variable when delayed feedback interrupts the intrinsic patterning. Marked individual differences occur, and age differences have been described. Thus, quantitative functions will vary according to many performance variables and individual variables.

All evidence indicates that there is little, if any, effective adaptation to conditions of delayed feedback. Trackers learn to perform fairly well with aided tracking devices, but this situation represents only partial feedback delay. With complete interruption of sensory signals, the basic organization of motion patterns is disturbed and the individual apparently cannot overcome the disturbance. Some adaptive changes in behavior occur, e.g., changes from continuous to discrete motions, but normal speed and accuracy of motion is not recovered.

The limited learning that occurs with delayed feedback convinces us that sensory feedback is not properly interpreted as a form of reinforcement, for reinforcement in a learning situation is moderately effective if delayed only a fraction of a second. What we are dealing with here is a more basic factor of movement organization than learning variables. We have seen in our studies of spatially displaced feedback that the human individual can adapt fairly well to a wide range and variety of geometric displacements, but no such flexibility is evident with respect to temporal displacement. The patterning of motion depends upon very precise timing of stimulus and response factors, and breaks down if this timing is disturbed.

The most effective way of adapting to delayed sensory feedback apparently is to eliminate or ignore the delayed signals as much as possible, and to utilize other sensory modes to control motion. That is to say, delayed vision is of so little use that the individual might as well perform blindly, with perhaps an occasional visual check to maintain his general orientation.

SUMMARY

1. Recent technological advances in magnetic tape recording of both auditory and visual signals have made possible studies of the effects of temporal displacement of movement-produced stimulus feedback. Other instances of delayed sensory feedback are provided by automated tracking devices and delaying the graphic trace of handwriting as produced by a telewriter or telescriber.

2. There is a tendency in learning psychology to interpret sensory feedback as a form of reinforcement. This interpretation would imply that feedback delay would retard learning or relearning, but not impair motion seriously or permanently.

3. Neurogeometric theory predicts that feedback delay is a serious disturbance because it interrupts the intrinsic temporal pattern of motion, and that the severity of the disturbance would vary with the type, complexity, and precision of motion. Further, we would expect persisting variability with delayed feedback instead of smooth learning, shifts from one mode of sensory control to others, and integrative changes in motion such as shifts from continuous to discrete motions.

4. Delayed auditory feedback causes a slowing down of speech, increased intensity, higher pitch, stuttering, and other articulatory disturbances. Analogous disturbances occur in other sound-producing motions. The three main types of speech errors are additions, omissions and substitutions. Maximum disturbance of rate and accuracy has been reported to occur with delay intervals of about 0.2 second. Accelerated speech feedback induces faster than normal speech.

5. There apparently is very little adaptation to delayed auditory feedback.

6. Automated tracking devices reduce accuracy of tracking because of the partial feedback delay to the operator of the effects of his movements. Specific studies of transmission lags in tracking systems have shown that progressive decrease in accuracy occurs with increasing delay intervals.

7. Studies of delayed graphic feedback of handwriting and drawing motions have shown that legibility and speed decreased and errors tended to increase with increasing delay intervals. No learning effect was observed.

8. One videotape recorder can be used to study "complete-task" delay of televised feedback, when the subject performs blindly and the televised record of his performance is played back at the completion of the task.

9. Studies of blind performance with consecutive feedback showed that little learning occurred when feedback was delayed to the end of the task. Maze tracing and star tracing were slow, dis-

organized and inaccurate. With a dot location task, delayed dynamic televised feedback of motion was found to be slightly more effective than delayed static feedback of the effects of motion in improving accuracy of blind performance. Performance was slightly faster with a 15-second delay interval than with a 30-second feedback delay.

10. Delayed televised feedback was simulated by having a trained observer duplicate the subject's maze-tracing movements after a delay interval and then presenting the televised image of the observer's movements on the subject's monitor. Three intervals were used: a short delay of 1-2 seconds, a half-task delay, and a complete-task delay. Very little learning occurred with any interval. With the short delay, motion degenerated into a series of jerky, discrete movements. Accuracy decreased with increase in magnitude of delay.

11. Concurrent delayed televised feedback was studied with two television recorders, one for recording and one for playback. Handwriting, drawing, tracing and dotting motions became very inaccurate, were slowed down considerably and were markedly disorganized by a 0.52 second delay. The most severely affected tasks were maze tracing and star tracing. Writing verbal material was less severely affected, and drawing simple geometric figures least. Continuous motions tended to become jerky. Errors in writing words were similar to those reported in studies of delayed graphic feedback, and analogous to speech errors with delayed auditory feedback.

12. We attribute the serious disturbances of delayed sensory feedback to the interruption of intrinsic temporal patterning of motion. The human individual tolerates considerable spatial displacement of feedback, but has very little tolerance for temporal displacement.

CHAPTER 14

INFANT CONTROL OF THE BEHAVIORAL ENVIRONMENT

In recent years there has been increasing interest in those aspects of behavior known as perceptual motivation or activity motivation. It has been recognized that the responses of many animals and particularly human individuals are often directed and sustained not by physiological drives but by perceptual-motor activities carried on for their own sakes. Our own theoretical position is that perceptual motivation is not an occasional or incidental phenomenon, but a basic and compelling condition of patterned behavior that persists throughout life.

We propose that the neurogeometric motion systems are organized so as to respond to stimulus differences and to generate further differences by movements of the body and its receptor organs. In the infant, these motion systems are not fully developed; responses which are elicited are for the most part generalized and nonprecise. During the course of maturation, we see progressive refinement of the spatial correspondence between stimulus pattern and motion pattern, as well as increasing control of the arrangement of environmental patterns by sustained motivated behavior. In order to explore the development of some of these perceptually organized behavior patterns in infants and young children, we have adapted our television methods and certain other procedures for use with very young children.

In our research with infants, we were interested generally in defining the course of development of integrated behavior patterns involving control of the perceived enivronment, and determining the ages at which different patterns emerge. We wished to discover whether such control is multi-dimensional, involving many sources of stimulation, and whether it is related to sustained motivated behavior.

Both general exploratory studies and controlled experiments were carried out. In the former, television set-ups, audio-tape recorders, infant-controlled visual slide projectors, infant-controlled audio-tape recorders, an infant-controlled rotating playpen, and a blanket test were used to explore the scope of child development in control of the perceived environment. Subsequently, two controlled experiments were carried out in order to investigate the course of development of integrated motion and motivation in the child in relation to the self-regulation of the perceived environment. In the first of these studies, a voice-controlled electronic relay unit was used to enable the child to start a rotating playpen in motion. The second analyzed the course of development of the child's motivation to keep in view an image of his mother or of an unfamiliar woman in a television monitor.

DEVELOPMENT OF MOTION IN THE CHILD

Among a number of psychological concepts of child development that have been proposed, there are two that have attracted widespread interest. The Freudian conception attributes the course of development to the elaboration of six stages of sexual differentiation, beginning with the oral stage of infant adaptation, passing through the anal, phallic, oedipal, and latent stages, culminating with the genital level of organization of action and motivation.[93]

The concept that human development is one of conditioned integration of simple reflex units of response is due primarily to Pavlov[205] in Russia and to Watson[318] in this country. This conditioning theory holds that the child starts his behavioral life with a large repertoire of simple reflexes. Through temporal association, these reflexes are organized into sequential patterns to form complex motions.

The postulated integration of motor behavior through sensory conditioning has been challenged through systematic study of fetal development in lower animals[50] and in man.[130] The general picture emerging from these studies is that the primary course of motor development in fetal life is one of differentiation of finer and finer movements from generalized mass movements of the body. Moreover, it is clearly established that this process of differentiation follows definite anatomic and functional patterns. The notion that learning is the basic integrative process in behavioral development is not commonly accepted by those who carry out systematic studies of developmental patterns in maturation. It is held generally that there are predisposing developmental factors which precede learning of motion patterns and define the limits of that learning.

Studies of displaced vision relate specifically to theoretical interpretations of the role of learning in perceptual-motor development. Some investigators in this field have interpreted their results as meaning that human subjects can recover completely from the effects of displacement, and achieve their adaptation by means of perceptual or sensory learning.[151, 275] As we have already seen, there are many reasons for qualifying such interpretations.

Another research area of interest here is that of sensory deprivation in young animals. The phenomena of sensory deprivation due to cataract blinding in childhood were cited originally by Helmholtz[116] as evidence of the experiential learning basis of perceptual organization. Recently, interest in these phenomena has been stimulated by studies of deprivation of vision[221] and other modes of perception[202] in chimpanzees and other animals.[157] As we noted in Chapter 2, the studies on chimpanzees indicate clearly that lasting impairment in visually guided behavior can ensue from artificial blinding for the first weeks or months of life. However, it is by no means clear that specific learning is an important factor in normal development of these perceptual-motor patterns. The most likely interpretation is that basic perceptual-motor patterns are genetically defined, but require a certain amount of environmental stimulation at the proper time for their normal development.

Another area of current research keeps alive the general psychoanalytic orientation while emphasizing the importance of learning in development. One group describes the course of development as being defined to an important degree by emotional and anxiety factors related to parent-child interaction.[67] In this view, reinforcement is the important integrative process. A series of studies in this tradition describes the developmental behavior of isolated infant monkeys in becoming attached to a feeding place and blanket as a substitute for normal attachment to the mother.[105, 106]

A few investigations have demonstrated that systematic space-organized behavior can emerge even when learning is not possible. Gibson and Walk,[98] for example, have described emotional reactions that occur in young babies as well as in other infant animals in response to what they call the "visual cliff" — an empty space lying below a clear glass surface on which the child or animal is made to walk. They interpret their findings as evidence of developmental processes of perceptual-motor activity leading to specific space-organized reactions prior to practice or learning in the particular situations observed.

We have described the development of space-structured motion in human infants as involving two distinct maturational phases.[268] The first occurs principally between 8 and 14 weeks of fetal life,[130] while the second occurs in the postnatal period up to three years. Both sequences of motor development involve space-structured movements. In the prenatal sequence, the organization is limited to the cutaneous locus of stimulation. The postnatal motor sequence involves the more complex structuring of postural, transport, and manipulative movements relative to gravity and to the geometric properties of space, differentiated by the various types of exteroceptors. Our view is that perceptual-motor learning in the child is limited by the degree of differentiation of these specialized systems of space-structured movements.

EXPLORATORY STUDIES

A series of exploratory studies were carried out in a children's hospital with several practical and theoretical objectives in mind. First, we were interested in new techniques that might be of value in the clinical evaluation of the disturbed hospitalized child. Secondly, we were hopeful of developing improved methods for testing very young infants, extending beyond mentalistic notions of intelligence. Finally, we wanted to take an objective look at the processes of environmental change affecting the hospitalized child, and to consider devices and points of view that might be used to effect better hospital care and faster recovery.

In five exploratory studies we observed some 43 hospitalized children and five nonhospitalized children between the ages of 3.5 months and 8 years. All of the hospital children were in the period of convalescence just prior to leaving the hospital. Almost all of these children had had major surgery and were in a relatively active state at the time of observation. A few essentially normal children who had been admitted to the hospital for clinical tests were also among the hospitalized group.

Reactions to Tape-Recorded Voices, Music, and Crying

In the first series of observations, the audiotape recorder was studied as a therapeutic tool, as a source of amusement, and as a test device to determine the responses of infants and young children to various kinds of music, to the sound of the mother or father, and to the sound of the child's own crying. A group of 17 hospitalized children ranging from 8 months of age up to 5 years were observed. Each child was brought into a small room and either placed in a crib or allowed to move about while the music and sounds were played. The observer, a young female medical student, was responsible for the care of the child during observations, and used maximum effort to keep him happy throughout the observation period of 30 to 45 minutes.

The pertinent results of these observations were that all but three of the children showed a definite interest in the music and actively responded to it. Some ceased crying when the music was played, and others went to sleep. Three or four children under two years cried when sound recordings of their own crying were played back to them in the experimental situation. The youngest child we studied, a boy of 8 months, responded systematically to both music and to the sound of his own crying. Among six children who were tested with several samples of different types of music, the younger ones reacted most to loud and fast music, while those 15

months and older were more interested in music with words.

Blanket and Sanded-Crib Study

A crib was prepared with a masonite floor covered with sanded paint, giving an uncomfortably rough surface for the child. A soft blanket was hung over the side of the crib and could be used by the child to cover the floor of the crib and protect his legs and hands. Five children were observed, ranging in age from one year to two years and two months. They were left in the crib for about 30 minutes. Only one child of the five, a girl of 17 months, used the blanket to protect her feet and hands from the sanded floor. The other children would not pull the blanket off the side of the crib, would not use it even if it were placed in their lap, nor would they crawl on it if it were placed at one end of the crib.

Control of Visual Projection

An electronic behavior-recording apparatus was designed by means of which an infant could control a film-strip projector and tape-recorder. A diagram of the apparatus used in these observations and in a subsequent study on the infant-controlled tape recorder is shown in Figure 14-1. This apparatus is based upon the techniques of electronic behavior recording described earlier. When the infant comes into contact with a plate located inside the crib, a relay is closed and operates the projector or starts the tape recorder. The recorder is a sensitive relay that passes a very small current through the body of a subject, and is closed when the subject touches an object also connected into the circuit. Thus, a tape recorder or visual projector can be connected so as to be activated when the child touches the appropriate surface. Needless to say, very special care was used in designing these cir-

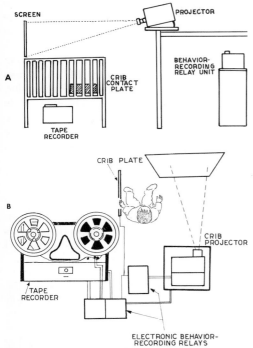

Figure 14-1. Arrangement of apparatus to study infant control of visual slide projector and auditory tape recorder. A. Side view of crib and other equipment. B. Top view, showing infant touching contact plate.

cuits in order to isolate the child from any injurious current source.

As shown in Figure 14-1, A, the 16-millimeter film-strip projector was located on a supporting shelf, and projected an image on a screen above one end of the baby's crib. A contact plate 24 inches long and 8 inches wide was attached to one side of the crib. Contact with this plate changed the colored image on the screen. A film strip of a country scene showing many shades of color was used, and alternate frames were covered with red dye to give additional color interest.

The seven infants studied varied in age from 3 months to 13 months. When infants showed no interest in the pictures, the observer would advance a few

of the frames to try to catch the child's attention. Only two of these infants displayed any real interest in the colored pictures, and none established a connection between the contact plate and the projection on the screen.

Control of Tape-Recorded Music and Sound

The set-up diagrammed in Figure 14-1 was used, except that in this case contact with the plate in the crib would turn on a tape recorder playing a recording of a female voice singing "Peter and the Wolf," or nursery songs. One contact by the child produced music that lasted two to three minutes. Ten children varying in age from 4 months to 22 months were observed.

The observations made here were similar to the first series of observations with the tape recorder in that all but one or two of the children showed definite reactions to the music. They either were soothed by the music and stopped crying, or reacted to the music in more positive ways. Only one of the ten children tested, however, seemed to form a limited connection between the contact plate and the activation of the recorder, even though at least six of the children controlled the recorder many times by making contact with the plate. If the testing had been prolonged, these young children might have learned the control technique, but they did not establish the reaction quickly.

Preliminary Television Studies

A closed-circuit television system was set up in an empty ward room and 10 children varying in age from 15 months to 8 years were observed. The technique (Figure 14-2) was to direct the camera toward the face and upper body of the child, and to permit him to view his own image in the television monitor. None had ever seen a television image of him-

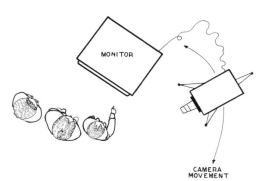

Figure 14-2. Closed-circuit television arrangement to show children their own televised images.

self before. All of the children but one reacted very positively to their own images on the monitor screen, in some cases becoming very excited. After the child had seen himself, the camera was moved so that he would lose the image and could regain it only by moving about. Motivated search of this sort occurred in all but two of the children. Most of them acted out particular movements when they saw their images. When the television picture was turned off, even the very youngest children asked the observer many times to turn it on so they could see themselves in the monitor again.

CONTROLLED EXPERIMENTS

Two types of controlled experiments were carried out. In the first, the capacity of the child to regulate his own movement in the environment by vocal response was observed. In the second, the motions made in order to maintain vision of a television image were studied in children of different ages.

Voice-Control of the Moving Environment

For these studies, a revolving wooden playpen was designed which could be

activated by the child's own vocalizations. A voice relay located near the moving playpen was activated by the child's voice and started rotation of the pen. Figure 14-3 illustrates the experimental set-up in a small hospital room. The photograph in Figure 14-3,A, shows the actual appearance of the revolving playpen and microphone. The pen made one revolution in 26 seconds. Figure 14-3,B, diagrams the arrangement of the playpen, microphone, and experimenter.

STUDY OF HOSPITALIZED CHILDREN. Subjects were used from two different populations: 20 children from the hospital, 4 to 37 months old, and a control group of nonhospitalized children, 6 to 36 months old. The hospital patients used in this experiment were selected

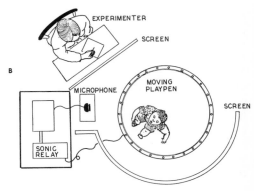

Figure 14-3. Set-up used to study voice-control of movement. A. Photograph of rotating playpen and voice relay. B. Diagram of experimental arrangement.

carefully by the hospital staff to ensure their good physical and behavioral condition. All of them had been admitted to the hospital for relatively minor surgery or treatment, e.g., clubfoot, mole removal, bad cold, and were tested just before their release. Tests were carried out between 10:00 and 11:15 A.M. or between 2:30 and 4:00 P.M., periods when the subjects were relatively relaxed and happy. At 9:30 A.M. and at 2:00 P.M., all of the hospital children were given orange juice or chocolate milk to drink. If necessary, diaper changes were made immediately before testing.

The general procedure followed with each child was to spend about fifteen minutes becoming acquainted with him, then to carry him to the test room where observations were made. If a child cried when placed in the playpen and continued to do so for three minutes, he was removed and not used as a subject. Each subject spent one 20-minute period in the test situation, where a control condition and an experimental condition were used successively. The control condition consisted of a 10-minute period when the playpen revolved continuously. For the 10-minute experimental condition, the playpen would make one revolution and then stop, remaining stationary until the child made a vocalization or other sound loud enough to activate the relay unit and thus start the playpen for one more revolution. In the first part of the experiment using 20 hospitalized children, 10 subjects were given the control condition first and the experimental condition second, while 10 subjects were given the experimental condition first, followed by the control condition. The two samples of 10 subjects each were matched as closely as possible according to age. The control group of 5 nonhospitalized children were given the control condition first, followed by the experimental condition.

The quantitative results of this study consist of data showing the mean frequencies of vocalization for the experimental and control conditions and for different age groups. The bar graph in Figure 14-4 summarizes the differences in mean number of vocalizations between the experimental and control condition for the 20 hospitalized and for the 5 nonhospitalized subjects. The hospitalized children gave roughly twice as many vocalizations during the experimental condition as during the control condition. This difference was significant at the 1 per cent level. The five nonhospitalized children gave more than a third more vocalizations in the experimental condition than in the control condition. The data from the group of 20 showed that the order of presentation of conditions had a significant effect on number of vocalizations, favoring the first 10-minute period. Thus, the difference for the group of five subjects was undoubtedly due to the experimental condition because all these five were tested with the control condition first.

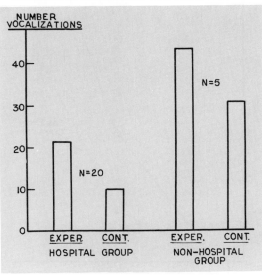

Figure 14-4. Mean number of vocalizations made by 20 hospitalized children and 5 of a control group during experimental condition, when sound would rotate the playpen; and control condition, when playpen rotated continuously.

There was a definite age factor in the number of vocalizations produced by the children, for both the experimental and the control conditions. As shown in Figure 14-5, the infants under one year gave almost no vocalizations in either condition, and the number of vocalizations increased sharply in the older age groups.

The children did not react uniformly in activating the playpen. Some children learned to activate the sound relay by positive responses, as a direct means of control. This was usually true of chil-

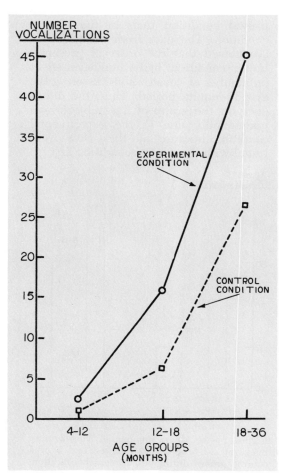

Figure 14-5. Number of vocalizations of hospitalized children in experimental and control conditions as a function of age.

dren two years old and older, who definitely established a connection between vocalizing and rotation of the pen. Children below two years sometimes controlled the playpen indirectly, or in a compensatory way, i.e., when they would cry out, the pen would start and they would stop crying. There may be a gradual transition from the use of crying to control the strange environment to the control by discrete vocalizations. In some cases, overt actions of the child in the playpen would start the rotation, and this action would be integrated with vocalizing behavior. An 18 month old boy, for example, was amazed when he stamped his foot and the pen started to turn, and thereafter made discrete vocalizations when the playpen stopped turning. A 2 year old quickly learned the connection between saying "out" and the sound of the relay unit, as well as movement of the pen. This child learned to activate the relay both by vocalizing and by stamping on the pen.

A few children were frightened by the rotation, and actually vocalized less during the experimental condition. There were some emotional reactions to both the starting and stopping of the playpen. Some children who started to whimper or grieve when placed in the playpen became more disturbed, or even enraged, when the pen started to move. Others were disturbed when the pen stopped moving. Continuous movement of the playpen had a definite excitatory effect on some infants, and a soothing and sleep-inducing effect on others.

Some very young children could formulate the nature of the situation in words. A little girl of 18 months said she didn't want the playpen to go around. Generally, however, only children above 2 years of age openly recognized the relationships between behavior and action of the pen.

There were four children aged one year or over who gave practically no responses that activated the relay. The first of these, a girl of 37 months, seemed passive and awed by the situation, and began to cry after about 17 minutes in the playpen. The second, a boy of 27 months, was very happy but very quiet and talked in a whisper throughout the experimental session. The third, a one year old, played with his shoelaces throughout the experimental period and eventually lay on the floor of the playpen, half asleep. The fourth, an 18 month old girl, was the one who did not want the playpen to go around. These four children, out of the 20 above one year of age in both groups, were the only ones who failed to give definite reactions, either direct or indirect, to the moving playpen. This study suggests that the moving environment has intrinsic stimulus value, as well as sustained motivating value, for children over one year of age. This motivation appears not only in positive and negative reactions to the moving stimulus, but in inducing relaxation and sleep behavior in some infants. Moreover, vocalizing reactions are readily integrated in this pattern of stimulus feedback to provide direct control of movement of the body and of the environment. There is no need for these reactions to be reinforced by primary organic forms of stimulation, such as food or bodily contact, in order to be learned very rapidly.

STUDY OF NONHOSPITALIZED CHILDREN. In a second experiment with the voice-controlled playpen, 75 nonhospitalized children were tested. These subjects were divided into five age groups — 4-8, 10-14, 16-20, 22-26, and 34-38 months — each group with 15 subjects. All but a few were children from a married-student housing facility. The procedure of testing was much the same as in the first experiment, except that a testing period of 16 minutes (8 minutes for the control condition and 8 minutes for the experimental condition) was used. The

control condition, with a continuously rotating playpen, was always given first. Because the first study showed that the initial period in the playpen produced more reactions, other variables being equal, it was judged that any increase in reaction found in the second period for the experimental condition could be considered significant. Prior to the test period, some 14 minutes were spent with each child and his mother in order to get to know the child and to explain the procedure of the experiment to the mother. Only the experimenter was in the testing room while observations were being made. Four toys were placed in the playpen during test periods.

The reactions of nonhospitalized children to the rotating playpen situation were in some ways different from those of the hospitalized children. The response frequencies from the younger children recorded here are significantly weighted with crying reactions, especially from the two youngest age groups. The motivating effect of the moving playpen was not adequate to overcome the negative factor of separation from the mother. Thus, the quantitative data of this study are not as clear as those from the first study in indicating frequency of discrete responses made to control the playpen.

The quantitative data obtained in this study are summarized in Figure 14-6, which presents separate curves for mean number of responses for the control and experimental conditions as a function of age. Points on the curve for the experimental condition that are marked with an asterisk denote ages at which there was a significant difference between experimental and control conditions. The main thing to note is that these curves of vocalization are much the same in form under both conditions. The frequency of vocalization was greatest for the 10-14 month old children, and — unlike the results with hospitalized children — drops off thereafter.

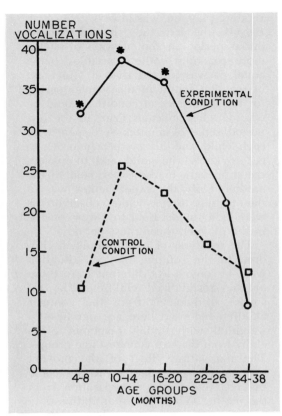

Figure 14-6. Number of vocalizations of non-hospitalized children in experimental and control conditions as a function of age.

Except for the oldest age group, the experimental condition produced more responses than the continuously moving playpen. This increase was due both to generally increased activity and vocalization produced by the stopping and starting of the pen and to direct response leading to control of the movement of the pen. The activity factor was probably most prominent in the two youngest age groups. The differences due to age have been assessed by analyses of variance, and approach significance at the 5 per cent level.

The experiments with the voice-controlled moving playpen have given two fairly clear results. For hospitalized

children, or for children who have become adapted to a particular environment, the moving playpen can provide a positive stimulus over which the child learns to level some direct voice control. As a device for motivating the child or baby when first introduced to a strange hospital situation, however, the voice-controlled moving playpen has limited or even negative value.

Maintaining a Visual Image

This experiment investigated the perceptual motivation of the child to keep within his field of vision a televised image provided on a closed-circuit television monitor. We were interested in finding at what age the child reacts to such a substitute visual image in a sustained, motivated way, and makes positive reactions to control and maintain this visual stimulus. The revolving playpen was used with a closed-circuit television chain, which provided a televised image of the child's mother or of another person for his observation while in the playpen. With these devices, we had a situation in which the child must compensate for movement of the playpen by means of coordinated motions in order to maintain vision of the television image.

Figure 14-7 illustrates the set-up and observation procedures for this experiment. A small RCA-TV Eye camera was used to televise the child's mother or a young woman who acted as a "stranger" for all of the subjects. The television monitor was located on a low table beside the playpen, so that it could be viewed by the child from inside the pen, which moved continuously throughout each test period. The playpen and monitor were surrounded by a white cloth screen, which hid the mother or stranger and the experimental observer from the child's direct vision. The observer watched the child through an opening in the screen and recorded by

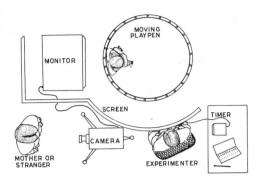

Figure 14-7. Experimental set-up used to study perceptual motivation of children to maintain view of television image.

means of a time clock the total time spent by the child watching the monitor. A photograph of the experimental situation is shown in Figure 14-8.

This experiment was designed to test differences in behavior due to the type of television image. Three image conditions were used: a control image in which a blank wall and window appeared on the monitor, an image of the child's mother, and an image of the female stranger. The person in these two experimental images performed two types of activities. The first behavior pattern showed the mother or stranger carrying out a number of activities, including throwing a large plastic ball, dancing about while clapping hands, and opening and closing a small umbrella while playing "peek-a-boo" behind it. During this time, the woman spoke informally to the child. In the second pattern, the mother or stranger stood still and read a nursery story about a small boy and girl taking a train ride. As shown in Figure 14-7, the position of the woman and, thus, the voice were on the same side of the room as the monitor, but in actual practice the position varied somewhat. Test observations of the children showed that they generally did not orient toward the voice when the screen was blank.

Thirty nonhospitalized children in five

age groups — 10-14, 16-20, 22-26, 28-32, and 34-38 months — were used as subjects, with six subjects in each group. Before each child was tested, the mother was instructed about her role in the experiment. Testing began a few seconds after the child was placed in the revolving playpen and lasted seven minutes. During this time, the child was given five testing periods of one minute each, alternating with 3-second rest periods. The monitor image was lit throughout, but there was no image on it during the rest periods. The five test images included the control image, the mother moving and reading, and the stranger moving and reading. The control image was presented first to all subjects, but thereafter the order of presentation was varied systematically.

The quantitative data of this experiment deal with the mean time spent by the five age groups in motivated watching of the television image. The graphs in Figure 14-9 show these mean durations for the different conditions of mother moving, stranger moving, mother reading, stranger reading, and control, plotted as a function of age. The graphs to the left represent the data for the movement condition, and those to the right, for the reading condition. Al-

Figure 14-8. Photograph of the playpen and television monitor.

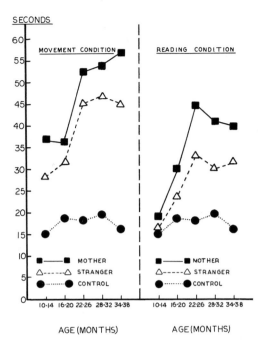

Figure 14-9. Mean time spent viewing the television monitor with different image conditions as a function of age.

though mean duration of response to the control image did not vary systematically with age, all of the experimental visual images produced motivated watching that increased in duration as a function of age. The age curves show a sudden rise between 20 and 26 months for watching the moving images, a more gradual rise between 14 and 26 months for watching the reading images. This may indicate a critical period of development in the child's perceptual motivation. Analyses of variance of the data for both movement and reading conditions show that the variation due to age was significant at the 1 per cent level for both of these conditions.

The graphs in Figure 14-9 show some differences in the time of viewing the mother image and the stranger image, but none of these differences was significant except for the movement condition with the youngest age group, which was significant at the 5 per cent level. These graphs also show that the children watched actively moving images longer than reading images. The differences between time spent in watching mother moving and mother reading were significant at the youngest and two oldest age groups, but were not significant at the critical age levels of 16 to 26 months. Over all, the children watched their mothers about one-third longer when she was active than when she was reading.

The strength of the perceptual motivation in this test situation is suggested by the quantitative data; the oldest group, for example, watched their mother moving for a mean time of more than 57 seconds out of a possible 60. Observing the children directly, however, was more convincing than the data. In order to watch the televised image, the children would walk slowly in a direction opposite the rotation of the pen, or else twist and turn their bodies so that the television screen remained visible. Almost without exception, the children made these active attempts to watch the monitor for at least a part of the testing period.

We have made no effort in this study to analyze the differential effects of the auditory and visual stimuli in defining the adaptive activity of the child, although the possibility of such differential effects is recognized. It may be also that combined visual and auditory effects were necessary to motivate the child to control the perceptual environment.

INTERPRETATIONS

According to some general ideas derived from the neurogeometric theory of motion, we have postulated that the differentiation of perceptual-motor activity in young infants and children shows progressive refinement of movement patterns at different levels of integration. Thus, the child's responses to object stimulation and patterns of environmental control involve first of all general postural activity, followed later by the use of body transport motion, and finally by the use of specific manipulative movements and articulated language. Further, we assume that so-called perceptual motivation is a significant factor in human behavior organization from infancy throughout life, and that manipulation and control of environmental patterns show progressive development as the child matures.

While we recognize that the exploratory studies reported here are limited and tentative, they seem to support our general ideas about the course of development of perceptual-motor coordination in the infant. We find evidence here that children from 10 to 18 months of age exercise some environmental control through generalized orientation motions, but as a rule do not respond specifically to the object characteristics of the environment. The period between 18 and 26 months is critical for the elaboration of many kinds of motivated space-organized movements which are adapted to control of stimulation. The effective movements used in this period usually are in the nature of general transport motions (in controlling the visual environment) or generalized vocalizing activities of a nonspecific nature. The more specific articulated kinds of control make their appearance as a rule only after two years of age.

Our observations confirm in some ways the findings of Gibson and Walk[98] that spatially organized orientation movements appear in the young child without specific prior training in the particular behavioral situation. Gibson and Walk observed that the depth perception of empty space under clear glass induced negative orientation reactions in the crawling child. We find that a wide variety of unlearned vocal and orientation reactions are characteristic of children from 6 months to 2 years in their reactions to changes in the perceived environment. Motivation to maintain the established visual environment to which the child has been adapted is especially characteristic of children from 1 to 2 years of age.

Since the first attempts to condition neonates and infants,[323, 326] it has been obvious that the Watsonian view describing human development in terms of specific learning is inadequate. Infants below 15 months of age do not condition easily, nor do they learn other types of specialized manipulations of object relations in their environment.[137] It appears that articulated control of the object environment involves maturational processes which occur typically after the age of one year and are not clearly developed until 18 months to 2 years. It is our opinion that learning of specific movements depends on this prior development of perceptual-motor coordinations.

Aside from their theoretical implications, the present studies have practical applications in the search for techniques that might aid the adaptation of the sick child to the hospital environment. Among the various procedures of environmental control investigated, such as infant-controlled tape recorders, visual displays, rotating playpens, and blanket covers, the visual-auditory techniques were the most clearly effective as a positive influence on the child's behavior. The closed-circuit television system, used to present the image and sound of parents and other persons and situations, was effective in inducing consistent orientation reactions in children between the ages of 16 months and 2 years, and perhaps earlier. Such techniques may prove useful as diagnostic procedures, as well as adaptive aids for the hospitalized infant.

SUMMARY

1. A number of observations and experiments were carried out to investigate the development of integrated behavior patterns involving control of the perceived environment in infants and young children.

2. In a series of exploratory studies, children from 3.5 months to 8 years of age, most of whom were hospital patients, were tested in situations where they could control visual, auditory, or tactual aspects of their environment. The younger children were most interested in the auditory stimuli (tape-recorded music and voices), but did not learn to control them by a simple contact device. Children under a year showed little interest in colored slides, but children from one to eight years were greatly interested in seeing themselves in a television monitor.

3. Two studies were carried out to study children's ability to learn to initiate movement of a revolving playpen by vocalizations. These sounds activated the pen by means of a voice relay. Hospitalized children gave about twice as many vocalizations during the experimental period, when the playpen would revolve once for every sound, as during the control period when the playpen revolved continuously. This means of control was not used under one year of age, but developed between one and one and a half years. Nonhospitalized children in general reacted unfavorably to the test situation, in which they were separated from their mothers, and for the most part did not learn to control the playpen.

4. In another controlled experiment, nonhospitalized children were tested in the slowly rotating playpen for the amount of time they would continually shift their orientation to watch a television monitor. Five televised images were used: a blank wall, mother active, mother reading, stranger active, and stranger reading. The period between about one and a half and two years was critical for development of perceptual motivation to watch either mother or stranger. The mother image was more effective than the stranger image, and an active image was more effective than a reading image.

5. These observations support our view that perceptual-motor coordinations and control of the perceptual environment develop progressively in infancy and childhood, involving first postural orientation movements, then transport movements, and finally the more precise manipulations and speech articulations. The more specific manipulative movements used to control the environment do not appear as a rule until about two years of age.

CHAPTER 15

EFFECTS OF DISPLACED AND DELAYED FEEDBACK: A RÉSUMÉ

We have seen how interest in a fundamental fact of physiological optics — inversion of the retinal image — has developed gradually into systematic investigation of the origins, development, and neural integration of behavior. The problem posed by ocular inversion and its significance in space perception was recognized by Leonardo, but not until Helmholtz was it taken finally from the realm of philosophical speculation to be defined in physiological terms. According to Helmholtz, perceived space is not absolute, but is defined according to the physiological make-up of the organism and its perceptual experience. In our own terms, the significance of the orientation of the retinal image is but a part of a larger problem of the geometricity of motion, i.e., the geometric correspondence between movement patterns and the patterns of the spatial environment.

We have attempted to show how the experimental analysis of displaced and delayed feedback represents a new chapter in the long search for truth about human motion and its neural regulation. Scientific study in this area has encompassed a number of phases, among them the discovery of the neural mechanisms of motion, the search for integrative mechanisms and the nature of their organization in specific activities, the analysis of movements in relation to control of tools and machines, and the study of perception and motion with spatial and temporal sensory displacement. Our interest in this latter phase stems from concepts of perceptual-motor integration which stress the feedback systems of motion and the

291

neural mechanisms upon which they depend. Specifically, we postulate that neurons of the central nervous system, which we call neurogeometric detectors or recorders, detect the space and time displacements between movements and their sensory feedback and thus regulate the pattern of motion relative to the properties of objects, surfaces, and gravitational forces of the perceived environment. These neurogeometric concepts not only stimulated our general interest in studies of displaced vision, but guided our specific research designs as well. We shall use this chapter to summarize the principal findings of our studies and to relate them to prior experimental results.

GENERAL PHENOMENA OF DISPLACED VISION

Most of the earlier studies of displaced vision were motivated by interest in what seemed to be a very direct question: With continued inversion or other displacement of the visual field, will the pictorially observed world eventually right itself so that it appears normal? Many investigators have been firmly convinced that space perception is learned, and have expended considerable effort to prove the learning hypothesis. But the experimental results on disoriented vision never have been simple, and never have given a straightforward answer to the question as formulated. Most of the studies of persons wearing inverting and reversing spectacles have indicated that they recover effective vision only in part, and, in some circumstances, only to a very minor degree.

As the number of experiments on displaced vision increased, the complexities of the observed effects multiplied almost beyond the scope of understanding. Experiments on mirror vision, which represented some of the first analytical research on the dimensions of disoriented visual perception, usually have not been considered along with studies based on the use of inverting spectacles. With the first animal studies, a new pattern of displaced vision phenomena was disclosed. Fish, salamanders, frogs, and birds subjected to displaced vision by anatomic or optical methods never adapted effectively, even when the displacements were effected before the animal had had any normal visual experience. Thus, one of the most important problems concerning displaced vision is to account for the differences between primates and lower animals.

The investigators interested in visual displacement in human individuals never have formulated the problem in its broader significance, i.e., as a fundamental question of the space organization of motion and the feedback mechanisms that regulate it. We consider this broader question one of the central problems of experimental psychology, yet in the displaced vision literature the emphasis has been on the more limited question of whether space perception can be learned. This preoccupation with proving or disproving the empirical theory has obscured the full significance of the displaced vision experiment, and, thus, has limited the scope of the experimental designs and their objective results.

In our own studies of displaced vision, we have attempted to examine the problem in a new experimental and theoretical context, in terms of the geometricity of the sensory feedback systems of human motion. For some years now investigators in behavior science have been interested in feedback mechanisms of response, but, except for the delayed sensory feedback studies, analyses of these processes have been confined for the most part to studies of machine systems, in which the feedback properties of action are determined generally by the timing of the machine. In the present research, we extend the analysis of feedback systems to the specific mechanisms of movement and to the space and time factors involved in its organization.

Our analysis of the phenomena of displaced vision is based on the belief that these phenomena reveal primary characteristics of motion organization and thus show indirectly how neural mechanisms are organized spatially to control the perceptual-motor relationship. When we examine the observations and experimental results of prior displaced vision studies along with our own more recent findings from this point of view, they provide new insight into the fundamental nature of the geometric organization of behavior.

Severity of Disturbance

As we have noted in Chapter 6, some of the most noteworthy immediate effects of visual displacement are emotional and motivational disturbances, which on occasion are quite severe. Nausea, depression, dizziness, feelings of frustration, and related effects have been reported. Although some of these emotional disturbances are due to the side-effects of wearing experimental optics, it is significant that they cannot be eliminated completely by our methods of using fixed prisms or television feedback. Performing in a displaced visual field is emotionally disturbing to many subjects, and performing with delayed sensory feedback is equally or even more disturbing.

These emotional disturbances reflect the severity of perceptual-motor discoordinations that occur with the more difficult spatial displacements as well as with feedback delay. Kohler[149] described an experimental condition so disturbing that his subjects had to be watched to prevent their injuring themselves. Although we had no comparable problems with subjects who were not required to move about, we did find an occasional subject who simply could not perform under the prescribed viewing conditions. These effects indicate the very basic nature of the disturbance brought about by visual displacement.

Differential Effects of Varied Conditions of Displacement

The various experiments on visual disorientation have shown clearly that the different dimensions and degrees of displacement produce their own special perceptual and motor effects. The problem is not just one of inverting the retinal image, as originally formulated before the turn of this century. One must distinguish conditions of inversion, reversal, and rotation of the visual field; reversal of depth cues; angular misdirection of the line of sight; and displacement of the locus of vision in various directions and to various degrees. Further, one can combine different dimensions of displacement, or apply displacement to monocular or binocular vision. In evaluating the experimental literature on displacement, one great difficulty is to determine which experiments have used equivalent conditions of disorientation and thus have produced comparable results.

In our own work, we have emphasized the differential effects of the different dimensions and degrees of displacement, and designed our experiments so as to define and quantify the differences. Our theoretical interpretations of motion regulation are based on a systematic understanding of these differential effects.

Direct and Compensatory Reactions

The significance of compensatory reactions under conditions of displaced vision has only recently received explicit recognition.[259, 260] Under some conditions of displacement, individuals are not limited to one type of reaction. They can perform direct movements, oriented as they normally are, which thus maintain the established relative directions between manipulative and travel movements and the postural axes of the body; or they can make compensatory movements, oriented so as to look normal in the displaced visual field. For example, compensatory handwriting movements in an inverted field make characters that are actually inverted but which appear to be upright. Objects can be handled so as to appear upright, or head positions can be assumed to compensate in part for angular displacement of vision.

We know now that the performance of compensatory reactions materially influences how the individual perceives a displaced visual field. Because earlier investigators did not identify such movements, we can only guess their role in the reported adaptation of subjects. We feel fairly certain that those cases for which nearly complete perceptual reorientation was claimed involved compensatory reactions of some sort, which corrected in part for the visual disorientation. The degree of perceptual adaptation to disoriented vision that can be achieved cannot be specified without analyzing the effects of various compensatory movements in that particular situation.

Normal and Breakdown Angles of Displaced Feedback

Our television studies have shown that so-called displacement of the visual field is the normal condition of perception and motion within certain angular ranges, and that the extent of these normal ranges can be specified quantitatively. For any given movement there is a normal range of displacement between the direction of movement and its sensory feedback within which little or no disturbance of behavior occurs. Beyond

this range, however, there is a breakdown range of displaced perceptual feedback in which the degree of disturbance is a function of the magnitude of displacement.

DEGREE OF ADAPTATION TO DISPLACED VISION

The critical fact that must be borne in mind in discussing adaptation to displaced vision is the observed difference between primates and lower vertebrates. The inframammalian forms studied can make no effective behavioral adaptation to various forms of displacement. Chickens cannot adapt to even limited angular displacement (7 degrees) of the line of sight. In contrast, monkey and man show considerable ability to adapt to different kinds of displacement.

In evaluating degree of adaptation, it should be emphasized that performance with displaced feedback is unreliable under stress. If the practiced subject in a displacement study is pressed to perform at maximum rates, his performance may disintegrate at once. Although this feature is never mentioned in the published reports of earlier investigators, we believe that they must have encountered its effects. It seems likely that any stressful condition imposed upon a subject, whether or not it is directly connected to the experiment, would result in deterioration of his performance. We would never trust ourselves in a vehicle driven by a person with displaced visual feedback, even though he apparently had adapted to the displacement condition.

The degree of perceptual and motor adaptation to displaced vision depends specifically on the nature and magnitude of the displacement, and so must be discussed relative to the experimental conditions. In general, the relative severity of initial disturbance with a given displacement condition is comparable to the final level of adaptation that can be achieved with that condition. That is, the greater the initial disturbance in behavior, the greater the difference between final level of adaptation and normal performance. (Although there are some exceptions to this rule, we cannot as yet fully evaluate their significance.) Thus, the comparisons we make among the effects of different displacement conditions apply as a rule both to initial disturbance and final level of adaptation.

Inversion

There have been very few studies of inversion uncomplicated by other displacement conditions. Kohler[149] had three subjects who wore an inverting mirror for 6, 9, and 10 days, and we have studied inverted vision produced both by a fixed prism and the television camera. Kohler claimed that his 9-day subject achieved "fully upright vision," although the same claim was not made for the other two. Our 20-day study of prism-inverted vision casts doubt on the belief that adaptation can ever be complete. Long before the end of the training period, the performance curves for handwriting movements leveled off, with the asymptote well above normal performance level. This effect was especially pronounced for contact movements. Although our television studies were not carried on for as long a period, they yielded similar results. Performance curves with televised inversion also showed a tendency to level off above normal performance levels.

Inversion-Reversal

The degree of adaptation that can be expected with combined inversion and reversal, with or without reversal of depth cues, is quite clearly less than complete. Subjects who have worn in-

verting and reversing spectacles have not adapted effectively, either in motor performance or in perception. Snyder and Pronko's[275] one subject was said to have made nearly complete adaptation after 30 days, but his error performance in a mirror tracing task was still a third above normal. The experimental evidence seems conclusive that only limited adaptation can be made to combined inversion and reversal.

Right-Left Reversal

Outside of some rather limited studies of Siipola[239] on right-left mirror reversal of vision, our television studies represent the only systematic work on right-left reversal of visual feedback not involving other displacement. We found rapid and nearly complete adaptation to simple reversal of vision in many types of common panel control, target location, drawing, and assembly motions. In more complex tasks such as handwriting, we found persisting effects of reversal on different component movements.

Kohler and one other subject wore reversing prisms that also reversed depth cues. Kohler's adaptation after 24 days was presumably less than complete, although he said that the other subject had achieved nearly complete reorientation after 37 days. However, neither subject corrected for the reversed depth cues. Furthermore, the experimental reports indicate that perceptual adaptation was often if not always dependent upon overt action within a situation.

Displacement of the Line of Sight

Human subjects make very rapid adaptations to prism-displacements of the line of sight within a limited range, up to about 15 degrees of horizontal displacement and undetermined in other dimensions. With 20- to 30-degree displacements, neither motor nor perceptual adaptation is complete. These results confirm our theoretical predictions concerning the existence of normal and breakdown ranges of perceptual displacement.

Displacement of the Locus of Vision

As Stratton's[297] original mirror study demonstrated, adaptation to fairly large angular displacements of the locus of vision within the mesial plane can be achieved readily. In our television studies, we find only limited changes in performance when the locus of vision is displaced forward in the mesial plane up to about 125 degrees. Our observations on this type of displacement are limited to assembly, drawing, writing, and dotting movements.

The tolerance of human subjects for displacement of the locus of vision is much more limited when the displacement is in the horizontal plane. Although simple movements can be performed effectively at larger displacement angles than more complicated movements, a horizontal displacement of 90 degrees is probably beyond the range in which any effective adaptation can be made.

ANGULAR DISPLACEMENT FUNCTION. We have determined the quantitative displacement function for horizontal displacement of the locus of vision for two tasks — maze tracing and circle drawing. In maze tracing, the accuracy of performance remains relatively constant with displacements from 0 to approximately 40 degrees. Beyond that range, accuracy decreases rapidly with increasing angles of displaced feedback. Performance time does now show this consistent relation with displacement angle. When circle drawing is judged according to success in making true circles, accuracy decreases after a very small range of displacement angles. Beyond about 10 degrees, the distortion of the circles is proportional to the degree of displacement.

All of the results on angular displacement confirm our postulates concerning normal and breakdown angles of displaced feedback. The range within which effective performance can be carried out varies with the dimension of displacement, and varies also with the type of movement or pattern of motion.

Relative Effects of Different Types of Displacement

It is difficult to compare the effects of different displacement conditions studied in earlier experiments, for all of the experimental optical devices used produced visual abnormalities in addition to the specific displacements desired. The use of television eliminates these side-effects, and permits direct comparisons of different dimensions and degrees of displacement. Needless to say, the difficult and expensive arrangements required by television and motion analysis instrumentation have limited the number of specific studies carried out and have influenced our experimental designs. Although some studies do not compare directly with others, we still have a considerable body of data from which direct comparisons can be drawn. In some cases, televised displacements can be compared with optically produced displacements.

Overall, the most severe effects of visual displacement are found with extreme angular displacements of the locus of vision or the line of sight in horizontal directions. Nonsystematic rotations of the visual field also produce severe effects, according to the limited observations available. Although subjects can reduce time of performance with these difficult displacement conditions, they never achieve really effective motor adaptation. This is particularly true of continuously visually guided movements.

Displacements of the locus of vision in the horizontal plane have relatively more severe effects than displacements in the mesial plane. It is difficult to make exact comparisons because the normal position of the eyes with respect to the plane of manual performance varies considerably, but in general we observed greater disturbance with some horizontal displacements than with any in the mesial plane.

If we compare the extensive work of Kohler on prism displacement of the line of sight with our own work on televised displacement of the locus of vision, it appears that the linear distortion is relatively more severe than the locus distortion. Kohler's subjects could not adapt effectively when the line of sight was displaced more than about 15 degrees, while effective adaptation can be made with locus displacement of about 40 degrees horizontally and even more mesially.

Among the systematic displacement conditions (inversion, reversal, and inversion-reversal), the effects of inversion are usually far more severe than of the other two conditions. Combined inversion and reversal of the visual field (180-degree rotation) is rarely as disturbing as inversion alone, but is consistently more disturbing than right-left reversal. With some types of tasks, not too highly organized visually, right-left reversal has little or no effect on either accuracy or time of performance. There are some individuals who show relatively severe effects with both reversal and inversion-reversal compared with mean performance of the majority of subjects. We assume that these individual effects may be related to sidedness.

Specificity of Adaptation

One of the most significant findings of displaced vision studies is that adaptation to any given condition of displacement is relatively specific to the task and to the condition of displacement. The assumption underlying all of the

earlier experiments involving the continuous wearing of experimental spectacles was that the effects of visual disorientation are quite general, and that adaptation to the new conditions would proceed "across the board." Conditions of normal vision were assumed to interfere with adaptation to displaced vision, and vice versa. Thus, it was believed that adaptation would proceed more rapidly with continuous wearing of spectacles than with periodic practice sessions of displacement.

It has been found consistently, however, that learning under conditions of displacement is much like the learning of any new task, and that the continuous wearing of spectacles to preclude normal vision does not materially change the rate and conditions of learning. Particular tasks or motions are learned as rapidly when displacement is limited to periodic practice sessions on successive days as when displacement is continuously imposed day after day. The continuous wearing of displacing devices does not result in a general reorientation of perception or motion, as implied in the experimental planning of Stratton,[295-297] Ewert,[74] and Kohler. Rather, the adaptation achieved consists of a series of specific reorientations, which can be learned and retained as efficiently with periodic as with continuous displacement.

EFFECTS ON OVERT MOTION

The motor effects of displaced visual feedback depend on the nature of the animal, the conditions of disorientation, and the pattern and directions of motion performed. In birds, frogs, and fish, visual tracking and striking movements are specifically displaced as a function of the dimensions of the displacement. The functional bilateral balance of behavior is disturbed in fish and frogs, so that the dynamics and motivation of general behavior are disturbed. Persistent rotation is observed when the animal is visually stimulated. A quite different effect occurs in the monkey, in which combined inversion and reversal of vision initially produces a comatose immobile state persisting intermittently for several days.

General Nature of Disturbance

The most severe motor effects in man occur with extreme angular displacements, or when diagonally oriented movements are performed under systematic inversion and reversal of the visual field. Movements continuously guided by vision, such as tracing and tracking, are the most severely affected. Smooth movements of this sort degenerate into jerky, discrete movements, which may be accompanied by marked tremor. Only maximum motivation keeps most individuals at work under such conditions. Under extreme conditions of disturbance, these effects may last over many days of practice, and any kind of stress causes a deterioration in level of adaptation previously achieved through practice. With practice, the motor disturbances can be eliminated more effectively with systematic displacements than with extreme nonsystematic displacements.

With simple right-left reversal of vision or with limited angular displacements, motor disturbance is not usually severe. Some movements, especially the components of complex motions, may show limited irregularities of control and increases in duration which gradually disappear with practice.

All types of movements may show specific directional disorientation when the visual feedback of motion is reversed or inverted. Thus, with inverted vision, the subject performs numerous inversions of movement. Such directional errors are most easily observed in movements of the eyes and head, and in

manual movements such as pointing or tracing. In more general types of task, the specific inversions or reversals of movement are not as clear.

Differential Effects on Motions of Different Complexity

One of the major objectives of our studies on displaced vision has been to analyze the effects of different displacements on motions of different complexity and direction, and on different components of a motion pattern. Our assumption was that the organization and effectiveness of a motion depends on its pattern and directional characteristics relative to the specific conditions of perceptual feedback. We believed that motions of relatively high levels of complexity or precision would be affected more by displaced vision than less complex or less precise motions because of the greater number of displaced perceptual-motor interactions involved.

Experimental results show clearly that simple motions like dotting are affected very little by visual displacement in comparison with more complex writing and drawing movements. Also, the simpler motions show a higher degree of recovery under displacement conditions.

Motions and tasks also can be characterized according to relative degree of visual demand or load. Motions with a high visual demand, such as precision tracing movements, typically are affected far more by visual displacements than motions such as assembly and panel control operations with a lower visual demand.

Differential Effects on Movements of Different Direction

Movements oriented in different directions are affected differently by different dimensions of displacement. In general, with any systematic displacement condition, by far the most difficult movements to make are those oriented diagonally with respect to the body axes. We interpret this to be due to the fact that continuous corrections must be made in both reference systems of motor control — the up-down gravity-oriented system and the bilaterally oriented right-left system. Comparable disturbances are found in all movements with extreme nonsystematic displacements. Because the primary reference system of motion is the body itself, adaptation to displaced feedback is easier if both the displacement and the motion are oriented systematically with reference to the body axes.

When movements made in different horizontal, vertical, and diagonal directions are timed under different conditions of systematic displacement, it is found that a movement in a specific direction varies in duration with different displacement conditions; it is also found that for any specific dimension of displacement, movements in different directions vary in duration. We believe that these interactions between the directional properties of movements and the relative orientation of perceptual feedback may be related to the high degree of differentiation and specificity that is characteristic of motions. In other words, we postulate that the relationship between the geometric characteristics of a movement and its perceived feedback makes it possible for this movement to be learned and retained as a specific response pattern, and that each of the countless discrete responses that make up the repertoire of human perception and motion owes its specificity to such a precisely defined geometric relationship.

Differential Effects on Different Component Movements

When transport and manipulative movements of a task are separately timed under different conditions of vis-ual displacement, differential effects are observed. In some cases the differences are striking. For example, one movement component may not be affected at all by a displacement, while another may be seriously impaired. There are usually marked differences in the effects of displaced feedback on the contact and travel movements of panel control operations and target location motions.

In attempting to specify the effects of a given displacement on different component movements, there are several factors that must be considered. The complexity and visual demand of a given component movement help determine how much it will be affected by displaced feedback, but the general directional orientation of the movement is also critical. We have not always found it possible to predict accurately the relative disturbance that will occur in different movement components because of the complexity of the factors involved.

Direct and Compensatory Movements

Under any condition of displaced vision, a pattern of motion can be executed with an apparent orientation in any direction — theoretically an infinite number of orientations. The number of discriminable orientations is quite limited, and among these are a few that will correct for the direction of visual displacement. These movements that have a visual feedback equivalent to normal orientation we call compensatory movements. They are movement patterns that appear upright in an inverted visual field, or right-left normal in a reversed field. It is the movement pattern itself with which we are concerned here, such as the written characters in handwriting. The hand or other body member will appear inverted in an inverted field, but can execute an apparently upright movement by means of compensatory reaction. The study of compensatory movements is important for two reasons: to determine whether they aid perceptual orientation with displaced vision, and to resolve the theoretical question as to whether they are learned faster because they compensate in part for the visual disorientation.

It is clear from both optical and television studies of compensatory reactions that such movements contribute toward a normal perceptual orientation of a displaced field. Most subjects performing in restricted visual fields such as we have used do not recognize the nature of the disorientation. Their problem is to learn a difficult new kind of visuomotor control, and if they are required to execute patterns which "look" normal, the field tends to look normal. The problem is quite different when subjects observe fields containing many familiar objects with an established orientation. Published reports of Kohler and others which indicate that perceptual orientation can vary for different parts of the same field lead us to believe that compensatory reactions may contribute toward these variations.

Compensatory and direct reactions have been studied with both systematic and nonsystematic displacements, and long-term adaptation with the two types of movement has been studied with inverted visual feedback. Initially, compensatory movements are slower than direct movements in displaced fields, but after a period of adaptation, the two types of movement are learned to about the same level of effectiveness. Extreme angular displacements seem to have a much more severe effect on compensatory than direct movements.

PERCEPTUAL ORIENTATION WITH DISPLACED VISION

There are many observations that permit us to describe in some detail the nature of the so-called perceptual reorientation that comes with the wearing of inverting or reversing devices. One of the most important determining factors is the critical attitude of the subject at the time he judges the orientation of the field. As Ewert[74] and Snyder and Pronko[275] have shown, a persistently critical attitude about the nature of the orientation precludes the judgment that the displaced field "looks normal." Apparently a subject who has spent some time trying to respond in a displaced field recalls afterward, if asked, that the field appeared normal. But if he is stopped in the midst of a task during the period of displacement and asked about the orientation, he notes discrepancies and reports them. We doubt that such discrepancies in perceptual orientation have ever been eliminated altogether in subjects wearing displacing devices.

We feel that Kohler's[151] claim that complete perceptual adaptation occurred in some subjects must be discounted for two reasons. In the first place, he himself reports that specific motor adaptation must occur in particular situations before perceptual reorientation is observed. This statement makes one doubt whether general perceptual reorientation without any discrepancies could be achieved. Secondly, although Kohler doesn't always report his procedures explicitly, the indications are that his subjects were asked to recollect the orientation of the visual field, and not to judge critically during performance.

There is no doubt that, with practice in restricted inverted and reversed visual fields, subjects come to view their own movements and objects within the field as having a consistent or normal appearance. There is no doubt also that restriction of the field enhances this effect. Most of our college student subjects who performed manipulative panel control tasks in restricted fields inverted by a fixed prism never knew that the visual feedback was inverted. The nature of the movements performed also influences the subjects' perception of the field. As we have said, most subjects performing writing and drawing movements in restricted displaced fields don't recognize the nature of the displacement.

The major fact to be noted about perceived orientation with displaced vision is the dominating role of motion in defining the perceived effects. The rapid adaptation that occurs with limited angular displacements exemplifies the flexibility of the movement systems of eyes, head, and hands in correcting and compensating for discrepancies that fall within a normal range of displaced feedback. With such limited displacements which can be compensated for in motion, there is no perceptual disturbance. The stabilizing of directional orientation with inverted and reversed vision, rather than being a pictorial "flipping over" of the perceived environment, is the outcome of a series of specifically learned displaced feedback relationships of motion. They may not represent maximally effective performance, but they can be perceived consistently once the novel sensory feedback interactions of movement are organized. We would not describe this adaptation as "rehabituation" or "redevelopment in perception," but as the learning or organization of a specific set of displaced feedback relations between perception and motion, which do not overlap materially with the perceptual-motor integrations of ordinary upright vision.

LEARNING FUNCTIONS WITH DISPLACED VISION

In evaluating the nature of adaptation to displaced feedback, some of the most useful data are quantitative descriptions of specific learning functions during and after exposure to the displacement. Stratton's[295-297] and Ewert's[74] careful daily records of activity under conditions of displacement give some general indications about the rate and conditions of

learning, but the first quantitative records were those of Peterson and Peterson,[208] Snyder and Pronko,[275] and Snyder and Snyder.[276] Most of the conclusions summarized in this section are drawn from our own studies.

Continuous versus Distributed Practice in Adapting to Displaced Vision

The learning of dotting, writing, and drawing tasks in inverted fields was compared under two practice conditions — when the trial sessions were massed within one day, and when they were distributed over a 20-day period. Although there were marked differences in learning curves for travel and manipulative movements and for the three different tasks, there were no differences caused by the distribution of practice sessions. The learning curves for both direct and compensatory movements were almost identical relative to the practice conditions.

These specific results and other general observations including retention tests, convince us that periods of normal vision do not interfere with learning to adapt to inverted or reversed vision. The experimental design that required subjects to wear experimental spectacles continuously was based on a theoretical assumption that cannot be substantiated.

Rates of Learning

In most of our studies with prism-inverted and televised displaced visual feedback, we have used daily exposures of one-half to two hours in length during which subjects are trained and tested in particular tasks. Typically, improvement with practice in the manual tasks we have used does not extend much beyond four or five days, and certainly not beyond eight to ten days. These rates of adaptation are much faster than those reported by Peterson and Peterson, and Snyder and Pronko and those implied by Stratton and Ewert, for the learning of motor activities. The differences are likely due to the fact that our displacement conditions did not involve depth reversals, disturbances of eye and head movements, or distortions of perceived movement, conditions that existed in one way or another in the previous studies.

Our learning curves for performance in displaced fields show smooth progress until the curves level off. The asymptotes are usually elevated above the level of performance with normal vision, except for some tasks and conditions that have been noted from time to time. Learning can progress to a normal level with very simple movements or tasks, or with minor displacement conditions. Learning curves that show the greatest initial elevation from the normal typically fall off at the fastest rates, but also level off at a relatively high elevation. That is to say, tasks and conditions that show the greatest initial disturbance typically show the poorest final adaptation.

Once learning levels off, we find no evidence of abrupt changes or improvements in performance that could be related to some dramatic perceptual-motor reorganization of performance. In our most extended studies, which lasted 20 days, all of the individual learning curves had leveled off in 10 days or sooner, with no evidence of belated reorganizations that could influence further learning. We have sometimes observed individual cases of abrupt changes in learning to respond to inverted or reversed feedback early in the training period, possibly caused by recognition of the nature of the displacement. In other individuals, however, such discovery may not influence the rate of learning at all.

Transfer Effects

Training in perceptual activities, such as reading, with inverted visual feedback does not transfer to specific motor performances under inversion. This is another indication of the specificity of adaptation with visual displacement.

Subjects who are trained with one condition of displacement show very little transfer effect when they are required to perform under other conditions of displacement. There is neither a significant positive transfer between displacement conditions nor a negative transfer, interference.

There is some limited transfer from one task to another, and between direct and compensatory movements, when the same condition of displacement is maintained. That is, subjects trained in one task, or with one type of movement, show some positive transfer when they are shifted to another task or another type of movement. In general, we find equivalent transfer phenomena with displaced vision as with normal learning: The degree of positive transfer is limited except between similar conditions of learning. The few instances of negative transfer that we have observed occur when movements of a particular reaction system must be made in opposite directions to the same general conditions of stimulation.

After-Effects and Retention

Kohler[149] reported that subjects who wore laterally displacing prisms for a period of time experienced perceptual after-effects for as long as several weeks after normal vision had been restored. In contrast, Wooster's[334] subjects who practiced localizing in fields displaced laterally by prisms experienced only momentary after-effects. We believe that the effects noted by Kohler may have been due to persisting deviation of the eyes from their normal position. We know that such positional modification can be achieved by prisms in correcting for strabismus, and might very well have occurred to a limited degree in Kohler's subjects.

The after-effects of inversion or reversal are generally quite limited, even after long periods of exposure to the displacement. The most persistent after-effects seem to occur in relation to activities that were relatively slow in adapting.

Although the learned adaptations to displaced vision interfere very little with behavior in normal visual fields, as evidenced by the limited after-effects observed, the specific response patterns that have been learned are retained over long periods of time with very little loss. Specific retention is tested by exposing the subject again to the displacement condition and requiring him to perform the task he learned under prior exposure. Peterson and Peterson[208] tested their subject's retention of responses learned under displaced vision eight months after the first displacement period, and Snyder and Snyder[276] reported tests made two years after the original exposure period. In both cases, the level of retention was very high. Snyder and Snyder found nearly perfect retention for assembly performance, card sorting, and object manipulation, and somewhat poorer retention for mirror drawing.

Our own data on long-term retention are limited to one subject who learned writing and drawing with prism-inverted vision during one day's massed practice and subsequent short practice sessions for six days thereafter. Retention tests of these performances made at yearly intervals for three years showed no marked change in either time of performance or quality of writing and drawing. For what it is worth, the subject reported after the last retention test that the task seemed easier than it had toward the end of the first learning period, according to his recollection.

SIZE DISTORTION OF VISUAL FEEDBACK

The problem of perceived size variation and constancy can be formulated experimentally as a problem of perceptual feedback in motion. We postulate that different stimulus and motion patterns can vary in magnitude within a certain normal range and still be perceived and reacted to as equivalent. Beyond this range of "perceptual-feedback" constancy, size variation in the visual field will lead to distortion in particular movements and movement relations, and consequent perceptions of size variation. According to this view, perceived size and extent of movement are regulated in terms of relative angular or geometric displacement of the stimulus feedback of motion. We assume that size distortion of televised visual fields will have less general effect on motion than any of the disturbing conditions of visual displacement, inasmuch as the intrinsic angular relationships of the perceived field do not change with change in size.

Experimental observations confirm the assumption just stated. Marked reduction or increase in size of the televised image of performance has very little influence on the accuracy and duration of either simple or complex motions. Highly precise tracing and writing motions can be carried out with little or no disturbance with both reduced and magnified visual feedback.

When artists were asked to observe objects with direct vision and draw them to true size in a televised performance field, it was found that magnification and reduction in size of the visual feedback produced wide variations in performance. In many cases, the subjects followed the visual cues in judging their movements and produced drawings that varied greatly in actual size. In other cases they overcompensated for the size distortion, producing very small drawings in reduced fields and large drawings in magnified fields. Some overestimated their movements most of the time, and some underestimated. The only consistency in their behavior was a marked reduction in accuracy in judging size of their drawings. None of the subjects excelled at the task. It is clear from the results that the tactual and kinesthetic systems are generally subordinate to the visual system in signaling the absolute size of motions. Most of the subjects drew reasonably accurate sizes with blind performance — when they could not see their hand or drawing — but when they were given size-distorted visual feedback their accuracy was less.

Comparisons between professional and amateur artists showed few if any significant differences in ability to draw accurate sizes in size-distorted visual fields. Years of training and experience do not seem to change the basic factors of perceptual feedback relative to behavior magnitudes. We also observed a marked decrease in interest and motivation to produce carefully executed drawings when the visual feedback was distorted.

DELAYED FEEDBACK OF MOTION

Television instrumentation has made it possible to delay the visual feedback of motion and analyze the effects on behavior. These observations on visual delay are comparable to investigations of delayed auditory feedback in speech and other motion patterns. The auditory studies, however, are complicated by the fact that only airborne sound can be delayed, while the immediate bone-conducted sound must be masked by raising the intensity of the delayed sound above normal level. In the television studies, control of visual feedback is complete, so that a clear-cut delay situation can be achieved.

We have made observations on two types of visual delay situations. Using simultaneous videotape recording and playback, we have effected delayed visual feedback with concurrent performance, comparable to the delayed auditory feedback studies. In this situation, the subject continues to perform while he is observing the delayed image of his movements. With just one videotape recorder and a tape loop we have observed the effects of delayed visual feedback on blind performance. In this case, the subject performs a task without any visual feedback of his movements, and then at the completion of the task is shown the delayed feedback of the entire performance.

Delayed Feedback with Blind Performance

When a task must be performed with no visual feedback of motion until the completion of the task, accuracy and speed are greatly decreased. Furthermore, there is little or no learning effect resulting from the presentation of the delayed visual feedback. In some cases, subjects improved significantly over several trials on the first day, but showed no learning effect on subsequent days. The limited improvement in performance that may occur may be no more than sometimes occurs with completely blind performance, when no visual feedback at all is given.

Delayed Feedback with Concurrent Performance

Delayed visual feedback with concurrent performance produces severe disturbances in the regulation of movement. Our limited observations have shown that a brief delay of about a half second seriously disturbs the execution of manual tasks requiring a fairly high degree of visual guidance. Tasks such as handwriting which demand less precise visual guidance are less severely affected.

One of the effects of delayed visual feedback is to produce repetitious movements comparable to the artificial stutter in speech produced by delayed auditory feedback. In tasks requiring precise visual control, such repetitive movements sometimes degenerate into a sort of tremor and nearly complete performance blocks. In handwriting, repetitions are seen in repeated letters. Although performance is not usually blocked in handwriting or in drawing geometric figures, movement times are greatly increased and accuracy decreased. Letters are sometimes omitted as well as repeated in writing tasks.

The effects of longer delays were studied by simulating a condition of delayed feedback, in which the subject observed the televised image of the hand of an observer duplicating the subject's own performance after a specified delay period. With short delays of 1 to 2 seconds, the subjects performed in a jerky manner, using discrete movements instead of smooth, continually controlled movements. With longer delays of about 30 seconds, jerky movements were not nearly as frequent, although overall accuracy was decreased. The performance with the longer delay was more like blind performance. Apparently the ability to perform smooth, continuously controlled movements, as in tracking and tracing, depends on a nearly simultaneous sensory feedback. When the visual feedback is delayed for a relatively long period, it is more or less ignored by the subject, who controls his movements by touch and kinesthesis.

These first experiments on delayed visual feedback are too limited to define the possibilities of learning to adapt to a continuously imposed delay. The study of simulated delayed feedback was continued for three days of practice, but learning effects were minimal for all magnitudes of delay.

Relative Effects of Delayed and Displaced Feedback

Although equivalent conditions of delayed and displaced feedback cannot be defined, it is interesting to compare the relative effects of the two types of distortion. It should be noted that subjects exposed to delayed visual feedback (concurrent with performance) have no real understanding of what is happening to them. As some subjects have said, everything looks all right, but everything that they do is wrong. Another subject said it feels almost like a disease or abnormality. We believe that the emotional disturbance and frustration produced by short-interval delay are definitely worse than the effects of geometric displacement, except possibly in the most extreme conditions of angular displacement.

The observed disturbances of motor performance are roughly equivalent with delayed feedback and the more difficult conditions of displaced feedback. In both cases, motions of high visual demand and complexity are affected much more than simpler or more discrete motions, or those having a low visual load. Jerky, tremor-like movements are observed under both types of visual distortion. Directional disorientation and at times complete loss of directional control also occur under both conditions. There are many equivalent phenomena of delayed and displaced vision that should be analyzed in more detail in future research.

SUMMARY

1. The significance of displaced vision research goes beyond the question of whether the individual can learn to see an inverted world upright to a consideration of the fundamental space organization of motion and its regulatory feedback systems.

2. Both motor and emotional effects of displaced vision can be very severe, even when the side-effects of wearing experimental optical devices are eliminated.

3. Lower animals cannot adapt to

displaced vision. In human subjects, adaptation is never complete, and depends on the nature of the displacement and the type of performance required. Usually the final level of adaptation reflects the degree of initial disturbance.

4. In general, inversion has more severe effects than inversion-reversal, and both of these conditions have more severe effects than reversal.

5. Adaptation is rapid and apparently complete to displacements of the line of sight up to about 15 degrees, but is limited beyond that. Adaptation is fairly good to horizontal displacements of the locus of vision up to 45 degrees or more, and even greater mesial displacements. All of these effects support our view of a normal range of angular displacement limited by a breakdown range. The exact limits depend on many movement variables.

6. Adaptation to displaced vision involves a series of specific perceptual-motor reorientations that are learned and retained fairly independently of normal motion patterns.

7. Visual displacement has greater effects on complex and precise motions than on less complex and less precise motions, and has differential effects on motions in different directions. Travel and manipulative components usually are affected differently.

8. Compensatory motions in displaced fields are initially slower than direct motions, but become just as effective. Also, compensatory motions probably aid in perceptual reorientation.

9. Displaced fields can look quite normal to a subject, especially if restricted in size and make-up, but are always subject to variable perceptual judgments due to critical attitudes, incomplete motor adaptation, and so on.

10. Learning in displaced fields is as good with intermittent exposure as with continuous. Learning curves are smooth and, except for simple tasks and limited displacements, level off above normal performance rates.

11. There is very limited transfer of training from one displacement condition to another or from one task to another. When conditions are similar, some positive transfer occurs.

12. After-effects of displacement are relatively limited, and retention of responses learned under displacement is very good. These effects speak for the specificity of the adaptive changes.

13. Size distortion of visual fields has relatively little effect on performance unless individuals are required to judge true size of their movements with reference to normal visual standards.

14. Delayed sensory feedback seriously disturbs motion organization, and there is little or no recovery. Smooth motions become jerky, and repetitive movements occur.

CHAPTER 16

THE NEURO-GEOMETRY OF MOTION

Although it would be satisfying to use the last chapter of a book for a final summing up of a theoretical position, such a definitive conclusion is not possible here, nor, in fact, desirable. Our purpose has been to raise questions about behavioral organization, to probe the weaknesses of certain other experimental and theoretical analyses, to develop some new ideas about the space-structuring of motion, and to test them insofar as possible in a sustained program of research — a program which has by no means reached an end. Thus, the set of concepts and postulates to which we refer as neurogeometric theory is — like so many other proposed descriptions of behavior and its mechanisms — an activity in progress, subject to elaboration and revision but probably never ready for conclusion.

We have evolved neurogeometric theory to its present form because it has proved useful in describing many diverse phenomena of behavior, and provocative in suggesting new lines of research. In this chapter we shall summarize some of the theoretical implications of the displaced vision research, point out applications of neurogeometric theory to other areas of behavior, and suggest problems of perceptual feedback worthy of future research effort.

THEORETICAL ACCOUNT OF DISPLACED VISION

The various theoretical analyses of displaced vision phenomena made by prior investigators have been presented in earlier chapters and need no further elaboration here. Suffice it to reexamine a few critical points.

Learning Interpretations

The empirical theorists have looked

upon the displaced vision experiment as a means of returning the individual to a state of undeveloped perception analogous to that of the infant. Kohler[151] in particular has stressed this interpretation, and then has described the process of adaptation to the experimental displacement as equivalent to normal perceptual development. The assumption is that if the adult can learn to perceive and move effectively in a displaced field, then normal perceptual development in the infant must be a process of learning.

We have pointed out a number of weaknesses in this position, principally that adaptation to displacement is variable, incomplete, and dependent on specific motor adjustments. This process of adjustment and reorientation as described in prior studies and as observed in our own bears no resemblance to what we know of perceptual-motor development in infants and children. Normal development in the child proceeds from gross generalized responses to finer, more specific responses, whereas adaptation to displaced vision starts with the learning of specific response patterns, and becomes general only in the sense that more and more specific adjustments can be learned. Further, these new perceptual-motor coordinations are quite independent of normal patterns of motion, and are retained for long periods of time as specific skills. The fact that human individuals can learn new coordinations in displaced visual fields proves nothing about the normal developmental process, nor does it explain the regulatory mechanisms of motion in either normal or displaced fields.

Local Sign Theory

Another problem has to do with the phylogenetic differences in response to displaced vision. No animal below primates ever has been shown to adapt to displacement conditions, whether pro-duced optically or anatomically. On this basis, Sperry[288] rejects altogether the learning account of perceptual-motor organization, and proposes his alternative view, which represents a revival of local sign theory in biochemical terms. While local sign doctrine seems meaningful with respect to the facts of anatomically displaced vision in lower animals, it fails to account for the flexibility of perceptual-motor organization found in monkey and man.

We have, then, these two sets of facts about displaced vision. The studies on man have shown that he can adapt with varying degrees of effectiveness to many different varieties of visual displacement. The studies on lower animals have shown that there are highly specific unlearned neural connections between receptors, central nervous system, and effectors in amphibia and other forms that determine fixed patterns of sensorimotor response. These facts have been used respectively to support the empirical theory of perception and a local sign theory of fixed genetic relationships in behavior, but neither of these theories gives a meaningful account of the mechanisms of motion, and how they can show progressively greater flexibility in phylogenetic development.

The Reafference Principle

A start toward analyzing the regulatory mechanisms of perceptual-motor integration has been made by von Holst,[128] who proposes the reafference principle to explain how motion is patterned in terms of movements already made. He assumes that the regulation of any movement involves an efference copy of a motor innervation pattern in the brain which can be negated by sensory reafference produced by the movement. When the reafference equals the efference copy, in magnitude and sign, movement stops. When there is a differential remainder between the two, movement is increased with a positive remainder and decreased with a negative remainder. In an alternative process, the differential remainder ascends to higher centers to give rise to perception.

Von Holst's doctrine of reafference represents a valuable approach to problems of motor control in animal behavior because of its emphasis on the role of sensory feedback in perceptual-motor coordination. The fundamental validity of the reafference principle is not going to be challenged seriously by experiment, any more so than the feedback idea itself. The principal weakness in this analysis is that it too fails to account for the marked flexibility of response in higher animal forms. Although von Holst's concepts of brain commands and brain copies make his theory comparable to the technologically oriented servo-system models of brain function, he finds it necessary to fall back on mentalistic notions such as perceptions in the higher centers to account for certain phenomena characteristic of human perceptual-motor behavior. These concepts defy experimental analysis.

On the other hand, von Holst's general principle of sensory compensation appears to be amenable to objective evaluation by such means as our studies on compensatory modes of response to various conditions of displaced vision. When the individual performs, for example, compensatory handwriting movements in a displaced field, the movements themselves appear displaced but the handwriting trace appears normally oriented. If von Holst's compensation principle has general validity, these compensatory reactions should be more adaptive and more efficient than noncompensatory reactions in a displaced field. However, our comparative studies of direct and compensatory reactions have shown that the latter possess no advantage over the former. As a matter of fact, direct reactions tend to

be more effective initially if they involve established patterns of motion, and the final level of performance is approximately the same for the two types of reaction.

We believe that compensatory reactions do facilitate adaptation to visual displacement only if they reduce the relative degree of displacement between sensory and motor patterns. For example, with relatively small angular displacements of vision, it is possible to make compensatory adjustments of the eyes or head that reduce or eliminate the disturbing effects of the displacement. To describe this, however, in terms of efference copies and reafference effects that "exactly compensate one another," as von Holst has put it, makes no allowance for human flexibility of response. We think it is more meaningful to apply the concept of normal ranges of displacement between sensory and motor patterns, and then to attempt to define these ranges according to the effective external and internal variables in a particular situation.

Neurogeometric Theory

Our own analysis of displaced vision phenomena is based on the general postulates of neurogeometric theory: that motion is multidimensional; that it is primarily space-structured; that this spatial patterning depends on neural sensitivity to spatial differences in stimulation; and that the temporal continuity of motion is determined by sensory feedback mechanisms. We believe that all patterned motion involves relative displacements between perception and motion, e.g., between the line of sight and the plane of manipulation, or between the vertical axis of the body with respect to gravity and a horizontal transport movement of the arm. These spatial relationships of different parts of the body are not fixed absolutely, but are subject to considerable variation. Thus, we look upon the various conditions of experimentally displaced vision as but exaggerations of quite ordinary variations in perceptual-motor displacement, and have investigated the effects of experimental displacement in the belief that we would thereby gain further understanding of normal integrative mechanisms.

MULTIDIMENSIONALITY OF MOTION. Our description of the three basic components of motion — posture, transport, and manipulation — was derived originally from many different observations and experimental analyses of patterned motion. These displaced vision studies support our view that various movement components are affected differentially by different variables. Whenever we timed travel and manipulative components separately, we found these differential effects. Movements in different directions and of different degrees of precision and complexity also were affected differently by a given displacement condition.

The neurogeometric specification of motion and perception enables us to define in physiological and behavioral terms what constitutes complexity in perceptual-motor organization. Complexity is a function not only of the number of space dimensions involved in a perceptual-motor feedback pattern, but depends also on the number of geometrically organized movements in the pattern. We have known since the early days of gestalt psychology that anisotropy of perceived patterns is a direct function of their complexity. The same is true of motor patterns. The greater the complexity of a movement pattern, the more it will be disturbed by space and time displacement, and the more limited will be its recovery.

AXIAL ORGANIZATION OF MOTION. One of our basic postulates is that motion is organized relative to the major axes of the body. The bilateral symmetry of vertebrates and many invertebrates

is not a happy accident, but an expression of the functional organization of the motion systems; this is a major factor to be considered in describing either neural integration or behavior.

We describe two of the three main motion systems as being organized axially. The postural base of all motion is regulated primarily according to gravitational stimulation, and thus is organized relative to the vertical axis of the body. Transport movements must be integrated with the postural base, but also are patterned bilaterally, and are regulated according to bilateral differences in stimulation. Thus, the body members execute transport movements relative to a set of right-left or horizontal axes. These two axially organized motion mechanisms function as reference systems of space orientation for finer manipulative movements.

In our investigations of different dimensions of visual displacement, we assumed from the start that the effects of a displacement would be related to its orientation with respect to the major body axes. Thus, we differentiated between systematic displacements, involving up-down inversion or right-left reversals, and intermediate nonsystematic displacements of various sorts. We predicted that visual inversion would disturb behavior more severely than right-left reversal, because the vertically organized postural system is the most primitive motion system and basic to all other organized motion. Further, we predicted that the most serious disturbances would be caused by certain extreme nonsystematic angular displacements. We believed that individuals would be able to correct for axial displacements more readily than for extreme displacements in other dimensions because the latter would demand continual readjustments and integration of both up-down and right-left motion systems.

These major expectations about axial

effects in adaptation to displaced vision were fulfilled almost without exception. Visual inversion was consistently more disturbing than right-left reversal, and extreme angular displacements were found that were more disturbing than inversion or 180-degree displacement.

We predicted further than combined inversion and reversal would be less disturbing than inversion, because the spatial relationships of an inverted-reversed behavioral field are internally consistent with a nondisplaced field. This prediction was confirmed generally, although there were some exceptions in our experimental findings.

NORMAL AND BREAKDOWN RANGES OF DISPLACEMENT. Human tolerance for minor relative displacements between the various sensory and motion systems of the body is a matter of common observation and needs no experimental confirmation. We know from experience that we can perform effective visually controlled manipulations with the eyes in many positions with respect to the hands. Thus we expected that minor angular displacements of the locus of vision would not seriously effect the efficiency of performance, but that displacement angles could be found that would cause movement breakdown. Our interest was in showing how these normal and breakdown ranges varied with different dimensions of displacement and different tasks.

The experimental evidence was clear that tolerance was greater for angular displacements in the mesial plane than in the horizontal plane. Also tolerance was greater when the task to be performed was relatively simple and not too precise. Quantitative breakdown functions were determined for specific tasks to show the general validity of the concept of normal and breakdown ranges of displacement.

We found significant evidence, however, that performance within a so-called normal displacement range is not necessarily equivalent at all angles. The efficiency of a specific motion pattern may remain approximately the same throughout a series of angular displacements, but the same performance may show differential effects throughout the same range if an additional variable is introduced. We refer to the study of mesial displacements in which the performance field was inverted for some of the trials. The same range of mesial displacements that had no apparent effect on upright performance had differential effects when the performance field was inverted. We believe that this is evidence for one of our other basic postulates — that motion patterns are organized according to the particular spatial requirements of a situation and derive their specificity or independence from their geometric organization.

SPECIFICITY OF MOTION. All our own experimental findings as well as the reports of prior studies attest to the specificity of adaptive changes that occur with displaced vision. In no case has there been clear evidence for general perceptual reorientation. Some of the most striking evidence for specificity of response comes from tests of retention showing almost perfect retention of skills learned in displaced fields after months and even years with no practice. Further evidence comes from the limited transfer demonstrated between different tasks learned under displacement conditions; only when tasks have similar performance elements does significant transfer occur. Subjects trained in a relatively inactive perceptual task — inverted reading — showed no significant transfer to inverted writing, even though verbal material was involved in both tasks.

The fact that every change in the orientation of the visual field and in the directional or spatial organization of a task has differential effects on performance is perhaps the most persuasive evidence for the geometric specificity of motion. This demonstration is one of the most important general findings of our displaced vision research. The relative independence of perceptual-motor skills has never been accounted for satisfactorily, but we believe that the basis for such specificity can be attributed to the almost limitless number of spatial relationships that can occur between perception and motion variables.

SIGNIFICANCE OF DELAYED FEEDBACK. The one outstanding effect of delayed sensory feedback is that it puts the individual in a situation to which it is almost impossible to adapt. Normal perceptual-motor coordinations cannot be recovered when critical sensory feedback signals are delayed. The only adaptive changes that do occur involve shifts in the perceptual-motor organization of the task. This intolerance for temporal displacement of feedback is in marked contrast to the wide tolerance of the human individual to spatial displacement, and his ability to relearn skills under many different types and degrees of spatial displacement.

We believe that these findings along with other results of our displaced vision studies show clearly that the learning process as an organizational factor in behavior is secondary to its primary neurogeometric organization. The relative geometricity of motion and its sensory feedback relationships define the nature, course and final level of perceptual-motor learning. The inconsistent and limited adaptation that occurs with delayed sensory feedback indicates that the primary organization of movement cannot be described as a time-coded process of establishing sequential response patterns on the basis of their effects. The wide variety of behavior patterns that can be performed and learned by the human individual reflects the flexibility of the spatial organization of his motions. The temporal requirements of motion systems are very rigid. Thus we believe that behavior is organized first of all on the basis of spatial differences, and that the concept of reinforcement as ordinarily defined is inadequate to account for the richness and variety of human behavior patterns.

On another level, the results of this research may have implications for certain aspects of training and education. If the basic neural processes of perceptual-motor learning in man are space-organized sensory feedback processes, then the optimal procedures of learning and education are best understood as auditory and visual feedback effects regulated by activity of the learner. Accordingly, our research on the neurogeometric organization of behavior provides a theoretical-experimental base for understanding audiovisual techniques in education and training. We already have described one application of these ideas in connection with the development of audio-visumatic techniques whereby learners control the auditory and visual feedback through their own overt responses.[258] Our results suggest that training techniques that permit self-regulated auditory and visual feedback would be far more effective for the learner than teaching boxes that depend entirely on the principle of verbal reinforcement.

GENERAL APPLICATIONS OF NEUROGEOMETRIC THEORY

The theory proposed in this book applies to neural function as well as to the organization of behavior. We propose what is essentially a cellular theory of neural integration as opposed to synaptic theory. The concept of the synapse as an integrative mechanism has always remained something of a mystery. We have very little knowledge about the synapse, except that it is a gap in the neural circuit at which integrative changes are supposed to occur, apparently without benefit of anatomic support. These changes are assumed to facilitate or inhibit neural conduction, and thus are believed to be the basis of learning as well as other integrative effects in behavior.

We prefer to believe that it is the internuncial cell or neuron itself that is the genetic and functional unit of neural integration, rather than the space between cells, and that the critical function of these neurons is not just to conduct impulses from one end to the other, but to respond to differences in two sources of stimulation. In brief, we assume that the temporal and spatial properties of sensori-neuromotor patterns are regulated by the internuncial neurons, in their role as differential detectors registering space and time displacements in the sensory feedback of motions.

Motor Functions of Neurogeometric Systems

We believe that neurogeometric detectors are involved in all systems of motor control, the most primitive as well as the most advanced. One of the most basic of such neuromotor systems is that involved in the reciprocal innervation of antagonistic muscles. One function of this balanced neural action is to maintain the postural support of the body. Another fundamental function is to maintain the sensitivity of receptors controlled by the motor system. For example, reciprocal tremor movements of the eyes continually shift their position and thus prevent the adaptation of retinal receptors.[222, 223]

To account for the reciprocal innervation of antagonistic muscle systems, Sherrington[237] postulated a sort of negative action imposed by inhibitory synaptic circuits, but the actual mechanism of neural inhibition has never been clear. According to neurogeometric theory, we need assume no such inhibitory principle. A detector neuron that

responds to differences either reacts or it doesn't react. The absence of response does not imply inhibition, but a balanced state of neural action in the cell with respect to two stimulus sources with which it is associated. We assume as a major hypothesis that reciprocal innervation can be accounted for in terms of such neurogeometric detectors. The response of one of a pair of antagonistic muscles displaces the member to which it is attached and thereby effects a differential stimulus condition that initiates the opposing response.

Another type of motor control that we describe in neurogeometric terms is the regulation of continuous tracking movements that are made to correspond in rate and direction to an external stimulus pattern. We believe that such motions depend on internuncial detectors which respond to differences between proximally located receptor cells.

Discrete start and stop movements are assumed to be controlled by inter-receptor detectors which record differences between specific loci of stimulation in two different receptor systems: in the eye or ear and some related locus of kinesthetic activity in a moving member. Some such spatial differentiation would function to stop the movement at a certain position. We believe that an almost countless number of specific cortical cells have evolved to detect differences between reference points within two receptor systems and account for the elaboration of the human cerebral cortex.

We assume also the existence of specific bilateral parallax movement regulators in the brain. These internuncial detectors innervate the appropriate muscles to maintain limited angular differences in position of the two eyes or of other symmetrical parts of the body in equivalent bilateral movements.

We believe that efferent-afferent detector neurons function in various ways to determine centrally controlled specific

movements like the saccadic movements
of the eyes. Such neurons could function
also to integrate different component
movements, such as postural and transport or transport and manipulative interactions. Certain extensive dendritic cell
mechanisms, such as the basket cells of
the cerebellum, are thought to be generalized efferent-afferent systems for
maintaining uniformity of action across
a widespread movement system and can
be made to feed activity into an entire
muscle mechanism when one part is
made active. It is possible also that
efferent-afferent cell systems are the primary circular reinforcing chains that
tend to produce repetitive motions once
a movement system is activated by
stimulation.

Development of Sensory Feedback Control

A basic problem of behavior of interest to us in connection with neurogeometric theory has to do with the
development of differential motor systems for control of sensory feedback,
for we believe that the primary organizational factor of adult behavior is the
motor control of sensory feedback. With
this problem in mind, we conducted our
exploratory studies on the abilities of
infants and children to control their
perceived visual, auditory, and tactual
environment. The results of these experiments indicated that infants up to 18
months of age have only the most
limited resources in regulating the perceived environment. During this early
period, the child develops highly articulated postural, body transport, and manipulative motions that are used in
general patterns of orientation and
manipulation, but this motor differentiation precedes by some months the
ability to control the sounds, sights, and
touches of the environment. These findings are in keeping with the general
point of view that the geometric organization of visual and auditory perception
follows the development of postural,
transport, and manipulative motion systems because refined perceptual activities are dependent on precise control of
the sensory feedback from the receptor
systems.

Our observations of infants suggest
that normal development of control of
the perceived environment is quite different from the events of adaptation to
displaced visual feedback in the adult.
The infant up to two years shows almost no specific manual control of the
visual environment, although he gives
consistent orientation reactions to televised sights of persons and to their
voices. In contrast, the adult individual
brings to the displaced vision situation
not only a great number of articulated
space-structured movements, but many
movements of this sort that can be
adapted immediately to control of the
disoriented surround.

Our studies on infant orientation to
televised images of persons have provided suggestive information about perceptual motivation in the infant. The
sights and sounds of persons, even of a
stranger, seem to be far more significant
objects of sensory control than movement of the environment, color, music,
and sounds, or the feel of a soft blanket
in an uncomfortable crib. However,
many of these other stimuli have definite
positive or negative value in motivating
some children.

Sensory Deprivation in Infancy

The process of adaptation to displaced
vision sometimes is considered analogous
to the process of developing visual skills
after a period of visual deprivation in
infancy or childhood. This point of view
originated with Helmholtz,[116] who related his empirical doctrine of perceptual development to observations on the
effects of infant blindness on visual
capacities after the blindness had been
corrected. Individuals who have suffered
infant blindness because of cataracts

typically show, after the cataracts have been removed, marked defects in visual perception and visuomotor coordination which gradually are reduced through experience. Helmholtz reasoned that such gradual acquisition of visual skills was good evidence for his empirical theory of perception — that space perception naturally comes about through learning. The same line of reasoning has been followed by empirical theorists with respect to displaced vision experiments; the fact that individuals can adapt to visual displacement is considered evidence that normal perceptual development is a learning process.

In recent years, observations on human individuals who have been given their sight only after a period of blindness have been supplemented by experimental observations on early sensory deprivation in chicks, rats, and chimpanzees.[58, 157, 202, 220, 221] We have summarized the most significant of these studies in Chapter 2. The results are in general agreement that early visual deprivation leads to impairment of visual behavior when sight is restored.

Although these studies seem to support a learning theory of perceptual development, we think that they can be interpreted otherwise. The visual defects observed in these studies have more of the characteristics of basic sensory and neural abnormalities than of deficiencies in specifically learned skills. We believe that early restriction of perceptual activity can interfere with the course of development of the integrative mechanisms of perception and motion, but that the general nature of these mechanisms under normal circumstances is genetically determined and not at the mercy of specific learning situations.

Phylogenetic Differences in Neurogeometric Organization

Observations on the phylogenetic differences in adaptation to displaced vision — no adaptation in flies, fish, frogs, salamanders, and birds, as contrasted with considerable adaptation in monkey and man — have definite implications for our understanding of the mechanisms of neural evolution. We believe that in the course of evolution, the brain developed as a neurogeometric system for the regulation of motion. The increased flexibility of response observed in higher animals is due to the progressive development of differential perceptual feedback systems for regulating and integrating transport and manipulative motions. The possibilities for varied response patterns have increased with the increase in number of neurogeometric detectors associated with different loci of activity.

It seems probable that the cortex has evolved specifically as a perceptual feedback mechanism for the control of fine manipulative movements of the body, especially those of the hands and face. Its projection areas are highly space-organized neurogeometric detector systems, made up of neurons that isolate and funnel specific patterns of stimulation relative to fine manipulation, and others that interrelate manipulative and transport movements of the body. We do not except the frontal lobes from this general conception of the cortex. These areas we conceive of as a projection system for the sensory feedback mechanisms of the internal organs. This view implies that cortical projection areas have expanded in evolutionary development not only in relation to the size of the receptor systems, but also in relation to degree of articulation of motor mechanisms related to particular receptor systems. There is general anatomic evidence that cortical expansion of the visual, auditory, and tactual systems during evolution has proceeded on this basis.

Tool Using

Our interest in the evolutionary changes in adaptation to displaced vision has led to a consideration of the behavioral and neural aspects of tool using, inasmuch as all tooling activities imply new dimensions and conditions of displaced perceptual feedback in motion. We have been especially interested in formulating experimentally some of the problems of perceptual feedback in tooled motions as compared with unaided manipulation.

Our exploratory studies bearing on these questions showed that visual displacement affected the movements of a panel control task differentially according to the particular dimension of visual displacement and the type and direction of movement. The potential variation of specific movement patterns made possible by different perceptual displacement conditions, movement directions, and types of movement components is more than sufficient to account for all of the variable tool-using activities of man. We found too that individuals can perform efficient tooling operations with a feedback of the trace or effect of their motions. They need not see the moving member directly, or even identify themselves with it in order to use the feedback for precise perceptual-motor coordinations.

These preliminary observations on displacing the perceptual feedback of tool using, which were described in Chapter 12, were included in this book to illustrate different approaches to analyzing the tooling functions performed by man. There is a pressing need for a more fundamental scientific conception of tool using and its significance in human behavior. It is fairly well established that the central factor in human evolution was man's use of tools, not only in survival but in positive control of the environment.[203] The evolutionary development of man's distinctively human characteristics — his upright posture, stereovision, apposition of thumb and fingers, mobility of head and eyes, forward disposition of shoulder and

arms, and oversized brain to level simultaneous control over these varied mechanisms of behavior — has been determined by tests of survival based on the fitting of motions to the use of tools. This adaptation of man to tools in control of the structural features of his environment has changed the details of the neurogeometric control of motion, but it has not altered the basic perceptual feedback systems that define the organization of behavior. The properties and dimensions of tool-using behavior are defined and limited by the fundamental organization of the sensory feedback mechanisms of the neuromotor system. The central problem in the design of tools and machines of modern man is that of the relative space and time displacement of visual feedback with respect to patterns of postural, transport, and manipulative movements demanded in their control.

Analysis of Specific Human Motions

In general, the research reported in this book describes a new approach to the analysis of human motion systems. We feel that some such modification of motion study methods is needed for careful decisive work in medicine, rehabilitation programs for the physically handicapped, machine design, industry, and work science. Heretofore the analysis of human motions, except for the work of Dodge,[66] Stetson,[291] and a few others, has been confined very largely to the timing of arbitrarily defined therbligs or operations, which has had no justifiable theoretical foundation except as it is applied to speed up work for increased profit.

In the research program defined here, we have approached the objective study of human motion by utilizing interrelated procedures of analyzing movement interactions and the effects of displaced and delayed sensory feedback. By these means we have tried to define the critical features of action and inter-action that are involved in such primary motion systems as those related to visuo-motor coordination, expressive motion, and gait, as well as the more specialized patterns of manipulative motion such as drawing, handwriting, painting, sculp-turing, assembly operations, and ma-chine work.

Experimental psychology in the past has devoted very little objective scien-tific effort to the understanding of these complex human skills. The general atti-tude has seemed to be that such out-standing forms of animal behavior are acquired through learning, through the effects of reinforcement, and thus are subject to the general laws derived from the study of maze running, lever press-ing, or the repetition of nonsense sylla-bles. Unfortunately, the general learning concepts that have been the subject of so much dedicated research effort and verbal analysis seem to have little meaning when applied to problems of prediction and control of patterned human skills.

Another segment of experimental psy-chology has devoted great effort and ingenuity and countless hours of care-ful experimentation to analyzing the differential sensory functions in behav-ior. This approach too has stopped short of an understanding of the differ-ential motor functions. Our feeling is that an analysis of sensory processes is incomplete without a related analysis of the integrated motion systems that make sensory differentiation possible. To understand how the individual be-haves according to the stimulus patterns of his environment, it is necessary to analyze the complete mechanisms of perceptual-motor integration.

Accordingly, we have developed and are still developing methods of studying perception and motion that reveal many of the detailed properties of movement integration, the geometricity of the sen-sory feedback processes of motion, and

the feedback time relations involved in different types of specialized motions. We believe that these methods of analysis could be extended to studies of all the educationally and occupationally significant motions of man.

STUDYING PERCEPTUAL FEEDBACK WITH TELEVISION

The research program described here has been more than an effort to produce an original theory, at best a fleeting achievement, and some experimental data. An equally important part of the venture has been to explore the possi-bilities of adapting a new visual tech-nology — that of closed-circuit television — to laboratory procedures and experi-mentation. This instrument has been peculiarly suited to our principal scien-tific interests. It is not only a desirable tool, but an essential tool for exploring and analyzing the temporal and spatial factors of the sensory feedback of mo-tion. A systematic laboratory science of the principles of the geometry of motion is made possible by television instru-mentation.

The television study of spatially and temporally displaced sensory feedback contributes to our understanding of all types of perceptual and motor patterns — manual skills, tool using, artistic instru-mentation, athletic performance, and general body and limb coordinations. But the implications of such study ex-tend beyond specific analyses of psycho-motor skill. The experimental tech-niques that permit us to separate both spatially and temporally the visual feed-back of motion from actual performance hold great promise for research in all aspects of behavior. We anticipate that television instrumentation will be used increasingly in studies of learning, per-ception, motivation, development, aging, behavior disorder, social interaction, and the effects of stress and drugs on human performance. Some of the experimental areas and their applications that interest us particularly are indicated below.

Critical Phenomena of Delayed Vision

The qualitative features and the quantitative functions of delayed visual feedback in behavior are almost entirely unexplored. Research already carried out barely defines methodology. Because of the close relation between perceptual feedback and the theoretically conceived processes of reinforcement in learning, the study of delayed visual feedback may become a critical technical approach to analyses of motivation and the learning process.

The specific problems of delayed vision are comparable to those of displaced vision, and should be analyzed in similar fashion. Among the problems that we hope to explore are the relation between magnitude of delay and performance efficiency for tasks of different visual demand and complexity, changes in pattern of movement coordination with increased magnitude of delay, the specificity of learning under different delay conditions, the maximum level of adaptation for different motions under different delay conditions, the after-effects of delayed visual feedback, and long-term retention of performance patterns learned under delayed feedback.

Remote Control of Space Vehicles

One area of applied science that needs immediate answers to questions about performance with delayed visual feedback is that of space exploration with satellites and roving space vehicles. The problem is one of controlling an unmanned vehicle from earth at a distance far enough to produce a material delay in transmitted signals. For example, if an operator on earth were attempting to control an unmanned vehicle on the moon by means of a television eye, his

visual feedback of the effect of his performance would be delayed 2.5 seconds. That is, the time required to transmit a signal to the moon plus the return trip for a visual signal to the operator would be approximately 2.5 seconds. When we imposed experimental delays of this magnitude on subjects, their performance deteriorated remarkably.

A somewhat different problem would be presented by a manned vehicle on the moon subject to dual control by the vehicle operator and a controller on earth. Here we would have all the problems of coordinating simultaneous dual control of a machine system complicated by the grave factor of delayed visual feedback.

Although we have not carried out long-term studies of adaptation to delayed visual feedback, and consequently cannot say with certainty to what degree an individual can overcome the disturbing effects of such delay, the results that we do have do not look promising. There is no evidence that effective adaptation to conditions of delayed feedback could be achieved by training.

Problems of Displaced and Delayed Feedback in Machine Systems

A critical factor involved in accurate operation of tracing and steering systems is that of time lags in stimulus feedback to the operator of the effect of his movements. These lags arise in part from electrical-mechanical linkages of the governing systems, but they also are due in some cases to the use of aided and automated forms of tracking and steering. Such systems introduce definite time lags as well as space displacements between the tracker's controlling movements and the perceptual feedback of the action of the cursor.

For some years, engineers have used design procedures referred to by the name "quickening" to eliminate lags in tracking and steering devices. Quickening amounts in effect to getting the information about steering action back to the operator as rapidly as possible. Unfortunately, the concept and procedure of quickening do not solve the fundamental problems of machine design for remote control. All systems of aided and power steering and tracking involve space displacement of visual feedback as well as delay. For example, when the rate control movements of tracking are automated, the positional relations between different movements in the tracking task are changed as well as the temporal relations between control movements and cursor action. The design features of tracking systems have been burdened with misconceptions in the past, and present engineering conceptions in this field have not gone beyond the general and superficial.

Tracking behavior is a product of multidimensional motor control, involving both transport (rate control) and manipulation (position control) of the tracking device. The aiding or automation of any component of the tracking task by means of compensatory displays or motor aiding involves both displacement and delay of the visual feedback of motion, with the consequence that such aiding may interfere with tracking accuracy rather than improve it.[168] Other things being equal, direct pursuit tracking systems cannot be improved upon, because they minimize the disturbing temporal and space displacements inherent in the aided systems. In rapidly moving platforms, however, as in high speed aircraft, the computer correction for the effects of speed and other physical characteristics of the moving system may preclude such direct tracking or steering. In such cases it may be impossible to avoid various forms of displaced and delayed compensatory feedback, put into the system by power and position aiding. What we need, then, are more detailed analyses of movement organization under the particular feedback conditions in question, in order to design the machine system for the most accurate and efficient human operation. To this end, television methodology readily lends itself.

Objective Study of Perceptual Constancy

The research on size-distorted visual feedback represents a new methodological approach to problems of size constancy in behavior. Many prior experimental studies in this area have studied the events of perceptual constancy in terms of the subject's verbal judgments of apparent size and other perceptual relationships. There are many experimental observations which indicate that such passive perceptual judgments may be quite variable and not a valid index of normal modes of response. When a subject is permitted to perform actively in size-distorted fields, he makes compensatory adjustments and other adaptive reactions which define his general response patterns in the situation.

The use of televised performance fields promises to be a valuable method for studying some of the critical factors that determine size constancy and size variation in perceptual behavior. The relative size of a televised visual image can be controlled over a wide range and can be shifted quickly from one size to another. More importantly, the subject can be required to perform overtly in the perceptual field, so that his responses can be measured and analyzed. We believe that these methods of behavior analysis are more meaningful than the methods of judgmental psychophysics.

Analysis of Motivation and Energy Expenditure

One of the weaknesses in behavior theory in past years has been its failure to give a meaningful account of human motivation. It has been assumed that human individuals as well as other animals are motivated primarily by their biological needs, expressed in physiological drive states. Yet much of ordinary human behavior — verbal and graphic skills, patterns of work, artistic and recreational pursuits — which we observe in ourselves and others seems to bear little relation to hunger, thirst, sexual drives, and the like. To bridge this gap between what the individual needs to sustain and reproduce himself and what he appears to be doing most of the time, it has been necessary to postulate a complex structure of learned or secondary motives that derive their strength from the primary needs of the living organism. In recent years this traditional description of motivation has been extended to include accounts of perceptual motivation, or activity motivation, but the main emphasis is still on physiological drives.

Our own point of view is that so-called perceptual motivation is more than an incidental source of human activity, and should be considered of primary importance in behavior organization. The nature of this motivating force can be described specifically in terms of the intrinsic make-up of the regulatory mechanisms of motion, for the neurogeometrically organized motion systems drive the individual to action as relentlessly as and more consistently than hunger or thirst. Further, the motion systems define specific patterns of behavior related to physiological needs.

Our studies of displaced and delayed feedback have shown some very clear motivational effects resulting from disorganization of the normal feedback relationships of motion. We have observed among other things frustration, blocking of activity, and general slowing down of behavior. In the study of artistic drawing in size-distorted fields, we observed a marked drop in effort to produce carefully executed drawings. On the other hand, we observed positive motivational effects of various perceptual conditions in infants and children. In other words, many variations in level of activity and general energy expenditure were directly due to perceptual feedback conditions.

We feel that these observations are significant in relation to the study of normal patterns of motivation, fatigue, monotony, and sleep, as well as of certain abnormal motivational effects in the neuroses and psychoses. If these events of behavior are determined in part by spatially and temporally organized sensory feedback interactions, then we believe that experimental feedback analysis will be an important method for motivational research.

Sensory Feedback Mechanisms in Educationally Significant Behavior Patterns

For many thousands of years, a significant part of human endeavor has been concerned with advancing and perfecting the specialized motions of drawing and handwriting — skills which have made possible not only our historical knowledge of the past, but also the structure of civilization as we know it. Yet the behavior patterns of handwriting and drawing have received only the most limited and often superficial attention in experimental psychology. For example, one branch of psychological handwriting study deals with the extension of graphology to provide a widely used clinical method of personality analysis. There has been almost no basic research on the nature of handwriting as a pattern of behavior and its significance in relation to other adaptive patterns of man.

One of the purposes of the research reported here has been to apply the techniques of displaced and delayed feedback analysis of motion to the study of the geometricity or form processes of behavior in both handwriting and drawing. Various experiments have shown that the processes of forming letters and drawing patterns are regulated by specific sensory feedback mechanisms, characterized by special properties of axial geometricity, relative angular displacement effects, and the intrinsic integration of specific transport and manipulative movements to define the overall pattern of motion. We believe that our television methods of analysis offer a valuable new approach to understanding the distinctive phenomena of handwriting and its development as a tool-using activity.

This type of television research also has a broader educational significance than suggested by the analysis of specific motion patterns. We believe that sensory feedback analysis by means of television systems can be used profitably in objective study of audiovisual techniques in education. Although communication techniques in the classroom have advanced far beyond the slate blackboard, this technological progress has been achieved without benefit of an adequate theoretical or experimental base. The main contribution of experimental psychology to the rationale of audiovisual techniques appears to be a set of concepts about learning and reinforcement and teaching boxes derived from studies of scheduled learning sequences in rats and pigeons. We submit that animal training skills do not provide a sufficient base for understanding the role and significance of audiovisual techniques in human learning.

Our work on sensory feedback mechanisms of educationally significant motions represents a new method for analyzing the nature of perceptual motivation and audiovisual design in education. Our results indicate that learning in man is not primarily time-coded, according to the effects of reinforcement, but rather is space-coded, and that the motivation, frustration, and organization of learning depend on

highly specialized geometric properties of the feedback mechanisms of component movements. Scientifically designed television and videotape systems can be applied to studying the development and control of the visual environment in the child, the artist, the writer, the tool user, and machine operator, and thereby provide an important new research technique.

SUMMARY

1. The facts of human adaptation to displaced vision have been used to support empirical theory of perceptual development although the two processes are very dissimilar. Perceptual development in the infant progresses from general to more specific responses, while adaptation to displaced vision involves learning specific adjustments.

2. Local sign theory as applied to the nonadaptive behavior of lower animals with displaced vision does not account for human flexibility of response, nor does the reafference principle, which accounts for perceptual-motor regulation in terms of the compensatory matching of efference copies and reafference.

3. Our experiments on displaced vision have provided direct evidence that motion is multidimensional, that its primary regulatory mechanisms are organized relative to the major body axes, and that there are normal breakdown ranges of visual displacement. This latter observation is in keeping with our view that all motion can be described in terms of relative displacements between different sensory and motor systems.

4. Specificity of perceptual-motor skills can be accounted for in terms of the countless number of spatial relationships that can occur between perception and motion variables. Motion patterns of different spatial organization that

appear equivalent under some circumstances can be shown to vary differentially with other conditions.

5. The individual's intolerance for delayed sensory feedback suggests that motion is not organized primarily in terms of time-coded reinforcement effects, but in terms of differential space patterns.

6. Neurogeometric theory is a cellular theory of neural integration as opposed to a synaptic theory. Differential detector neurons are assumed to be the basis of all levels of neuromotor regulation of motion.

7. Development of perceptual control of the environment in children follows the differentiation of the motion systems and is dependent on it.

8. Sensory deprivation in infancy leads to deficiencies in perceptual-motor coordination which can be interpreted in terms of sensory and neural abnor-

malities resulting from the restriction.

9. Human evolution has involved progressive development of differential feedback systems, especially of the cerebral cortex. There is need for more meaningful analyses of tool using, since this is the critical behavioral factor defining man's evolution.

10. No branch of experimental psychology has provided an adequate research base for understanding specific human motion patterns. Our methods of analysis have been developed to fill this need.

11. Closed-circuit television is an important research tool which can be used to study delayed visual feedback, problems of remote control of space vehicles, problems of displaced feedback in machine systems, the critical variables in perceptual size constancy, variation in motivational states, and educationally significant behavior patterns.

REFERENCES

1. Adrian, E. D.: The Basis of Sensation: The Action of the Sense Organs. New York, W. W. Norton & Company, Inc., 1928.

2. Ampex Corporation. VTR goes to sea with U. S. Navy. Ampex Head Lines, 2 (2): 1-2, 1960.

3. Angulo y González, A. W.: The prenatal development of behavior in the albino rat. J. Comp. Neurol., 55: 395-442, 1932.

4. Arai, T.: Mental fatigue. Teachers College, Columbia Univ., Contr. Educ. No. 54, 1912.

5. Argentieri, D.: Leonardo's optics. Leonardo da Vinci. New York, Reynal & Company, 1956, pp. 405-436.

6. Asch, S. E., and Witkin, H. A.: Studies in space orientation. I. Perception of the upright with displaced visual fields. J. Exp. Psychol., 38: 325-337, 1948.

7. Asch, S. E., and Witkin, H. A.: Studies in space orientation. II. Perception of the upright with displaced visual fields and with body tilted. J. Exp. Psychol., 38: 455-477, 1948.

8. Ash, I. E.: Fatigue and its effects upon control. Arch. Psychol., 4, Whole No. 31, 1914.

9. Atkinson, C. J.: Adaptation to delayed side-tone. J. Speech Hearing Dis., 18: 386-391, 1953.

10. Baillet, A.: La vie de M. Descartes. Paris, published anonymously, 1693.

11. Bain, A.: The Senses and the Intellect. 3rd Ed. New York, Appleton, 1879.

12. Barcroft, J., and Barron, D. H.: The development of behavior in foetal sheep. J. Comp. Neurol., 70: 477-502, 1939.

13. Barnes, R. M.: Motion and Time Study. 4th Ed. New York, John Wiley & Sons, Inc., 1958.

14. Bartley, S. H., and Chute, E.: Fatigue and Impairment in Man. New York, McGraw-Hill Book Company, Inc., 1947.

15. Bates, J. A. V.: Some characteristics of a human operator. J. Inst. Elec. Engr., 94: 298-304, 1947.

16. Beaunis, H.: Recherches sur la contraction simultanée des muscles antagonistes. Gaz. Med. Paris, 56: 340, 1885.

17. Benedict, F. G., and Benedict, C. G.: The energy requirements of intense mental effort. Proc. Nat. Acad. Sci., 16: 438-443, 1930.

18. Benedict, F. G., and Carpenter, T. M.: The influence of muscular and mental work on metabolism and the efficiency of the human body as a machine. Washington, D. C., U. S. Government Printing Office, 1909.

19. Benedict, F. G., and Cathcart, E. P.: Muscular work: A metabolic study with special reference to the efficiency of the human body as a machine. Washington, D. C., Carnegie Inst., 1913.

20. Benedict, F. G., and Murschhauser, H.: Physiology: Energy transformations during horizontal walking. Proc. Nat. Acad. Sci., 1: 597-600, 1915.

21. Bergeijk, W. A. van, and David, E. E., Jr.: Delayed handwriting. Percept. Mot. Skills, 9: 347-357, 1959.

22. Berkeley, G.: An essay toward a new theory of vision. In B. Rand (Editor), Classical Psychologists. Boston, Houghton Mifflin Company, 1912.

23. Birmingham, H. P., and Taylor, F. V.: A human engineering approach to the design of man-operated continuous control systems. U.S.N. Res. Lab. Report No. 4333, 1954.

24. Black, J. W.: The effect of delayed sidetone upon vocal rate and intensity. J. Speech Hearing Dis., 16: 56-60, 1951.

25. Black, J. W.: Systematic research in experimental phonetics: II. Signal reception: Intelligibility and side-tone. J. Speech Hearing Dis., 19: 140-146, 1954.

26. Black, J. W.: The persistence of the effects of delayed side-tone. J. Speech Hearing Dis., 20: 65-68, 1955.

27. Block, S.: Effect of visual requirements on simultaneous motions. J. Methods-Time Measurement, 3: 65-67, 1956.

28. Block, S.: Research on blind grasp. J. Methods-Time Measurement, 5: 10-14, 1958.

29. Borelli, G. A.: De Motu Animalium. (Opus posthumum.) Rome, A. Bernabò, 1680-'81.

30. Braune, W., and Fischer, O.: Der Gang des Menschen. Leipzig, Hirzel, 1895.

31. Bridgman, C. S., and Smith, K. U.: Bilateral neural integration in visual perception after section of the corpus callosum. J. Comp. Neurol., 83: 57-68, 1945.

32. Brown, G. G.: Perception of depth with disoriented vision. Brit. J. Psychol., 19: 117-146, 1928.

33. Brunswik, E.: Thing constancy as measured by correlation coefficients. Psychol. Rev., 47: 69-78, 1940.

34. Buffa, E. S.: The additivity of universal standard data elements. II. J. Industrial Engineering, 8: 327-334, 1957.

35. Buffa, E. S., and Lyman, J.: The additivity of the times for human motor response elements in a simulated industrial assembly task. J. Appl. Psychol., 42: 379-383, 1958.

36. Burian, H. M.: Influence of prolonged wearing of meridional size lenses on spatial localization. Arch. Ophthal., 30: 645-666, 1943.

37. Buxton, C. E.: The application of multiple factorial methods to the study of motor abilities. Psychometrika, 3: 85-95, 1938.

38. Carmichael, L.: The development of behavior in vertebrates experimentally removed from the influence of external stimulation. Psychol. Rev., 33: 51-58, 1926.

39. Carmichael, L.: Sir Charles Bell. Psychol. Rev., 33: 188-217, 1926.

40. Carmichael, L.: Robert Whytt: A contribution to the history of physiological psychology. Psychol. Rev., 34: 287-304, 1927.

41. Carmichael, L., and Dearborn, W. F.: Reading and Visual Fatigue. Boston, Houghton Mifflin Company, 1947.

42. Cattell, J. M.: Some psychological experiments. Science, 98: 1-14, 1926.

43. Chase, R. A.: Effect of delayed auditory feedback on the repetition of speech sounds. J. Speech Hearing Dis., 23: 583-590, 1958.

44. Chase, R. A., Harvey, S., Standfast, S., Rapin, I., and Sutton, S.: A comparison of the effects of delayed auditory feedback on speech and key-tapping. Communications Lab., Columbia Univ., and Dep. Biometrics Res., State of N. Y., Res. Report, 1958.

45. Chase, R. A., Harvey, S., Standfast, S., Rapin, I., and Sutton, S.: Studies on sensory feedback: The effect of delayed auditory feedback on speech and key-tapping. Communications Lab., Columbia Univ., and Dep. Biometrics Res., State of N. Y., Res. Report, 1959.

46. Chase, R. A., Sutton, S., First, D., and Zubin, J.: A developmental study of changes in behavior under delayed auditory feedback. Communications Lab., Columbia Univ., and Dep. Biometrics Res., State of N. Y., Res. Report, 1959.

47. Chase, R. A., Sutton, S., Rapin, I., Standfast, S., and Harvey, S.: Sensory feedback influences on motor performance. Communications Lab., Columbia Univ., and Dep. Biometrics Res., State of N. Y., Res. Report, 1959.

48. Chernikoff, R., Birmingham, H. P., and Taylor, F. V.: A comparison of pursuit and compensatory tracking under conditions of aiding and no aiding. J. Exp. Psychol., 49: 55-59, 1955.

49. Chernikoff, R., Birmingham, H. P., and Taylor, F. V.: A comparison of pursuit and compensatory tracking in a simulated aircraft control loop. J. Appl. Psychol., 40: 47-72, 1956.

50. Coghill, G. E.: Anatomy and the Problem of Behaviour. Cambridge, Cambridge Univ. Press, 1929.

51. Cohen, L. and Strauss, L.: Time study and the fundamental nature of manual skill. J. Consult. Psychol., *10:* 146-153, 1946.

52. Conklin, J. E.: Effect of control lag on performance in a tracking task. J. Exp. Psychol., *53:* 261-268, 1957.

53. Conklin, J. E.: Linearity of the tracking performance function. Percept. Mot. Skills, *9:* 387-391, 1959.

54. Coronios, J. D.: Development of behavior in the fetal cat. Genet. Psychol. Monogr., *14:* 283-386, 1933.

55. Cox, C. M.: Comparative behavior in solving a series of maze problems of varying difficulty. J. Exp. Psychol., *11:* 202-218, 1928.

56. Craik, K. J. W.: Theory of the human operator in control systems: I. The operator as an engineering system. Brit. J. Psychol., *38:* 56-61, 1947.

57. Craik, K. J. W., and Vince, M.: The psychological and physiological aspects of control mechanisms, Part II, with special reference to ground-tank and A. A. tank gunnery. Med. Res. Council, Mil. Pers. Res. Com., Gr. Brit., Report No. BPC 44/322, 1944.

58. Cruze, W. W.: Maturation and learning in chicks. J. Comp. Psychol., *19:* 371-409, 1935.

59. Culler, E., and Mettler, F. A.: Conditioned behavior in the decorticate dog. J. Comp. Psychol., *18:* 291-303, 1934.

60. Daniel, R.S., and Smith, K. U.: The sea-approach behavior of the neonate loggerhead turtle *(Caretta caretta)*. J. Comp. physiol. Psychol., *40:* 413-420, 1947.

61. Dart, R. A.: Adventures with the Missing Link. New York, Harper & Brothers, 1959.

62. Darwin, C.: The Expression of the Emotions in Man and Animals. New York, Appleton, 1873.

63. Davis, R., Wehrkamp, R., and Smith, K. U.: Dimensional analysis of motion: I. Effects of laterality and movement direction. J. Appl. Psychol., *35:* 363-366, 1951.

64. Delabarre, E. B.: A method of recording eye-movements. Amer. J. Psychol., *9:* 572-574, 1898.

65. Delgado, J. M. R., Roberts, W. W., and Miller, N. E.: Learning motivated by electrical stimulation of the brain. Amer. J. Physiol., *179:* 587-593, 1954.

66. Dodge, R.: Five types of eye movement in the horizontal meridian plane of the field of regard. Amer. J. Physiol., *8:* 307-329, 1903.

67. Dollard, J., and Miller, N. E.: Personality and Psychotherapy: An Analysis in Terms of Learning, Thinking, and Culture. New York, McGraw-Hill Book Company, Inc., 1950.

68. Douglas Aircraft Company. Integrated instrument development. Report No. ES-26040, 1955.

69. duBois-Reymond, E.: Untersuchungen über thierische Elektrizität. Berlin, Reimer, 1849.

70. Dusser de Barenne, J. G.: The labyrinthine and postural mechanisms. In C. Murchison (Editor), A Handbook of General Experimental Psychology. Worcester, Mass., Clark Univ. Press, 1934, pp. 204-246.

71. Eisely, L. C.: Man, the firemaker. Sci. Amer., *191* (3): 52-57, 1954.

72. Elkind, J. I.: Tracking response characteristics of the human operator. USAF Human Factors Oper. Res. Lab., Air Res. Dev. Com., Memo No. 40, 1953.

73. Erismann, T., and Kohler, I.: Upright vision through inverting spectacles. Penn. State College: Psychol. Cinema Reg. No. 2070, 1953.

74. Ewert, P. H.: A study of the effect of inverted retinal stimulation upon spatially coordinated behavior. Genet. Psychol. Monogr., *7:* 177-363, 1930.

75. Ewert, P. H.: Factors in space localization during inverted vision: I. Interference. Psychol. Rev., *43:* 522-546, 1936.

76. Ewert, P. H.: Factors in space localization during inverted vision: II. An explanation of interference and adaptation. Psychol. Rev., *44:* 105-116, 1937.

77. Ewing, G. R.: Automeasurement. Proc. Amer. Inst. Industrial Engineering, *12:* 1-10, 1956.

78. Fairbanks, G.: Systematic research in experimental phonetics: I. A theory of the speech mechanism as a servosystem. J. Speech Hearing Dis., *19:* 133-139, 1954.

79. Fairbanks, G.: Selective vocal effects of delayed auditory feedback. J. Speech Hearing Dis., *20:* 333-346, 1955.

80. Fairbanks, G., and Guttman, N.: Effects of delayed auditory feedback upon articulation. J. Speech Hearing Res., *1:* 12-22, 1958.

81. Fenn, W. O.: Frictional and kinetic factors in the work of sprint running. Amer. J. Physiol., *92:* 583-611, 1930.

82. Fenn, W. O.: Mechanics of muscular contraction in man. J. Appl. Physics, *9:* 165-177, 1938.

83. Fenn, W. O., and Hursch, J. B.: Movements of the eyes when the lids are closed. Amer. J. Physiol., *118:* 8-14, 1937.

84. Ferrier, D.: The Functions of the Brain. London, Smith Elder, 1876.

85. Fitts, P. M. (Editor): Psychological research on equipment design. Washington, D. C., U. S. Government Printing Office, 1947.

86. Fitts, P. M.: Engineering psychology and equipment design. In S. S. Stevens (Editor): Handbook of Experimental Psychology. New York, John Wiley & Sons, Inc., 1951, pp. 1287-1340.

87. Fitts, P. M., and Crannell, C.: Location discrimination: II. Accuracy of reaching movements to twenty-four different areas. USAF Air Mat. Com. Tech. Report No. 5833, 1950.

88. Fleishman, E. A.: Dimensional analysis of psychomotor abilities. J. Exp. Psychol., *48:* 437-454, 1954.

89. Fleishman, E. A.: Dimensional analysis of movement reactions. J. Exp. Psychol. *55:* 438-453, 1958.

90. Flourens, P.: Recherches expérimentales sur les propriétés et les fonctions du système nerveux dans les animaux vertébrés. Paris, Baillière, 1824.

91. Foley, J. P., Jr., An experimental investigation of the effect of prolonged inversion of the visual field in the Rhesus monkey. J. Genet. Psychol., *56:* 21-51, 1940.

92. Forbes, T. W.: Auditory signals for instrument flying. J. Aeronaut. Sci. *13:* 255-258, 1946.

93. Freud, S.: An Outline of Psychoanalysis. (Trans. by J. Strachey) New York, W. W. Norton & Company, Inc., 1949.

94. Fritsch, G., and Hitzig, E.: Über die elektrische Erregbarkeit des Grosshirns. Arch. Anat. Physiol. wiss. Med., *37:* 300-332, 1870.

95. Galambos, R.: Microelectrode studies on the auditory nervous system. Ann. Otol. Rhinol. Laryngol., *66:* 503-505, 1957.

96. Gesell, A.: The ontogenesis of infant behavior. In L. Carmichael (Editor): Manual of Child Psychology. New York, John Wiley & Sons, Inc., 1946.

97. Gesell, A., and Thompson, H.: Twins *T* and *C* from infancy to adolescence: a biogenetic study of individual differences by the method of co-twin control. Genet. Psychol. Monogr., *24:* 3-121, 1941.

98. Gibson, E. J., and Walk, R. D. The "visual cliff." Sci. Amer., *202* (4): 64-71, 1960.

99. Gibson, J. J.: Adaptation, after-effect and contrast in the perception of curved lines. J. Exp. Psychol., *16:* 1-31, 1933.

100. Gilbreth, F. B.: Bricklaying System. New York, Clark, 1909.

101. Gilbreth, F. B., and Gilbreth, L. M.: Applied Motion Study. New York, Sturgis and Walton, 1917.

102. Grandjean, E., and Egli, R.: Physiological and medical investigations of occupational fatigue. Proc. Int. Congr. Occup. Health, Helsinki, *3:* 418-420, 1957.

103. Granit, R.: Receptors and Sensory Perception. New Haven, Yale Univ. Press, 1955.

104. Grether, W. F.: Efficiency of several types of control movements in the performance of a simple compensatory pursuit task. In P. M. Fitts (Editor): Psychological research on equipment design. Washington, D. C., U. S. Government Printing Office, 1947.

105. Harlow, H. F. The nature of love. Amer. Psychologist, *13:* 673-685, 1958.

106. Harlow, H. F., and Zimmerman, R. R.: Affectional responses in the infant monkey. Science, *130:* 421-432, 1959.

107. Harris, S. J., Brožek, J., and Smith, K. U.: The effects of caloric restriction on the travel and manipulation components of human motion. Int. Z. angew. Physiol. einschl. Arbeitsphysiol., *17:* 34-41, 1958.

108. Harris, S., and Smith, K. U.: Dimensional analysis of motion: V. An analytic test of psychomotor ability. J. Appl. Psychol., *37:* 136-141, 1953.

109. Harris, S. J., and Smith, K. U.: Dimensional analysis of motion: VII. Extent and direction of manipulative movements as factors in defining motions. J. Appl. Psychol., *38:* 126-130, 1954.

110. Harrison, R. G.: An experimental study of the relation of the nervous system to the developing musculature in the embryo of the frog. Amer. J. Anat., *3:* 197-220, 1904.

111. Hartson, L. D.: Contrasting approaches to the analysis of skilled movements. J. Gen. Psychol., *20:* 263-293, 1939.

112. Hecker, D., Green, D., and Smith, K. U.: Dimensional analysis of motion: X. Experimental evaluation of a time-study problem. J. Appl. Psychol., *40:* 220-227, 1956.

113. Held, R., and Hein, A. V.: Adaptation of disarranged hand-eye coordination contingent upon re-afferent stimulation. Percept. Mot. Skills, *8:* 87-90, 1958.

114. Held, R., and Schlank, M.: Adaptation to disarranged eye-hand coordination in the distance-dimension. Amer. J. Psychol., 72: 603-605, 1959.

115. Helmholtz, H. L. F. von: Muller's Arch. Anat. Physiol., 276-364, 1850.

116. Helmholtz, H. L. F. von: Physiological Optics. Vol. 1. (Trans. from 3rd German edition, Ed. by J. P. C. Southall) Rochester, New York, Optical Society of America, 1924.

117. Helson, H., and Howe, W. H.: A study of factors determining accuracy of tracking by means of handwheel control. Off. Sci. Res. Dev. Report No. 3451, The Foxboro Co., 1942.

118. Helson, H., and Howe, W. H.: Relative accuracy of handwheel tracking with one and both hands. Off. Sci. Res. Dev. Report No. 3455, The Foxboro Co., 1943.

119. Hess, E. H.: Space perception in the chick. Sci. Amer., 195 (1): 71-80, 1956.

120. Hess, E. H.: Effects of meprobamate on imprinting in waterfowl. Ann. N. Y. Acad. Sci., 67: 724-733, 1957.

121. Hick, W. E.: The discontinuous functioning of the human operator in pursuit tasks. Quart. J. Exp. Psychol., 1: 36-51, 1948.

122. Hilgard, E. R., and Marquis, D. G.: Conditioning and Learning. New York, Appleton-Century, 1940.

123. Hill, A. V.: The maximum work and mechanical efficiency of human muscles and their most economical speed. J. Physiol., 56: 19-41, 1922.

124. Hill, A. V.: Muscular Movement in Man. New York, McGraw-Hill Book Company, Inc., 1927.

125. Hill, A. V.: Production and absorption of work by muscle. Science, 131: 897-903, 1960.

126. Högyes, A.: Über den Nervenmechanismus der assoziierten Augenbewegungen. Mschr. Ohrenheilk. Laryngo-Rhinol., 46: 809-841; 1027-1083; 1353-1413; 1554-1571, 1912.

127. Holland, J. G.: Technique for behavioral analysis of human observing. Science, 125: 348-350, 1957.

128. Holst, E. von: Relations between the central nervous system and the peripheral organs. Brit. J. Anim. Behav., 2: 89-94, 1954.

129. Holst, E. von, and Mittlestädt, H.: Das Reafferenz-Prinzip. Die Naturwissenschaften, 20: 464-476, 1950.

130. Hooker, D.: The origins of overt behavior. Ann Arbor, Univ. of Michigan Press, 1944.

131. Howell, F. C.: The Villafranchian and human origins. Science, 130: 831-844, 1959.

132. Hubbard, A. W., and Stetson, R. H.: An experimental analysis of human locomotion. Amer. J. Physiol., 124: 300-313, 1938.

133. Huey, E. B.: On the psychology and physiology of reading. Amer. J. Psychol., 11: 283-302, 1900.

134. Huiskamp, J., Smader, R. C., and Smith, K. U.: Dimensional analysis of motion: IX. Comparison of visual and nonvisual control of component movements. J. Appl. Psychol., 40: 181-186, 1956.

135. Hull, C. L.: Aptitude Testing. New York, World, 1928.

136. Hull, C. L. Principles of Behavior: An Introduction to Behavior Theory. New York, Appleton-Century, 1943.

137. Hunter, W. S., and Bartlett, S. C.: Double alternation behavior in young children. J. Exp. Psychol., 38: 558-567, 1948.

138. Ittelson, W. H.: The Ames Demonstrations in Perception. Princeton, Princeton Univ. Press, 1952.

139. Jabbur, S. J., and Towe, A. L.: Effect of pyramidal tract activity on dorsal column nuclei. Science, 132: 547-548, 1960.

140. Janssen, M. J.: Présentation du revolver photographique et d'épreuves obtenues avec cet instrument. Bull. Soc. Fran. Phot., 22: 100-108, 1876.

141. Jaynes, J.: Imprinting: The interaction of learned and innate behavior. I. Development and generalization. J. Comp. Physiol. Psychol., 49: 201-206, 1956.

142. Jaynes, J.: Imprinting: The interaction of learned and innate behavior. II. The critical period. J. Comp. Physiol. Psychol., 50: 6-10, 1957.

143. Jenkins, W. O.: The discrimination and reproduction of motor adjustments with various types of aircraft controls. Amer. J. Psychol., 60: 397-406, 1947.

144. Kalmus, H., Denes, P., and Fry, D. B.: Effect of delayed acoustic feed-back on some non-vocal activities. Nature, 175: 1078, 1955.

145. Kalmus, H., Fry, D. B., and Denes, P.: Effects of delayed visual control on writing, drawing and tracking. Language and Speech, 3: 96-108, 1960.

146. Kappauf, W. E., and Smith, W. M.: Design of instrument dials for maximum legibility: II. A preliminary experiment on dial size and graduation. USAF Air Mat. Com. Mem. Report No. MCREXD-694-1N, 1948.

147. Kilpatrick, F. P.: Two processes in perceptual learning. J. Exp. Psychol., 47: 362-370, 1954.

148. Koffka, K.: Principles of Gestalt Psychology. New York, Harcourt, Brace and Company, 1935.

149. Kohler, I.: Über Aufbau und Wandlungen der Wahrnehmungswelt, insbesondere über 'bedingte Empfindungen.' Oest. Akad. Wiss., phil.-hist. Klasse Sitzungsber., 227 (1), 1951. (Translation available by G. Krauthamer.)

150. Kohler, I.: Warum sehen wir aufrecht? Die Pyramide, 2: 30-33, 1951.

151. Kohler, I.: (Rehabituation in perception.) Die Pyramide, 5, 6, & 7, 1953. (Translation available by H. Gleitman, Ed. by J. J. Gibson.)

152. Kohler, I.: Experiments with prolonged optical distortion. Acta Psychol., 11: 176-178, 1955.

153. Köhler, W.: Gestalt Psychology. New York, Liveright Publishing Corporation, 1929.

154. Kottenhoff, H.: Situational and personal influences on space perception with experimental spectacles: I. Prolonged experiments with inverting glasses. Acta Psychol., 13: 79-97, 1957.

155. Kottenhoff, H.: Situational and personal influences on space perception with experimental spectacles: II. Semiprolonged tests with inverting glasses. Acta Psychol., 13: 151-161, 1957.

156. Lake, C. W., Jr.: Automeasurement — mechanizing time study. Proc. Industrial Engineering Inst. (9th ann.), 29-36, 1957.

157. Lashley, K. S., and Russell, J. T.: The mechanism of vision: XI. A preliminary test of innate organization. J. Genet. Psychol., 45: 136-144, 1934.

158. Lauru, L.: Physiological studies of motions. (Trans. by L. Brouha.) Advanc. Mgmt., 22: 17-24, 1957.

159. Leakey, L. S. B.: Olduvai gorge. Sci. Amer., 190 (1): 66-71, 1954.

160. Lee, B. S.: Some effects of side-tone delay. J. Acoust. Soc. Amer., 22: 639-640, 1950.

161. Lee, B. S.: Effects of delayed speech feedback. J. Acoust. Soc. Amer., 22: 824-826, 1950.

162. Lee, B. S.: Artificial stutter. J. Speech Hearing Dis., 16: 53-55, 1951.

163. Lehmann, H.: Das statische-dynamische Arbeitsequivalent. Industr. Psychotech., 5: 212-233, 1928.

164. Lettvin, J. Y., Maturana, H. R., McCulloch, W. S., and Pitts, W. H.: What the frog's eye tells the frog's brain. Proc. Inst. Rad. Engr., 47: 1940-1951, 1959.

165. Levine, M.: Tracking performance as a function of exponential delay between control and display. USAF Wright Air Dev. Cent. Tech. Report No. 53-236, 1953.

166. Licklider, J. C. R.: Quasi-linear operator models in the study of manual tracking. In R. D. Luce (Editor), Developments in Mathematical Psychology. Glencoe, Ill., The Free Press of Glencoe, 1960.

167. Lifson, K. A.: Errors in time-study judgments of industrial work pace. Psychol. Monogr., 67: No. 5, 1953.

168. Lincoln, R. S., and Smith, K. U.: Systematic analysis of factors determining accuracy in visual tracking. Science, 116: 183-187, 1952.

169. Lorenz, K. Z.: The evolution of behavior. Sci. Amer., 199 (6): 66-78, 1958.

170. Loucks, R. B.: An experimental evaluation of the interpretability of various types of aircraft attitude indicators. In P. M. Fitts (Editor), Psychological research on equipment design. Washington, D. C., U. S. Government Printing Office, 1947.

171. Lowry, S. M., Maynard, H. B., and Stegemerten, G. J.: Time and Motion Study and Formulas for Wage Incentives. 3rd Ed. New York, McGraw-Hill Book Company, Inc., 1940.

172. Magni, F., Melzack, R., Moruzzi, G., and Smith, C. J.: Direct pyramidal influences on the dorsal-column nuclei. Arch. Ital. Biol., 97: 357-377, 1959.

173. Marey, E. J.: Animal Mechanism. New York, Appleton, 1874.

174. Marey, E. J.: C. R. Acad. Sci., Paris, 94: 683-684, 1882.

175. Marquis, D. G., and Hilgard, E. R.: Conditioned responses to light in monkeys after removal of the occipital lobes. Brain, 60: 1-12, 1937.

176. Marquis, D. P.: Can conditioned responses be established in the newborn infant? J. Genet. Psychol., 39: 479-492, 1931.

177. Martindale, R. L., and Lowe, W. F.: Use of television for remote control: A preliminary study. Kirtland AFB Spec. Weap. Cent. Res. Report No. TN-58-12, 1958.

178. Matthews, S., and Detwiler, S.: The reactions of *Amblystoma* embryos following prolonged treatment with chloretone. J. Exp. Zool., *45:* 279-292, 1926.

179. McCarthy, D.: Language development in children. In L. Carmichael (Editor): Manual of Child Psychology. 2nd Ed. New York, John Wiley & Sons, Inc., 1954, pp. 492-630.

180. McCormick, E. J.: Human Engineering. New York, McGraw-Hill Book Company, Inc., 1957.

181. McFarland, R. A: Human Factors in Air Transport Design. New York, McGraw-Hill Book Company, Inc., 1946.

182. McGinnis, J. M.: Eye movements and optic nystagmus in early infancy. Genet. Psychol. Monogr., *8:* 321-430, 1930.

183. McKendrick, J. G.: Life in Motion, or Muscle and Nerve. London, Adam and Charles Black, Ltd., 1892.

184. McLeod, R. B.: Spatial disorientation in landing an airplane. Science, *92:* 604, 1940.

185. Mechler, E. A., Russell, J. B., and Preston, M. G.: The basis for the optimum aided-tracking time constant. J. Franklin Inst., *248:* 327-334, 1949.

186. Mengle, L. I.: Three-dimensional TV system. Radio TV News, 1958.

187. Miles, W.: The two-story duplicate maze: Tracing the stylus maze with a maximum of indirect visual guidance. J. Exp. Psychol., *10:* 365-377, 1927.

188. Miller, N. E., and Dollard, J.: Social Learning and Imitation. New Haven, Yale Univ. Press, 1941.

189. Mitchell, M. J. H.: Direction of movement of machine controls: III. A two-handed task in a discontinuous operation. Min. Supply Psychol. Lab., Cambridge, Eng., Report No. SM 10018 (S), 1947.

190. Moore, A. D.: Perceptual disorientation during landing of airplane. Science, *92:* 477-478, 1940.

191. Mosso, A.: Fatigue. (Trans. by M. Drummond and W. B. Drummond.) New York, G. P. Putnam's Sons, Inc., 1904.

192. Motycka, J., and Auburn, T.: Electronic data processing comes to time study. J. Industrial Engineering, *8:* 11-18, 1957.

193. Mowrer, O. H.: The law of effect and ego psychology. Psychol. Rev., *53:* 321-334, 1946.

194. Mowrer, O. H., Ruch, T. C., and Miller, N. E.: The corneo-retinal potential difference as the basis of the galvanometric method of recording eye movements. Amer. J. Physiol., *114:* 423-428, 1936.

195. Münsterberg, H.: Psychology and Industrial Efficiency. Boston, Houghton Mifflin Company, 1913.

196. Muybridge, E.: Animal Locomotion. Philadelphia, J. B. Lippincott Company, 1887.

197. Myers, C. S.: Industrial Psychology. New York, People's Inst. Publ. Co., 1925.

198. Nadler, G.: Therblig relationships: I. Added cycle work and contact therblig effects. J. Industrial Engineering, *6:* 3-4, 1955.

199. Nadler, G. and Goldman, J.: Electronics for measuring motions. Science, *124:* 807-810, 1956.

200. Nadler, G., and Goldman, J.: The Unopar. J. Industrial Engineering, *9:* 58-65, 1958.

201. Nissen, H. W.: Phylogenetic comparison. In S. S. Stevens (Editor): Handbook of Experimental Psychology. New York, John Wiley & Sons, Inc., 1951, pp. 347-386.

202. Nissen, H. W., Chow, K. L., and Semmes, J.: Effects of restricted opportunity for tactual, kinesthetic, and manipulative experience on the behavior of a chimpanzee. Amer. J. Psychol., *64:* 485-507, 1951.

203. Oakley, K. P.: Man, the Tool-maker. Chicago, Univ. of Chicago Press, 1957.

204. Olds, J.: Pleasure centers in the brain. Sci. Amer., *195* (4): 105-116, 1956.

205. Pavlov, I. P.: Conditioned Reflexes. (Trans. and Ed. by G. V. Anrep.) London, Oxford Univ. Press, 1927.

206. Pearl, B. E., Simon, J. R., and Smith, K. U.: Visual tracking: IV. Interrelations of target speed and aided-tracking ratio in defining tracking accuracy. J. Appl. Psychol., *39:* 209-214, 1955.

207. Peters, R. W.: The effect of changes in side-tone delay and level upon rate of oral reading of normal speakers. J. Speech Hearing Dis., *19:* 483-490, 1954.

208. Peterson, J., and Peterson, J. K.: Does practice with inverting lenses make vision normal? Psychol. Monogr., *50,* No. 5: 12-37, 1938.

209. Pfister, H.: Über das Verhalten der Hühner beim Tragen von Prismen. Unpublished doctoral dissertation, Univ. of Innsbruck, 1955.

210. Poffenberger, A. T.: Principles of Applied Psychology. New York, Appleton-Century, 1942.

211. Poppen, J. R.: Equilibria functions in instrument flying. J. Aviat. Med. 7: 148-160, 1936.

212. Pratt, K. C.: The neonate. In L. Carmichael (Editor): Manual of Child Psychology. 2nd Ed. New York, John Wiley & Sons, Inc., 1954, pp. 215-291.

213. Pratt, K. C., Nelson, A. K., and Sun, K. H.: The behavior of the newborn infant. Ohio State Univ. Stud., Contr. Psychol. No. 10, 1930.

214. Prentice, W. C. H., and Beardslee, D. C.: Visual "normalization" near the vertical and horizontal. J. Exp. Psychol., 40: 355-364, 1950.

215. Rawnsley, A. I., and Harris, J. D.: Comparative analysis of normal speech and speech with delayed side-tone by means of sound spectrograms. USN Med. Res. Lab. Report No. 248, 1954.

216. Ray, W. S.: A preliminary report on the study of fetal conditioning. Child Development, 3: 175-177, 1932.

217. Rhule, W., and Smith, K. U.: Effects of inversion of the visual field on human motions. J. Exp. Psychol., 57: 338-343, 1959.

218. Rhule, W., and Smith, K. U.: Effect of visual pretraining in inverted reading on perceptual-motor performance in inverted visual fields. Percept. Mot. Skills, 9: 327-331, 1959.

219. Richer, M. P.: Note sur la contraction du muscle quadriceps dans l'acte de donner un coup de pied. Compt. Rend. Soc. Biol., 2: 204-205, 1895.

220. Riesen, A. H.: The development of visual perception in man and chimpanzee. Science, 106: 107-108, 1947.

221. Riesen, A. H.: Arrested vision. Sci. Amer., 183 (1): 16-19, 1950.

222. Riggs, L. A., and Ratliff, F.: Visual acuity and the normal tremor of the eyes. Science, 114: 17-18, 1951.

223. Riggs, L. A., Ratliff, F., Cornsweet, J. C., and Cornsweet, T. N.: The disappearance of steadily fixated visual test objects. J. Opt. Soc. Amer., 43: 495-501, 1953.

224. Rosapelly, M.: Apparatus for larynx movements. In P. J. Rousselot, Principes de Phonétique Expérimentale. Vol. 1. Paris, Welter, 1897, p. 98.

225. Rousselot, P. J.: Principes de Phonétique Expérimentale. Vol. 1. Paris, Welter, 1897.

226. Rubin, G., and Smith, K. U.: Learning and integration of component movements in a pattern of motion. J. Exp. Psychol., 44: 301-305, 1952.

227. Rubin, G., Von Trebra, P., and Smith, K. U.: Dimensional analysis of motion: III. Complexity of movement pattern, J. Appl. Psychol., 36: 272-276, 1952.

228. Schwartz, R. P., and Heath, A. L.: The pneumographic method of recording gait. J. Bone & Joint Surg., 14: 783-794, 1932.

229. Schwartz, R. P., and Heath, A. L: The definition of human locomotion on the basis of measurement. J. Bone & Joint Surg., 29: 203-214, 1947.

230. Schwartz, R. P., Heath, A. L., and Wright, J. N.: Electrobasographic method of recording gait. Arch. Surg., 27: 926-934, 1933.

231. Searle, L. V.: Psychological studies of tracking behavior: IV. The intermittency hypothesis as a basis for predicting optimum aided-tracking time constants. USN Res. Lab. Report No. 3872, 1951.

232. Seashore, R. H.: Stanford motor skills unit. Psychol. Monogr., 39, No. 2: 51-66, 1928.

233. Seashore, R. H.: Work and motor performance. In S. S. Stevens (Editor): Handbook of Experimental Psychology. New York, John Wiley & Sons, Inc., 1951, pp. 1341-1362.

234. Seashore, R. H., Buxton, C. E., and McCollom, I. N.: Multiple factorial analysis of fine motor skills. Amer. J. Psychol., 53: 251-259, 1940.

235. Senden, M. von: Raum- und Gestaltauffassung bei operierten Blindgeborenen vor und nach der Operation. Leipzig, Barth, 1932.

236. Sherman, M., and Sherman, I. C.: Sensorimotor responses in infants. J. Comp. Psychol., 5, 53-68, 1925.

237. Sherrington, C. S.: The Integrative Action of the Nervous System. New Haven, Yale Univ. Press, 1906.

238. Sholtz, H.: Physical strain among foundry workers. Trade Union Inf. Rep. Eur. Prod. Agcy., 3: 13-24, 1958.

239. Siipola, E. M.: Studies in mirror drawing. Psychol. Monogr., 46, No. 6: 66-77, 1935.

240. Simon, J. R.: The duration of movement components in a repetitive task as a function of the locus of a perceptual cue. J. Appl. Psychol., 40: 295-301, 1956.

241. Simon, J. R., and Smader, R.: Dimensional analysis of motions: VIII. The role of visual discrimination in motion cycles. J. Appl. Psychol., 39: 5-10, 1955.

242. Simon, J. R., and Smith, K. U.: Theory and analysis of component errors in aided pursuit tracking in relation to target speed and aided-tracking time constant. J. Appl. Psychol., 40: 367-370, 1956.

243. Simons, J. C.: Walking under zero-gravity conditions. USAF Wright Air Dev. Cent. Tech. Note No. 59-327, 1959.

244. Simonson, E.: Fatigue of the central nervous system. Clin. Proc. Cape Town, 2: 112-116, 1943.

245. Simonson, E., and Brožek, J.: Flicker fusion frequency: Background and applications. Physiol. Rev., 32: 349-378, 1952.

246. Skinner, B. F.: The generic nature of the concepts of stimulus and response. J. Gen. Psychol., 12: 40-65, 1935.

247. Skinner, B. F.: The Behavior of Organisms: An Experimental Analysis. New York, Appleton-Century, 1938.

248. Skinner, B. F.: Science and Human Behavior. New York, The Macmillan Company, 1953.

249. Smader, R., and Smith, K. U.: Dimensional analysis of motion: VI. The component movements of assembly motions. J. Appl. Psychol., 37: 308-314, 1953.

250. Smith, K. U.: The postoperative effects of removal of the striate cortex upon certain unlearned visually controlled reactions in the cat. J. Genet. Psychol., 50: 137-156, 1937.

251. Smith, K. U.: The relation between visual acuity and the optic projection centers of the brain. Science, 86: 564-565, 1937.

252. Smith, K. U.: The behavior of decorticate guinea pigs. J. Comp. Psychol., 27: 433-447, 1939.

253. Smith, K. U.: The neural centers concerned in the mediation of apparent movement vision. J. Exp. Psychol., 26: 443-466, 1940.

254. Smith, K. U.: Experiments on the neural basis of movement vision. J. Exp. Psychol., 28: 199-216, 1941.

255. Smith, K. U.: Bilateral integrative action of the cerebral cortex in man in verbal association and sensori-motor coordination. J. Exp. Psychol., 37: 367-376, 1947.

256. Smith, K. U.: Learning and the associative pathways of the human cerebral cortex. Science, 114: 117-120, 1951.

257. Smith, K. U.: Discrimination in animals. In C. P. Stone (Editor): Comparative Psychology. 3rd Ed. New York, Prentice-Hall, Inc., 1951.

258. Smith, K. U.: Audiovisumatic teaching: a new dimension in education and research. Aud.-vis. Com. Rev., 8: 85-103, 1960.

259. Smith, K. U.: The geometry of human motion and its neural foundations: I. Perceptual and motor adaptation to displaced vision. Amer. J. Phys. Med., 40: 71-87, 1961.

260. Smith, K. U.: The geometry of human motion and its neural foundations: II. Neurogeometric theory and its experimental basis. Amer. J. Phys. Med., 40: 109-129, 1961.

261. Smith, K. U., and Bloom, R.: The electronic handwriting analyzer and motion study of writing. J. Appl. Psychol., 40: 302-306, 1956.

262. Smith, K. U., and Bojar, S.: The nature of optokinetic reactions in mammals and their significance in the experimental analysis of the neural mechanisms of visual functions. Psychol. Bull., 35: 193-219, 1938.

263. Smith, K. U., and Bridgman, M.: The neural mechanisms of movement vision and optic nystagmus. J. Exp. Psychol., 33: 165-187, 1943.

264. Smith, K. U., and Daniel, R. S.: Observations of behavioral development in the loggerhead turtle (Caretta caretta). Science, 104: 154-156, 1946.

265. Smith, K. U., and Kappauf, W. E.: A neurological study of apparent movement. J. Gen. Psychol., 23: 315-327, 1940.

266. Smith, K. U., Kappauf, W. E., and Bojar, S.: The functions of the visual cortex in optic nystagmus at different velocities of movement in the visual field. J. Gen. Psychol., 22: 341-357, 1940.

267. Smith, K. U., McDermid, C. D., and Shideman, F. E.: Analysis of the temporal components of motion in human gait. Amer. J. Phys. Med., 39: 142-151, 1960.

268. Smith, K. U., and Smith, W. M.: The Behavior of Man: Introduction to Psychology. New York, Henry Holt & Company, Inc., 1958.

269. Smith, K. U., and Warkentin, J.: The central neural organization of optic functions related to minimum visible acuity. J. Genet. Psychol., *55:* 177-195, 1939.

270. Smith, K. U., and Wehrkamp, R.: A universal motion analyzer applied to psychomotor performance. Science, *113:* 242-244, 1951.

271. Smith, P. A., and Smith, K. U.: Effects of sustained performance on human motion. Percept. Mot. Skills, *5:* 23-29, 1955.

272. Smith, W. M.: Photoelectric technique for measuring eye movements. Science, *130:* 1248-1249, 1959.

273. Smith, W. M., McCrary, J. W., and Smith, K. U.: Delayed visual feedback and behavior. Science, *132:* 1013-1014, 1960.

274. Smith, W. M., Smith, K. U., Stanley, R., and Harley, W.: Analysis of performance in televised visual fields: preliminary report. Percept. Mot. Skills, *6:* 195-198, 1956.

275. Snyder, F. W., and Pronko, N. H.: Vision with spatial inversion. Wichita, Univ. of Wichita Press, 1952.

276. Snyder, F. W., and Snyder, C. W.: Vision with spatial inversion: A follow-up study. Psychol. Rec., *17:* 20-31, 1957.

277. Sontag, L. W., and Wallace, R. F.: A study of fetal activity: Preliminary report of the Fels Fund. Amer. J. Dis. Child., *48:* 1050-1057, 1934.

278. Spelt, D. K.: The conditioning of the human fetus *in utero*. J. Exp. Psychol., *38:* 338-346, 1948.

279. Spence, K. W.: Theoretical interpretations of learning. In S. S. Stevens (Editor): Handbook of Experimental Psychology. New York, John Wiley & Sons, Inc., 1951, pp. 690-729.

280. Sperry, R. W.: Action current study in movement coordination. J. Gen. Psychol., *20:* 295-313, 1939.

281. Sperry, R. W.: Reestablishment of visuomotor coordinations by optic nerve regeneration. Anat. Rec., *84:* 470, 1942.

282. Sperry, R. W.: Effect of 180 degree rotation of the retinal field on visuomotor coordination. J. Exp. Zool., *92:* 263-279, 1943.

283. Sperry, R. W.: Optic nerve regeneration with return of vision in anurans. J. Neurophysiol., *7:* 57-69, 1944.

284. Sperry, R. W.: Restoration of vision after crossing of optic nerves and after contralateral transplantation of eye. J. Neurophysiol., *8:* 15-28, 1945.

285. Sperry, R. W.: Orderly patterning of synaptic associations in regeneration of intracentral fiber tracts mediating visuomotor coordination. Anat. Rec., *102:* 63-76, 1948.

286. Sperry, R. W.: Mechanisms of neural maturation. In S. S. Stevens (Editor): Handbook of Experimental Psychology. New York, John Wiley & Sons, Inc., 1951, pp. 236-280.

287. Sperry, R. W.: The eye and the brain. Sci. Amer., *194* (5): 48-52, 1956.

288. Sperry, R. W.: The growth of nerve circuits. Sci. Amer., *201* (5): 68-75, 1959.

289. Sperry, R. W.: Cerebral organization and behavior. Science, *133:* 1749-1757, 1961.

290. Stetson, R. H.: A motor theory of rhythm and discrete succession. Psychol. Rev., *12:* 250-270; 293-350, 1905.

291. Stetson, R. H.: Motor phonetics: a study of speech movements in action. Amsterdam, N. Holland Publ. Co., 1951.

292. Stetson, R. H., and Bouman, H. D.: The action current as measure of muscle contraction. Science, *77:* 219-221, 1933.

293. Stetson, R. H., and McDill, J. A.: Mechanism of the different types of movement. Psychol. Monogr., *32*, No. 3: 18-40, 1923.

294. Stone, L. S.: Functional polarization in retinal development and its reestablishment in regenerating retinae of rotated grafted eyes. Proc. Soc. Exper. Biol. & Med., *57:* 13-14, 1944.

295. Stratton, G. M.: Some preliminary experiments in vision without inversion of the retinal image. Psychol. Rev., *3:* 611-617, 1896.

296. Stratton, G. M.: Vision without inversion of the retinal image. Psychol. Rev., *4:* 341-360; 463-481, 1897.

297. Stratton, G. M.: The spatial harmony of touch and sight. Mind, *8:* 492-505, 1899.

298. Strauss, H.: Über die hirnlokalisatorische Bedeutung des einseitigen Ausfalls des optokinetischen Nystagmus und der hemianopischen Aufmerksamkeitsschwäche. Z. ges. Neurol. Psychiat., *143:* 427-435, 1933.

299. Taylor, F. V.: Human engineering and psychology. In S. Koch (Editor): Psychology: A Study of a Science. Vol. 5. New York, McGraw-Hill Book Company, Inc., 1959.

300. Taylor, F. W.: The Principles of Scientific Management. New York, Harper & Brothers, 1911.

301. Ter Braak, J. W. G.: Untersuchungen über optokinetischen Nystagmus. Arch. Néerl. Physiol., *21:* 310-375, 1936.

302. Thorndike, E. L.: Animal intelligence: An experimental study of the associative processes in animals. Psychol. Rev. Monogr. Suppl., *2,* No. 4, 1898.

303. Thorndike, E. L.: Animal Intelligence. New York, The Macmillan Company, 1911.

304. Thorndike, E. L.: Educational psychology. II. The psychology of learning. New York, Teachers College, Columbia Univ., 1913.

305. Thouless, R. H.: Individual differences in phenomenal regression. Brit. J. Psychol., *22:* 216-241, 1932.

306. Tiffany, W. R., and Hanley, C. N.: Adaptation to delayed side-tone. J. Speech Hearing Dis., *21:* 164-172, 1956.

307. Van Wagenen, W. P., and Herren, R. Y.: Surgical division of commissural pathways in the corpus callosum: relation to spread of an epileptic attack. Arch. Neurol. & Psychiat., *44:* 740-759, 1940.

308. Vince, M. A.: Corrective movements in a pursuit task. Quart. J. Exp. Psychol., *1:* 85-103, 1948.

309. Vince, M. A., and Mitchell, M. J. H.: Direction of movement of machine controls: II. Min. Supply Psychol. Lab., Cambridge, Eng., Report No. SM 2861 (S), 1946.

310. Viteles, M. S.: Industrial Psychology. New York, W. W. Norton & Company, Inc., 1932.

311. von Trebra, P., and Smith, K. U.: The dimensional analysis of motion: IV. Transfer effects and direction of movement. J. Appl. Psychol., *36:* 348-353, 1952.

312. Warkentin, J., and Carmichael, L.: A study of the development of the air-righting reflex in cats and rabbits. J. Genet. Psychol., *55:* 67-80, 1939.

313. Warkentin, J., and Smith, K. U.: The development of visual acuity in the cat. J. Genet. Psychol., *50:* 371-399, 1937.

314. Warrick, M. J.: Direction of movement in the use of control knobs to position visual indicators. In P. M. Fitts (Editor), Psychological Research on Equipment Design. Washington, D. C., U. S. Government Printing Office, 1947.

315. Warrick, M. J.: Effect of transmission-type control lags on tracking accuracy. USAF Air Mat. Com. Tech. Report No. 5916, 1949.

316. Washburn, S. L.: Tools and human evolution. Sci. Amer., *203* (3): 62-75, 1960.

317. Watson, J. B.: Behavior: An Introduction to Comparative Psychology. New York, Henry Holt & Company, Inc., 1914.

318. Watson, J. B.: Psychology from the Standpoint of a Behaviorist. 2nd Ed. Philadelphia, J. B. Lippincott Company, 1924.

319. Wehrkamp, R., and Smith, K. U.: Dimensional analysis of motion: II. Travel-distance effects. J. Appl. Psychol., *36:* 201-206, 1952.

320. Weisenburg, T., and McBride, K. E.: Aphasia: A clinical and psychological study. New York, Commonwealth Fund, 1935.

321. Weiss, P.: Self-differentiation of the basic patterns of coordination. Comp. Psychol. Monogr., *17:* No. 4 (Whole No. 88), 1941.

322. Welford, A. T.: Skill and Age. London, Oxford Univ. Press, 1951.

323. Wenger, M. A.: An investigation of conditioned responses in human infants. Univ. Iowa Stud., Child Welfare, *12,* No. 1: 7-90, 1936.

324. Werner, H., and Wapner, S.: The Innsbruck studies on distorted visual fields in relation to an organismic theory of perception. Psychol. Rev., *62:* 130-138, 1955.

325. Wertheimer, M.: Experimentelle Studien über das Sehen von Bewegung. Z. Psychol., *61:* 161-265, 1912.

326. Wickens, D. D., and Wickens, C.: A study of conditioning in the neonate. J. Exp. Psychol., *26:* 94-102, 1940.

327. Wiener, N.: Cybernetics, or Control and Communication in the Animal and the Machine. New York, John Wiley & Sons, Inc., 1948.

328. Winchester, R. A., Gibbons, E. W., and Krebs, D. F.: Adaptation to sustained delayed side-tone. J. Speech Hearing Dis., *24:* 25-28, 1959.

329. Windle, W. F.: Genesis of somatic motor function in mammalian embryos: a synthesizing article. Physiol. Zool., *17:* 247-260, 1944.

330. Wing, K. G., and Smith, K. U.: The role of the optic cortex in the dog in the determination of the functional properties of conditioned reactions to light. J. Exp. Psychol., *31:* 478-496, 1942.

331. Witkin, H. A.: Perception of body position and of the position of the visual field. Psychol. Monogr., *63,* No. 7 (Whole No. 302), 1949.

332. Witkin, H. A., and Asch, S. E.: Studies in space orientation: III. Perception of the upright in the absence of a visual field. J. Exp. Psychol., *38:* 603-614, 1948.

333. Witkin, H. A., and Asch, S. E.: Studies in space orientation: IV. Further experiments on perception of the upright with displaced visual fields. J. Exp. Psychol., *38:* 762-782, 1948.

334. Wooster, M.: Certain factors in the development of a new spatial co-ordination. Psychol. Monogr., *32,* No. 4 (Whole No. 146), 1923.

335. Yoakum, C. S.: An experimental study of fatigue. Psychol. Monogr., *11,* No. 3 (Whole No. 46), 1909.

INDEX

Date Due
